1972

Public Health Concepts
in
Social Work Education

Public Health Concepts
in
Social Work Education

*Proceedings of seminar held at
Princeton University, Princeton, N. J.
March 4-9, 1962*

Council on Social Work Education

in cooperation with

Public Health Service
Department of Health, Education, and Welfare

No. 62-35-1   Price: $5.00

Table of Contents

v

Foreword

From a tenuous beginning almost 60 years ago, social work education has won a respected place for itself in the structure of professional education in the United States. No profession is more self-critical nor more persistent in its search for ways of lifting the level of professional education and therefore of practice.

The Seminar on Public Health Concepts in Social Work Education held March 4-9, 1962, at Princeton, New Jersey, reported herein, is the most recent attempt of the Council on Social Work Education to further the improvement of education for social work. This seminar, which was made possible by the Public Health Service of the Department of Health, Education and Welfare, brought together 125 educators and practitioners of public health and social work. It was their opportunity and task to analyze those concepts and methods developed in public health which gave promise of being applicable for use in social work.

The objective of this meeting is nowhere stated with greater clarity than in Dr. Theodore J. Bauer's paper (see page 1): "This seminar is based on the premise that our professions can best meet our challenges, our need for adjustments, by reemphasizing our fundamental concepts of the interrelatedness of health and social problems. The purpose of our getting together is to explore methods of translating these concepts into active practice in today's society."

The participants included a member of the faculty from each of 63 schools of social work in the United States and Canada, highly knowledgeable and interested officials from the various units of the Public Health Service, and others representing several disciplines and various aspects of public health education and practice.

The seminar was administered by the Council on Social Work Education under a contract with the Public Health Service, which not only provided the funds but whose staff gave expert advice in its planning and conduct. This is one of the few ventures of this kind in which so many units of the Public Health Service have participated. We trust that the results will justify further joint endeavors of this nature.

The seminar gave new insight into the continuing responsibility of the Council on Social Work Education for curriculum development and the value of greater collaboration between the social worker and the public health practitioner. Its ultimate influence, however, will not be known for some time. What was said, summarized in these proceedings, will be read and pondered by social work educators throughout the country. We can expect no automatic transfer of public health concepts to social work education and practice. But it is reasonable to expect that social work will, in time, utilize many of the concepts and methods discussed in achieving its own professional objectives and in enhancing its skills.

I wish to acknowledge Council appreciation to Dr. Luther Terry, the Surgeon General of the Public Health Service, and his staff for making this seminar possible. The Bureau of State Services merits special mention because of the leadership it provided for this undertaking and the unfailing support which it gave from the very beginning. Particularly helpful was the appointment by Dr. Bauer, Chief of the Bureau of State Services, of a committee of social work educators and public health personnel to facilitate the planning of the seminar under the inspired leadership of Dr. Leslie W. Knott.

Mention must also be made of another member of the Public Health Service staff, Ruth Taylor, without whose continuous help it is difficult to believe that this volume could have been completed.

The Council also deeply appreciates the time and the effort

of the 125 participants who placed their knowledge and talents at the service of social work education for the ultimate enrichment of social work practice.

In any successful undertaking of this nature, there is usually one person whose efforts are required to translate plans into reality, to help tie the many separate elements into an ordered whole, and to carry the project to completion. Miss Grace White was the one who performed these services for this project. She had been educational consultant on the staff of the Council on Social Work Education and is now in the Department of Social Services at the University of Kentucky Medical Center. She served the seminar as educational director from its inception. Her real satisfaction will come as the values derived from the seminar find their way into practice.

ERNEST F. WITTE
Executive Director
Council on Social Work Education

New York, New York
September 1962

PROGRAM SCHEDULE
Seminar on Public Health for Schools of Social Work

Sunday, March 4, 1962

1:00 P.M.-6:00 P.M.	Registration
6:30 P.M.	Reception and Buffet Supper
8:00 P.M.-9:30 P.M.	**Opening General Session**
Presiding Chairman:	LESLIE W. KNOTT, M.D., *Chief* *Division of Chronic Diseases* Public Health Service U.S. Department of Health, Education, and Welfare

Greetings from Region II
   Trois Johnson, M.D., *Community Health Services Consultant*
   Public Health Service, Region II, U.S. Department of HEW

Welcome to New Jersey
   Roscoe P. Kandle, M.D., *State Commissioner of Health*
   New Jersey State Health Department

"Why Are We Here?"
   Theodore J. Bauer, M.D., *Assistant Surgeon General*
   Chief, Bureau of State Services
   Public Health Service, U.S. Department of HEW

Great Expectations
   Ernest F. Witte, Ph.D., *Executive Director*
   Council on Social Work Education

Objectives and Plans for the Seminar
   Grace White, *Educational Consultant*
   Council on Social Work Education
   Educational Director of the Seminar

Monday, March 5, 1962

9:00 A.M.-12:00 N.   **Second General Session**

Presiding Chairman: CLIFFORD H. COLE, M.D., *Program Officer*
Bureau of State Services, U.S. Department of HEW

Public Health Goals
John D. Porterfield, M.D., *Deputy Surgeon General*
Public Health Service, U.S. Department of HEW

Programing—Principles and Elements
Leslie W. Knott, M.D., *Chief*
Division of Chronic Diseases
Public Health Service, U.S. Department of HEW

Discussions and Questions

1:30 P.M.-2:45 P.M.   **Third General Session**

Presiding Chairman: ERNEST F. WITTE, Ph.D., *Executive Director*
Council on Social Work Education

Effective Community Health Services
George James, M.D., *First Deputy Commissioner*
New York City Department of Health

3:15 P.M.-4:30 P.M.   *First Discussion Group Session*
Subject: Public Health Concepts, Goals, and Methods

Tuesday, March 6, 1962

9:00 A.M.-11:45 A.M.   *Second Discussion Group Session*
Subject: Reciprocal Concerns Regarding Social Functioning and Health

2:30 P.M.-5:15 P.M.   **Fourth General Session**

Presiding Chairman: ELMER L. HILL, M.D., *Chief*
Public Health Training Branch
Division of Community Health Practice
Public Health Service, U.S. Department of HEW

Potentials and Limitations of Epidemiology
John M. Cassel, MBBCh., M.P.H., *Professor of Epidemiology*
School of Public Health, University of North Carolina

Applied Epidemiology and Its Use in the Control of Mental Illnesses
  Roger W. Howell, M.D., *Professor of Epidemiology*
  School of Public Health, University of Michigan

Epidemiology and Its Application to Social Work
  Maurice B. Hamovitch, Ph.D., *Professor of Social Work*
  School of Social Work, University of Southern California

Discussions and Questions

Wednesday, March 7, 1962

9:00 A.M.-12:00 N. *Third Discussion Group Session*
           Subject: Extending the Utilization of Epidemiology in
                     Social Work Practice and Education

1:30 P.M.-4:30 P.M. **Fifth General Session**

Presiding Chairman: MRS. ROSALIE ABRAHAMS, *Staff Assistant*
                     Coordination and Liaison Branch
                     Division of Chronic Diseases
                     Public Health Service, U.S. Department of HEW

  The Five Faces of Prevention
    Claire Ryder, M.D., *Chief, Chronic Disease Program*
    Division of Chronic Disease Program
    Public Health Service, U.S. Department of HEW

  Programing for Prevention in a Rural Area
    Frank Kiesler, M.D., *Director*
    Tri-County Mental Health Center
    Grand Rapids, Minnesota

  *Therapy, Prevention, and Developmental Provision: A Social
  Work Strategy*
    Alfred J. Kahn, D.S.W., *Professor of Social Work*
    New York School of Social Work, Columbia University

Discussions and Questions

Thursday, March 8, 1962

9:00 A.M.-12:00 N. *Fourth Discussion Group Session*
          Subject: Implications for the Social Work Curriculum

2:30 P.M.-5:00 P.M. **Sixth General Session**

Presiding Chairman: CURTIS G. SOUTHARD, M.D., *Chief*
                      Community Services Branch, National Institute
                      of Mental Health
                      Public Health Service, U.S. Department of HEW

"Who Is the Patient in Public Health?"
    Roscoe P. Kandle, M.D., *State Commissioner of Health*
    New Jersey State Health Department

Community Planning for Health: The Social Welfare Experience
    Robert Morris, D.S.W., *Associate Professor of Community
    Planning*
    Florence Heller Graduate School of Advanced Studies in
    Social Welfare, Brandeis University

Discussion and Questions

8:00 P.M.-9:30 P.M. **Seventh General Session**

Panel Discussion: Post Master's Preparation for Practice in a
                    Particular Field of Social Work

Friday, March 9, 1962

9:00 A.M.-11:15 A.M. *Fifth Discussion Group Session*
          Subject: Implications for the Social Work Curriculum

11:30 A.M.-12:30 P.M. **Closing General Session**

Presiding Chairman: KATHERINE A. KENDALL, PH.D.,
                      Associate Director
                      Council on Social Work Education

The Role of Social Work in Meeting the Challenge to Public Health
    David E. Price, M.D., *Assistant Surgeon General*
    Deputy Director, National Institutes of Health
    Public Health Service, U.S. Department of HEW

Group Leaders and Consultants*

Group Leaders
  Eleanor Barnett
  Frederick Ferris
  Ludwig Geismar
  Rita McGuire
  Joseph Meisels
  Kathleen O'Donoghue
  Edgar Perretz
  Robert Rutherford
  Meyer Schwartz
  Rose Segal
  John Turner

Recorders
  Mary Baker
  Sophia Bloom
  John Eichenberger
  Ira Gibbons
  David Levine
  Charles Mitchell
  Eleonor Morris
  Joan Smith
  Ethel Swengel
  Alan Wade
  Sophie Wojciechowski

Consultants
  Katherine Kendall
  Ruth Knee
  Eileen Lester
  Albert Rhudy
  Ruth Taylor
  Milton Wittman

Research Consultants
  Arnold Gurin
  Maurice Hamovitch
  Alfred Kahn
  Jennie Mohr
  Paul Schreiber

Panel

Sophia Bloom
Katherine Kendall
Eileen Lester

Marie McNabola
Esther Spencer
Grace White, *Leader*

Seminar Analyst: Milton Wittman

Advisory Committee*

Clifford H. Cole, M.D.
Elmer L. Hill, M.D.
Ruth Knee
Eileen Lester

Kathleen O'Donoghue
Meyer Schwartz
Ruth Taylor

* Affiliations shown in List of Participants, p. xviii.

Planning Committee[1]

Leslie W. Knott, M.D., *Chairman*
Marion Andrews
Eleanor Barnett
Clifford H. Cole, M.D.[2]
Frederick Ferris
Fredrik F. Fredlund[3]
Ira Gibbons
Elmer L. Hill, M.D.
Ruth Knee

Eileen Lester
Kathleen O'Donoghue
Albert Rhudy
Robert F. Rutherford
Meyer Schwartz
Lucille Smith[4]
Ruth Taylor
Grace White
Milton Wittman

Staff of the Seminar

Grace White,
Educational Director

Irmgard Scherer,
Secretary-Recorder

---

[1] Affiliations shown in List of Participants, p. xviii
[2] Program Officer, Bureau of State Services
Public Health Service, U.S. Department of HEW
[3] Chief, Management Advisory Branch
Office of the Chief, Bureau of State Services
Public Health Service, U.S. Department of HEW
[4] Chief, Health Services Organization Branch
Division of Public Health Methods
Office of the Surgeon General
Public Health Service, U.S. Department of HEW

Contributors of Papers[*]

Theodore J. Bauer, M.D., Assistant Surgeon General
Chief, Bureau of State Services
Public Health Service, U.S. Department of HEW

John M. Cassel, MBBCh., M.P.H., Professor of Epidemiology
School of Public Health, University of North Carolina

Maurice B. Hamovitch, Ph.D., Professor of Social Work
School of Social Work, University of South Carolina

Roger W. Howell, M.D., Professor of Epidemiology
School of Public Health, University of Michigan

George James, M.D., M.P.H., First Deputy Commissioner
New York City Department of Health

Alfred J. Kahn, D.S.W., Professor of Social Work
New York School of Social Work, Columbia University

Roscoe P. Kandle, M.D., M.P.H., State Commissioner of Health
New Jersey State Health Department

Frank Kiesler, M.D., Director
Tri-County Mental Health Center
Grand Rapids, Minnesota

Leslie W. Knott, M.D., M.P.H., Chief
Division of Chronic Diseases
Public Health Service, U.S. Department of HEW

Robert Morris, D.S.W., Associate Professor of Community Planning

---

[*] The titles and affiliations shown are those held at the time of the Seminar.

Florence Heller Graduate School of Advanced Studies in Social Welfare
Brandeis University

John D. Porterfield, M.D., M.P.H., Deputy Surgeon General
Public Health Service, U.S. Department of HEW

David E. Price, M.D., D.P.H., Assistant Surgeon General
Deputy Director, National Institutes of Health
Public Health Service, U.S. Department of HEW

Claire Ryder, M.D., M.P.H., Chief, Long Term Illness Program
Division of Chronic Diseases
Public Health Service, U.S. Department of HEW

Ernest F. Witte, Ph.D., Executive Director
Council on Social Work Education

Milton Wittman, D.S.W., Chief, Social Work Section, Training Branch
National Institute of Mental Health
Public Health Service, U.S. Department of HEW

List of Financial Contributors*

BUREAU OF MEDICAL SERVICES
    DIVISION OF HOSPITALS
    DIVISION OF INDIAN HEALTH

BUREAU OF STATE SERVICES
    COMMUNICABLE DISEASE CENTER
    DIVISION OF ACCIDENT PREVENTION
    DIVISION OF CHRONIC DISEASES
    DIVISION OF COMMUNITY HEALTH SERVICES
    DIVISION OF ENVIRONMENTAL ENGINEERING AND FOOD PROTECTION
    DIVISION OF HOSPITAL AND MEDICAL FACILITIES
    DIVISION OF NURSING
    DIVISION OF OCCUPATIONAL HEALTH

NATIONAL INSTITUTES OF HEALTH
    NATIONAL INSTITUTE OF MENTAL HEALTH

---

* All of which are units of the Public Health Service, Department of Health, Education, and Welfare.

List of Participants*

MRS. ROSALIE G. ABRAHAMS
*Staff Assistant, Coordination and
    Liaison Branch*
Division of Chronic Diseases
Public Health Service, U.S. Dept.
    of HEW

MRS. BLANCHE ADAMS
Associate Professor of Social Work
Raymond A. Kent School of
    Social Work
University of Louisville

JAMES ANDERSON
Assistant Professor
School of Social Work
Wayne State University

MARION ANDREWS
Chief, Social Service Branch
Division of Indian Health
Public Health Service, U.S. Dept.
    of HEW

MARY R. BAKER
*Consultant on Careers in Social
    Work*
Council on Social Work Education

ELEANOR BARNETT
Associate Professor
Graduate School of Social Work
University of Denver

TESSIE BERKMAN
Professor of Social Work
Graduate School of Social Work
New York University

SOPHIA BLOOM
Associate Professor of Social Work
Schools of Social Work and
    Public Health
University of Pittsburgh

LOUISE BOATMAN
Associate Professor
School of Social Work
University of Buffalo

ELEANOR BRADLEY
Social Work Supervisor
School of Social Work
University of British Columbia

WILLIE V. BRATTON
Associate Professor
School of Social Work
University of Tennessee

MRS. ISABELLE K. CARTER
Associate Professor
School of Social Work
University of North Carolina

CATHERINE M. CASEY
Chief, Social Work Section
Massachusetts Department of
    Public Health

MILTON CHERNIN
Dean
School of Social Welfare
University of California (Berkeley)

MRS. HORTENCE S. COCHRANE
Associate Professor
School of Social Work
Syracuse University

ELEANOR COCKERILL
Professor of Social Casework
Graduate School of Social Work
University of Pittsburgh

MERRISS CORNELL
Professor, Research and Statistics
School of Social Work
Ohio State University

---

* The titles and affiliations shown are those held at the time of the Seminar.

VALENTIN CRUZ
Assistant Professor
School of Social Welfare
University of Ottawa

ROGER CUMMING
Director, Social Work Service
Veterans Administration
Washington, D. C.

KATHARIN DEN BLEYKER
Assistant Professor
Graduate School of Social Work
University of Utah

MRS. LEONA R. DOHERTY
Assistant Professor of Social Work
Worden School of Social Service
Our Lady of the Lake College

ADRIANE V. DUFFY
*Program Coordinator, Social Work
    Program*
New Jersey State Department of
    Health

JOHN EICHENBERGER
Assistant Professor
Graduate School of Social Work
University of Nebraska

THEODORE ERNST
Assistant Professor
School of Social Work
University of Missouri

FREDERICK J. FERRIS
Dean
National Catholic School of
    Social Service
Catholic University of America

MRS. JACINTA M. GARCÍA-CABRERA
*Assistant Professor and Field Work
    Supervisor*
School of Social Work
University of Puerto Rico

LUDWIG L. GEISMAR
Associate Professor
Graduate School of Social Work
Rutgers, The State University

IRA L. GIBBONS
Associate Professor
School of Social Work
Howard University

MARY C. GILLIS
Chief, Social Service Branch
Division of Hospitals
Public Health Service, U.S. Dept.
    of HEW

GERALDINE GOURLEY
*Medical Social Consultant,
    Tuberculosis Program*
Division of Preventive Medicine
New Mexico Department of
    Public Health

MARGARET Y. GRAHAM
Chief Staff Development Specialist
Bureau of Family Services,
    U.S. Dept of HEW

MITTIE GRUBER
Associate Professor
School of Social Welfare
Louisiana State University

JENNETTE GRUENER
Professor
Jane Addams Graduate School of
    Social Work
University of Illinois

MRS. GEORGETTE D. GUAY
Professor of Medical Social Service
School of Social Work
Laval University

ARNOLD GURIN
Lecturer in Social Work
School of Social Work
Michigan State University

WILLIAM HALL
Assistant Professor
Schools of Social Work and
    Public Health
University of Minnesota

MAURICE B. HAMOVITCH
Professor
School of Social Work
University of Southern California

FLORENCE HASELKORN
Assistant Professor
School of Social Work
Adelphi College

ELMER HILL, M.D.
*Chief, Public Health Training
    Branch*
Division of Community Health
    Services
Public Health Service, U.S. Dept.
    of HEW

MRS. GENEVIEVE HILL
Professor of Social Work
School of Social Work
Atlanta University

JOSEPH I. HUNGATE, JR.
Visiting Associate Professor
School of Social Work
University of Texas

BETTY HUTCHINSON
Medical Social Consultant
Anne Arundel County Dept. of
    Health, Maryland

VIRGINIA INSLEY
Chief, Medical Social Work Section
Division of Health Services
Children's Bureau, U.S. Dept. of
    HEW

ALFRED KAHN
Professor of Social Work
New York School of Social Work
Columbia University

ALFRED H. KATZ
*Associate Professor of Social Welfare
    in Medicine*
Schools of Medicine, Public Health
    and Social Welfare
University of California at
    Los Angeles

CONSTANCE E. KELLAM
Assistant Professor
School of Social Work
Loyola University

MRS. KATHERINE A. KENDALL
Associate Director
Council on Social Work Education

MRS. RUTH I. KNEE
Psychiatric Social Work Consultant
Community Services Branch
National Institute of Mental Health
Public Health Service, U.S. Dept.
    of HEW

LESLIE W. KNOTT, M.D.
Chief, Division of Chronic Diseases
Public Health Service, U.S. Dept.
    of HEW

THERESE LaLANCETTE
Mental Health Nurse Consultant
Public Health Service, Region II
    U.S. Dept of HEW

WARREN C. LAMSON
Chief, Professional Resources Section
Community Services Branch
National Institute of Mental Health
Public Health Service, U.S. Dept.
    of HEW

NEOTA LARSON
Chief, Welfare Branch
Division of Claims Policy
Bureau of Old Age and Survivors
    Insurance
U.S. Dept of HEW

THERESE LAVOIE
Senior Lecturer
L'Ecole de Service Social
Université de Montréal

JANIE LEE
Field Instructor
School of Social Service
St. Louis University

EILEEN E. LESTER
*Medical Social Consultant, Long
    Term Illness Program*
Division of Chronic Diseases
Public Health Service, U.S. Dept.
    of HEW

DAVID L. LEVINE
Professor
School of Social Welfare
Florida State University

MARTIN B. LOEB
Professor
School of Social Work
University of Wisconsin

MRS. LUCILE MCADOO
*Associate Professor, Director of
    Field Work*
National Catholic School of Social
    Service
Catholic University of America

MARION MCGINNIS
Associate Professor
School of Social Work
University of Maryland

RITA MCGUIRE
Associate Professor
School of Social Service
Fordham University

MRS. BERNICE A. MCINTOSH
Assistant Professor
School of Social Work
Howard University

MARIE MCNABOLA
Training Specialist
Social Work Section, Training
    Branch
National Institute of Mental Health
Public Health Service, U.S. Dept.
    of HEW

ANNE MCQUADE
Mental Health Nursing Consultant
Visiting Nurse Service
New York City

JOSEPH F. MEISELS
Chairman
Graduate Department of Social
    Work
University of Kansas

FRED MERRITT
Associate Professor

School of Social Work
University of Hawaii

HENRY J. MEYER
*Professor of Social Work and
    Sociology*
School of Social Work
University of Michigan

CHARLES F. MITCHELL
Director, Division of Mental Health
Texas Department of Health

JENNIE MOHR
Director of Research Program
School of Social Work
Simmons College

ELEANOR MORRIS
Medical Social Consultant
Public Health Service, Region II
    U.S. Dept. of HEW

ROBERT MORRIS
*Associate Professor of Community
    Planning*
Florence Heller Graduate School for
    Advanced Studies in Social
    Welfare
Brandeis University

MRS. MARTHA BALL NAYLOR
*Nursing Consultant, Long Term
    Illness Program*
Division of Chronic Diseases
Public Health Service, U.S. Dept.
    of HEW

J. WAYNE NEWTON
*Chairman, Community Organization
    Department*
School of Social Work
Boston College

KATHLEEN O'DONOGHUE
*Co-ordinator, Human Growth and
    Behavior Sequence*
School of Social Work
Boston College

BEATRIX PARK
Professor
School of Social Work
Boston University

EDGAR A. PERRETZ
Associate Professor of Social Work
School of Social Work
University of Toronto

HELEN PINKUS
Associate Professor
School for Social Work
Smith College

MARY POOLE
Associate Professor of Social Work
Dept. of Public Health and
    Preventive Medicine
University of Pennsylvania

KURT REICHERT
Director, Office of Public Health
    Social Work
New York State Department of
    Health

ALBERT E. RHUDY
Medical Social Consultant, Heart
    Disease Control Program
Division of Chronic Diseases
Public Health Service, U.S. Dept.
    of HEW

MYRON JOHN ROCKMORE
Chief, Psychiatric Social Service
Connecticut State Dept. of Mental
    Health

MAYSIE ROGER
Professor
School of Social Work
University of Manitoba

NATHAN ROSENBERG
Research Psychologist
Division of Accident Prevention
Public Health Service, U.S. Dept.
    of HEW

MRS. ELAINE ROTHENBERG
Assistant Professor
School of Social Work
Richmond Professional Institute of
    the Colleges of William and
    Mary

ROBERT F. RUTHERFORD
Director
School of Social Work
Simmons College

MARGARET M. RYAN
Social Work Consultant
Division of Training
Office of Vocational Rehabilitation,
    U.S. Dept. of HEW

CLAIRE RYDER, M.D.
Chief, Long Term Illness Program
Division of Chronic Diseases
Public Health Service, U.S. Dept.
    of HEW

BERNHARD SCHER
Chairman
Department of Social Work
West Virginia University

PAUL SCHREIBER
Director
School of Social Work
Hunter College of the City
    University of New York

EDITH SCHROEDER
Associate Professor
School of Social Work
University of Oklahoma

MARGARET L. SCHUTZ
Associate Professor and Director of
    Field Work
George Warren Brown School of
    Social Work
Washington University

MEYER SCHWARTZ
Associate Professor
Graduate School of Social Work
University of Pittsburgh

ROSE SEGAL
Associate Professor of Social Work
    and Social Research
Carola Woerishoffer Graduate Dept.
    of Social Work and Social
    Research
Bryn Mawr College

VIRGIL V. SHOOP
Mental Health Consultant in Social Work
Public Health Service, Region VI
U.S. Dept. of HEW

MRS. JEAN SHORES
Assistant Professor
School of Social Welfare
University of California at
Los Angeles

RUTH P. SHORT
Community Organization Specialist
California State Dept. of Mental
Hygiene

JOAN M. SMITH
Associate Professor
School of Social Work
University of Connecticut

MRS. ESTHER C. SPENCER
Chief, Bureau of Public Health Social Work
California State Department of
Public Health

ISABEL STAMM
Professor of Social Work
New York School of Social Work
Columbia University

ETHEL SWENGEL
Associate Professor
School of Social Work
Boston University

MERLIN TABER
Instructor of Social Work
School of Social Work
State University of Iowa

MRS. HAZEL TAYLOR
Acting Director
Office of Public Health Social Work
New York City Department of
Health

MRS. RUTH B. TAYLOR
Chief Medical Social Consultant, Tuberculosis Program
Communicable Disease Center

Public Health Service, U.S. Dept.
of HEW

LT. COL. FERNANDO G. TORGERSON
Social Service Consultant
Office of the Surgeon General,
U.S. Army

HELEN H. TUCK
Associate Professor
School of Social Work
McGill University

THOMAS J. TUCKER
Chief, Medical Social Consultant
Division of Maternal and Child
Health
Pennsylvania Department of Health

JOHN B. TURNER
Associate Professor
School of Applied Social Sciences
Western Reserve University

ALAN D. WADE
Assistant Professor
School of Social Service
Administration
University of Chicago

ELLEN J. WALSH
Chief, Social Service Department
The Clinical Center
National Institutes of Health
Public Health Service, U.S. Dept.
of HEW

EDWARD WALTER
Associate Professor
School of Social Work
University of Washington

ELIZABETH L. WATKINS
Assistant Professor of Social Work in Public Health
Schools of Public Health and Social
Work
University of Michigan

MRS. MILDRED WATSON
Field Work Instructor
School of Social Work
University of Denver

GENEVIEVE C. WEEKS
Assistant Professor
Division of Social Service
Indiana University

GRACE WHITE
Social Work Associate
Department of Social Services
Medical Center
University of Kentucky

ERNEST F. WITTE
Executive Director
Council on Social Work Education

MILTON WITTMAN
Chief, Social Work Section,
  Training Branch
National Institute of Mental Health
Public Health Service, U.S. Dept.
  of HEW

MRS. SOPHIE WOJCIECHOWSKI
Field Instructor, Student Unit
School of Social Work
Adelphi College

ILSE S. WOLFF
Mental Health Nursing Consultant
Connecticut State Dept. of Health

Preface

Exploration of the goals and philosophy, the concepts and primary methods of a field of service can be a stimulating adventure for educators and practitioners alike, as the Seminar on Public Health for Schools of Social Work proved. Part of the adventure lay in discovering that some concepts and practices which had seemed to be distinctive to one field were common to both. Other practices of public health were found to be distinctive to that field. The new territory explored was their meaning and their implications for the practice of social work, and hence their significance to social work education.

This report of the seminar contains the full texts of all papers presented in the general sessions and summaries of the group discussions which interspersed them. The report cannot convey the satisfaction of clarification and increased understanding which resulted from journeying together for five days. It may, however, stimulate readers to explore the major concepts and methods and possibly to seek communication with educators and practitioners who also want a better understanding of a field of practice other than their own. Some observations by a public health social worker about the implications of the seminar for social work education appear in the concluding chapter of this report.

Design of the Seminar

Two major objectives were set forth by the Planning Committee, which was widely representative of public health and of social work education:

To stimulate within the field of social work better realization

and better understanding of the dynamic aspects of what
the field of public health can contribute to the well-being
of the individual and the community.

To promote within social work education better understanding of the field of public health and to encourage working
together in developing ways in which this content may be
incorporated in the social work curriculum.

The objectives posed a problem in selection of content. An
analysis of the structure and programs of public health could have
pointed up the contribution made by public health to the well-
being of the individual and the community. New problems, new
programs, new approaches, new knowledge have broadened the
goals of public health. While these had to be understood to meet
the first objective, they alone were not enough. Understanding of
the dynamic aspects of a field called for more than knowledge of
the program of services. It called for emphasis on the goals,
philosophy, guiding principles, and selection and evaluation of
methods. The second objective could not be met until it became
clear to the educators how these goals, philosophy, concepts, and
methods were akin to or differed from those of social work.
Furthermore, public health content had to be seen in its range
and substance and then considered from the standpoint of its
potential contribution to social work practice, and therefore, its
appropriateness for social work education.

During the period of planning with the Advisory Committee
several clusters of questions emerged, many of which could not
be "answered" by one speaker, or even several speakers. They
necessitated joint exploration by practitioners and educators in
group discussion. The selection of the content for presentations
by speakers and for small group sessions was directed toward
finding at least partial answers to these persisting questions:

1. One idea lies at the core of the relationship between public health and social work. What is the relationship between health and social functioning? What are the reciprocal concerns and common interests of the two fields?
   Where do they converge and how are they interdependent? What are the interrelationships between health and

social welfare agencies in delivering services to meet human needs? In short, what is common ground?

2. What concepts of public health are most characteristic? What light can the public health concept of primary prevention throw on social prevention? Can hazards to adequate social functioning be as clearly defined as hazards to health, and by similar methods? What applicability to social work lies in the concept of program emphases on high risk groups and populations? Is the public health field encountering problems in its effort to prevent chronic disease similar to those which social work encounters in trying to prevent chronic social disorders?

3. What approaches are used by each field to reach shared and distinctive goals? What methods are effective, and to what ends? How are they selected and evaluated? Are public health methods adaptable to social work? Would social work practice be enriched by further knowledge and utilization of these methods?

All participants were requested to prepare for the seminar. Source material and suggested reading were provided to the public health practitioners so they might become well versed in the nature of social work education and the curriculum policy of the Council on Social Work Eduation. Source material and suggested reading were provided to the social work educators so they might become familiar with public health concepts and with the organization and nature of public health services at the various levels of government. The sessions were planned to understanding on this base of information.[1]

Public health physicians were asked to carry the major task of presenting public health content in the general sessions. Three subjects—epidemiology, prevention, and community planning—were presented in the dual frameworks of public health and social work, with companion papers by public health physicians and social work educators. Social work educators led the group sessions, and social workers from the Public Health Service served

---

[1] The annotated bibliography distributed to the participants at the Seminar appears in the Appendix of this report.

as consultants. The faculty was supplemented in the discussion groups by 40 actively participating resource persons primarily from federal, state, and local public health programs; most were social workers but there were also public health physicians and nurses, and a psychologist. The social sciences were also represented by several faculty members of schools of social work.

All discussion groups were designed to provide the maximum opportunity for varied points of view from a wide range of expert knowledge. Each group included representatives of the several disciplines in public health practice, a social worker from a federal program related to health and medical care other than the Public Health Service, and social work educators in each major curriculum area. Public health content currently appears in a variety of courses and in field instruction in schools of social work, as shown by summaries of curriculum offerings related to public health prepared for the seminar by participants from the schools. By design, the group sessions on implications for the curriculum were not centered on any particular sequence but on three major facets of social work—collecting and analyzing information and knowledge to be used in problem solving, policy making and programing, and the provision of services to individuals, groups, and communities.

Observations on the Significance of the Seminar

The objectives set by the Planning Committee were seen as long-range objectives as well as aims for the seminar. As an event, the seminar represents the culmination of almost two years of planning but it also represents a springboard for further activities in the Public Health Service, in the Council on Social Work Education, and in the individual schools of social work. Channels of communication were significantly widened for public health personnel as well as for social work educators. Participants found that communication among disciplines and among practitioners and educators enriched all. Wide geographic representation enabled the social workers to get a broader view of public health personnel and public health practice, and gave the public health people a broader view of social work education and its philosophy. This broader base of acquaintance will facilitate further exchange of information, teaching materials, and faculty selection.

As a field of practice, Public health utilizes a number of disciplines. Rarely do practitioners of several disciplines in one field sit down together for a significant period to ponder how the educational preparation of one discipline might be enriched by selected content from that field. Even more rarely is the opportunity provided for several disciplines to explore this question with a substantial number of educators from one discipline and thus to be exposed to the points of view about education for that particular practice. Such was the opportunity afforded by the seminar. One by-product has been the alertness of public health personnel to the possibilities of fruitful explorations with other groups of educators. It was implicit that the potential value of social work concepts for other educational programs would emerge.

Since the seminar was planned for social work educators, discussions of curriculum focused on social work education. They aimed to stimulate thinking about specific content, new approaches, and untapped sources of rich teaching material. As stated in the second objective set for the seminar, one aim was to encourage social work educators and public health personnel to work together in developing ways in which public health content might be incorporated effectively into the social work curriculum. A process was set in motion that will be continued in the schools as faculties search for better ways to meet their curriculum objectives. No effort was made to translate into curriculum structure the material of the seminar which was recognized to be of value. The reports of the group discussions reflect no conclusions regarding specific ways of incorporating public health content in the curriculum, but they do reflect strong interest in exploring a wide range of concepts and consideration of specific content that seemed promising. Interest was shown in examining some concepts at greater depth, methods of public health as curriculum objectives were discussed, and the possibilities for usage were weighed. The curricula of a number of schools will undoubtedly be enriched as a direct consequence of insights gained during the seminar.

Public health seeks to employ more social workers than are

now prepared for the particular responsibilities defined in its positions for social workers. A session was devoted to the available types of advanced education and training programs and to the competencies needed in the practice of social work in public health. Its aim was to lead this group of educators into further consideration of the profession's need to provide methods of training beyond the master's degree program, not only for the field of public health but for the competent practice of social work in any field.

The seminar's significance cannot be measured at this time. The schools' immediate response to the invitation and the quality of participation by their representatives evidenced its timeliness and importance. The grasp of new concepts and the progression of thought in their application to social work and education for social work give promise of far-reaching results.

GRACE WHITE
Educational Director

THE PAPERS

Why Are We Here?*

by THEODORE J. BAUER, M.D.

Background for Expectations

On behalf of the Public Health Service, I want to welcome you to this seminar and express our appreciation to you for coming. This is an experiment, a first-of-its-kind occasion. To evaluate it, we need to consider at the outset what we expect. As far as the Public Health Service is concerned, our expectations stem directly from new emphases in our programs which I would like to review briefly. I think this background will give you a better understanding of why we sought this meeting with you.

For some time, it has been apparent that health services and facilities needed adjustments to meet the changing conditions of modern life. From a health standpoint, these changed conditions fall into two broad categories.

Our New World

One is external. The world we live in today is radically different from the world of yesterday. The land, the water, even the air is different: permeated with new chemicals, new radioactive materials, new threats to health. More obvious changes are the new suburbias and shopping centers, the concentration of two-thirds of the population in metropolitan areas, the traffic-jammed superhighways. These changes too have a direct relationship to health.

The second category of change is more personal and relates to the effects on people of the changing conditions of life. Owing to medical progress, people are living longer; chronic diseases and injuries now loom as the major threats to health. Treatment

---

* Paper delivered March 4, 1962.

of these problems calls for a wide range of services. At the same time, owing to the mobility of the population and its concentration in sprawling urban areas, the problem of providing such services has become more complex.

Two years ago a task force was appointed by the Surgeon General of the Public Health Service to consider how our federal programs might better aid the states and communities in adjusting health activities to these changing conditions. The outcome of the work of this task force was the decision to establish two special units in the Public Health Service: one concentrating on environmental threats to health, the other on the development of services and facilities that people need to maintain optimum health under modern living conditions.

In dealing with environmental health problems, research is the crying need. We simply do not know enough about the long-term effects of low level exposure to chemicals, radioactive material, and other contaminants to know what we must control and how to do it. Plans are now under way to develop a National Environmental Health Center, comparable in many ways to the National Institutes of Health, except that instead of dealing with specific disease categories, it will deal with elements in the environment that contribute to disease and disability. Like the NIH, this center will support research projects and training programs for research personnel in non-federal agencies in addition to conducting its own research and training programs. The proposed Environmental Health Center will also be the headquarters for operating programs which take existing knowledge and see—by technical assistance, enforcement action and other measures—that this knowledge is widely applied.

Using What We Know

In dealing with personal health problems, however, we already have a tremendous amount of life and health saving knowledge which is not being fully used.

Although there are still great gaps in our knowledge—we have no preventives for chronic diseases comparable to vaccines for communicable diseases, nor do we have the specific cures we need—nevertheless we do have an excellent medical reseach program in the NIH itself and in the outside research it supports. What we do not have is an adequate system for making better use of the knowledge we already possess. It is this problem that concerns us and that, we hope, will concern you too.

Needed: A Continuum of Health Care

To make the best possible use of modern health knowledge, we need to devise measures for providing a continuum of health care to the individual. At present too much is left to chance. Whether a child is protected against the growing list of communicable diseases for which we have vaccines depends upon the kind of family he happens to be born into. Whether cancer, glaucoma, diabetes, and the other so-called silent diseases are discovered at their most treatable, and often painless, stages depends upon the degree of concern the individual has for his health. Relatively few apparently have enough knowledge or concern to seek and pay for medical checkups when they feel well. And the kind and quality of care the person with a chronic condition receives depends not only upon the alertness of his physician in keeping up with all the new developments in this field, but also on the availability of a variety of facilities and services, many of which are now lacking or inadequate in most communities. Because too much is left to chance, because care is so fragmented, we estimate that approximately 150,000 Americans die and more than a million are seriously disabled every year from conditions that could have been prevented.

Congress has recognized this as a national problem; much legislation in recent years has been designed to help states and communities develop programs to deal with it. You are probably most familiar with the legislation which fosters training, research, and the development of community services related to mental health.

The most recent and comprehensive measure to strengthen state and community programs was taken last fall when Congress passed the Community Health Services and Facilities Act. This law authorizes more federal aid in modernizing health and medical services so that people will have a greater opportunity to get the kind of care they need, when and where they need it. It provides funds for state health departments to foster growth and development of home nursing, homemaker and restorative services, and other measures of particular benefit to the chronically ill and aged. It authorizes more aid for the construction of nursing homes. And it provides for project grants which can be used by public and other nonprofit health and welfare agencies to devise better methods of delivering health services to the people.

New Model—with Social Services Built In

I regard this legislation as a new charter to public health. For the first time we have a national commitment to do the modernization job that has long needed doing. It is in relation to this tremendous new opportunity that I am so excited about the potentialities of this seminar. For if this modernization is to be effective, it must include a strong social service component. What we expect from you are some answers as to how that component can become a built-in feature of these emerging, these modernized, health services. We think you are the key people to help us because you are training the social workers of the future, the men and women we shall be looking to as we build these modern programs.

The task before us will not be easy, either for you or for us. There has always been a strong relationship between the professions of public health and social work, but in recent years we have tended to go our separate ways. We both repeat the same credos—the importance of treating the "whole person," the interrelationship of the social, emotional, and physical. But in actual practice the social worker has become more and more preoccupied with the social and emotional. The public health worker, on the other hand, has relied over-heavily on the physical sciences. He has looked to penicillin to wipe out VD, to vaccine to eradicate polio, to fluoridation to reduce tooth decay. Too often he has tended to forget that it is not the drugs, the vaccines, the chemicals, but people's attitudes about them that spell the difference between the success or failure of a public health program.

Despite our separation—perhaps even because of it—during this period of specialization both professions have matured. We know much more about the control of health and social problems than we did back in the days when health and social workers ganged up on the hapless client with a "no VD shots, no groceries" approach.

The Public Expects Effective Action

Nevertheless, there is ample evidence that both health and social problems have multiplied faster than our ability to cope with them. The public is becoming increasingly concerned about these unmet health and social needs and challenges us to find more effective answers.

This seminar is based on the premise that our professions can best meet our challenges, our need for adjustments, by re-emphasizing our fundamental concepts of the interrelatedness of health and social problems. The purpose of our getting together is to explore methods of translating these concepts into active practice in today's society.

Social work is recognized as contributing to the patient a continuum of services—pre-hospital, hospital, and after care. Social work has competencies we in public health need and lack. Considering our needs first in their most narrow and selfish context, we need more social workers as employees in community health agencies as well as in hospitals. We need them to staff counseling centers where patients and their families can be guided to the health and health-related services they need. We need them as members of coordinated home-care teams to help families deal with the familial and personal problems inherent in long-term illness. We need their skills in community organization to help communities develop plans and set priorities for the modernization of their health services. The number and variety of opportunities for social workers in health agencies are rapidly increasing.

Beyond the immediate staffing needs within health agencies, there is the broader need for directors and staffs of social agencies to team up with public health workers on problems of mutual concern. Your "hard core" families are also our "hard core" families; their health problems are as unresolved as their social problems. I have noted a growing trend for health and welfare agencies to work together, in inter-agency committees, case conferences, and training opportunities, and in other ways, but I believe much more could and should be done along this line.

Our Common Problems and Prospects

Perhaps I can best sum up our needs by simply saying that in dealing with today's major health problems we realize we must draw heavily upon the social sciences and particularly upon the competencies of the social work profession. We can do so only if the members of that profession recognize the mutuality of our problems and share our interest in mounting a joint attack upon them. That is why we are suggesting that certain aspects of public health may have a legitimate place in the school of social work curriculum. We are not suggesting special courses in public health; we are not proposing a return to the old type of public health course which all too often seemed to have the objective of turning social workers into pseudo specialists in certain types of diseases. We *are* asking for an exploration of ways in which social work students might be sensitized to the newer types of health problems and to the contribution they can make toward their solution.

We are optimistic enough to believe that the benefits of such an approach will not be entirely one-sided—that public health may also make a contribution to your profession. The physical condition of a client often has an important bearing on his social problems. This is particularly true of the chronically ill and aged, whose plight is demanding increasing attention from both our professions. I believe we have barely skimmed the surface in exploring how we might work together more profitably in programs of medical care and rehabilitation. Not only our medical knowledge but our public health concepts are useful in advancing our social programs.

I will not attempt to spell out how a more effective merging of our competencies might be achieved. I merely want to assure you that if you, in considering the ideas presented at this seminar, discover ways you think we can be helpful to each other, we shall be happy to make whatever contribution we can. For our part, we shall consider this conference a success if we gain, as I know we shall, your thoughtful consideration of the issues presented during these five days.

Great Expectations[*]

by ERNEST F. WITTE

Our Common Heritage

This meeting underscores our conviction that public health and social work not only have much in common but that each has unique knowledge and skills which, properly utilized, can enhance performance in the other field.

We have in common the roots from which we have grown. They are found in the common interests of those early pioneers who may be considered our common founders. Some of these roots go back to colonial times. Increased immigration and the development of slums became the concern of reformers who saw the effects of overcrowding on health and sanitation, on poverty and dependency, on family life, and organized in various ways to do something about them. Among those who contributed to the early development of both public health and social work were such leaders as Dorothea Dix, Jane Addams, Florence Kelley, Dr. Benjamin Rush, Lemuel Shattuck, Jacob Riis, and Justice Brandeis (especially because of his successful defense of the Oregon ten-hour maximum day for women). These are but a few of those to whom we owe a common debt; if you were preparing such a list, it might be entirely different from mine.

This early identification of public health and social work tended to disappear as the two fields developed their special interests and training programs. As social work evolved, it placed increasing emphasis on direct services to individuals, whereas public health moved in the opposite direction. Important to note,

[*] Paper delivered March 4, 1962.

however, is that recent developments in both fields appear to be bringing us back to a realization that we have many common problems on which we ought to work together. Perhaps the developments in public health as reported by the late Dr. Joseph W. Mountin help to explain why our two fields are again drawing closer together:

> In addition, a new approach to health itself is being fostered by professional groups as well as in the popular mind. Health is now being thought of, not in terms of disease or mortality figures, but in a positive way, in terms of physical fitness, mental and emotional adjustment, and social satisfaction and usefulness. In other words, health is no longer considered solely as an end, but also as a means. The public health responsibility cannot be considered liquidated once we have reduced infant mortality to the vanishing point, or conquered malaria or syphillis, or even cancer and heart disease. It must be geared to promoting ever higher standards of human efficiency and satisfaction.
>
> As an important corollary of this approach, public health workers are obliged to take a new look at the origins of social pathology. Health problems cannot be isolated from the environment—both physical and social—in which they exist. Such factors as the individual's job, his family life, his housing, his recreation must all be assayed for their impact on health and disease. In other words, we must now not only put emphasis on the individual and his needs, but also consider him in relation to his whole complex socioeconomic environment.[1]

This comes rather close to my own thinking (which in this case reflects that of social workers generally) that our public health services have too long neglected preventive and early corrective medical care for the individual. It has always seemed less than enough to discover the dental needs, for example, of the school child, or his need for corrective help with his vision, or his nutritional needs, and then do nothing to assure corrective action.

---

[1] Joseph W. Mountin, "The Health Department's Dilemma," *Public Health Reports,* 67:225, March 1952.

I must add in all honesty that we in social work education have highly selfish motives in our concern with public health. We think you have developed concepts and methods which may contribute significantly to the improvement of social work education and practice about which I want to comment later.

Concerns of the Council

Some of you are less familiar than others with the responsibilities and interests of the Council on Social Work Education. The Council is a fledgling, both in age and size, compared to the Public Health Service. It is not quite ten years old and has an authorized professional staff of twelve, but at the moment is short two of these. Within this voluntary organization provision has been made for responsible participation by all parts of the national community concerned with making social work education produce social workers of competence.

The Council embraces 56 accredited schools of social work in the United States and seven in Canada, some 115 undergraduate departments offering a sequence of courses bearing on social welfare, the National Association of Social Workers, 44 national organizations performing welfare functions, and representatives of higher education and of the interested public. It is not always easy to meld the diverse interests of all these groups, but in the main we have not encountered insurmountable obstacles.

The objectives of the Council are two: to improve and to extend education for social work. I shall not take time to detail the many varied activities in which we engage in the furtherance of these objectives, activities which are outlined in our leaflet, *Focus and Direction for Social Work Education.*[2]

Health and Welfare Are Inseparable

Naturally, as an organization concerned with social work curriculum development, we are deeply interested in all aspects of health and medical care, for these are inseparably a part of the welfare of people, irrespective of any other problems involved.

---

[2] *Focus and Direction for Social Work Education* (New York: Council on Social Work Education, 1960; revised, August 1962).

The importance of health and medical care is increasingly brought to the attention of social work as the life span increases and more individuals at both ends of it require care and assistance of some kind. No one was particularly surprised to learn, for example, that "the great majority of adult welfare recipients [in New York State] are not simply persons in economic need, but are sick people who require medical and social services to restore their health, to conserve what health they have, or to make their remaining days as comfortable as possible."[3] Unfortunately, our public action is not always consistent with our knowledge of such problems.

The interest of social work education in all aspects of health and medical care has contributed to the development over a considerable period of a particular interest in public health concepts and methods. This interest has waxed and waned for various reasons, but there has been, I believe, steadily increasing recognition that we ought to make a systematic effort to understand public health better.

From its inception the Council, like its predecessor, has had close working relations with certain units of the Public Health Service, particularly the National Institute of Mental Health. Our staff has had both formal and informal opportunities to consult with the Public Health Service staff and vice versa. We followed with interest, and at times apprehension, the recent self-study by the Public Health Service. We have been involved with various units in our mutual concern over manpower shortages in both fields, and we are currently working with the NIMH to develop a comprehensive roster of mental health manpower which we expect to be of great value in resolving this problem. We hope this effort may be expanded, at least to include all manpower in the health field.

A Combined Curriculum?

The focus of this seminar, however, is on the use in social work education of certain concepts and methods developed in

---

[3] Introduction to *No. 1 Cause of Dependency; 1958 Annual Report, New York State Department of Social Welfare* (Albany: New York State Department of Social Welfare, 1959), p. vii.

public health. We have not been unaware that there might be benefits to social work education in a closer study of public health concepts and methods, but our attempts have been sporadic and not well organized. In 1956, for example, a subcommittee of the Council's Committee on the Advanced Curriculum examined the possibilities of developing a combined curriculum, drawn from schools of public health and social work, which would prepare students for a social work career in public health. This was recognition, I think, that in some respects the social work curriculum was not then equipping social workers to practice in the public health field so that they could make their maximum contribution. We now recognize that our task is to prepare well-qualified social workers for practice in any field; this does not preclude utilizing knowledge from another field that has value for social work nor permitting students to acquire knowledge in another field by taking courses in other schools of the university, when this does not interfere with their education for their own field.

In 1959 the Council and Cornell University co-sponsored a conference on the common training required by United States personnel going abroad to give technical advice and professional help to less-developed nations. Public health personnel took a responsible part in helping to plan this conference and make it a success. Dr. John J. Hanlon discussed "Public Health and Social Change" and in a remarkably comprehensive but down-to-earth fashion made these developments and their implications for joint concern very clear. I quote one brief passage from his talk:

Importance of the Family

Over a long period, social action to combat or remedy the various types of social problems was fractioned into separate, more or less insulated activities. This was natural since the recognition of each specific problem and its espousal for public action usually originated with one or several visionary individuals. Sometimes these persons were dedicated to the amelioration of a particular problem because of some personal or familial experience. This was the cause above all which motivated them and those they gathered about them. The result was a tendency toward parochialism of interest and action evidenced by separate health reforms, housing reforms, penal reforms, political reforms, and so on. Gradually a relationship among all these apparently unrelated social problems became recognized on more or less theoretical and empirical grounds, but attempts to correlate remedial action lagged essentially up to the present generation.

Perhaps the single most significant contribution to this recent development has been the recognition of and emphasis upon the family, in contrast to the individual, as the basic integer. Beyond this, in the free world at least, the basis and fabric of the nation are centered upon the totality of the families within it. This is evidenced in agriculture, advertising, home and automobile design, and for tax purposes.[4]

Our conjectures on areas of common concern and helpfulness were borne out in the exchange of knowledge made possible by this conference on education for international service. Furthermore, possibly because in less complicated and structured societies one gets a clearer picture of relationships, it became obvious that the better social work and public health understand each other's objectives and methods, the more effectively can each work to achieve its own goals and contribute to the achievement of their common goals.

In a follow-up conference in 1961, co-sponsored by the Association of Schools of Public Health and the Council on Social Work Education, we dealt with how to make professional education better serve students coming from abroad for professional study in the United States. Although only a few faculty members have been exposed to this type of exchange, we believe the knowledge gained is shared through published reports and established channels for curriculum development.

Another development related to the objectives of this seminar was the decision in 1958 by our Accreditation Commission to collect descriptions of social work practice in selected fields, including public health. These descriptions were the raw material from

---

[4] *Interprofessional Training Goals for Technical Assistance Personnel Abroad: Report of an Interprofessional Conference on Training of Personnel for Overseas Service, Ithaca, New York, June, 1959* (New York: Council on Social Work Education, 1959), pp. 145-46.

which we derived a series of statements on practice, including one on medical social work. This has helped to clarify areas of concern in curriculum development.

Another Council venture into the health field was our co-sponsoring with the American Association on Mental Deficiency of a conference on mental retardation and social work education. Here was a neglected responsibility with large health and social components. There was obvious need to insure that the generic social work curriculum help students to understand "the inter-relatedness of the bio-psychosocial factors which produce mental retardation; the dynamic nature of retardation and its consequent responsiveness to social intervention; the growth potential and the ability to change in the retarded individual; the existence of individual differences among the retarded."[5]

As further indications of our sustained move toward a better working knowledge of public health, I would list the following:

In 1955 the Council was involved in a conference called by the tuberculosis unit of the Public Health Service to discuss the possible interest of selected schools of social work in the development of a cooperative research program.

In 1957 and 1958 the Council, the National Association of Social Workers, and the American Public Health Association considered desirable educational qualifications of social workers in public health programs.

At our Annual Program Meeting in Montreal in 1961 we held an institute on "Public Health Concepts: Their Implication for Social Work Education." That institute in some ways helped to lay the groundwork for this seminar.

The experience that perhaps has done as much as any other to stimulate Council interest in the utilization of public health concepts in social work education has to do with the work of Community Research Associates. In 1960, at the request of the Hill Family Foundation, Council staff analyzed all reports of experiments on preventive programing in social work published by Community Research Associates and the St. Paul Family-Centered

---

5 Alfred H. Katz, ed., *Mental Retardation and Social Work Education: Proceedings of a Conference held at . . . Milford, Michigan, June 16-19, 1959* (Detroit: Wayne State University Press, 1961), p. 5.

Project to determine their implications for the social work curriculum. Subsequently we brought together a group of social work educators to discuss how the concepts of prevention and control developed in these and related experiments were being or might be utilized in the curriculum.[6]

The relevance of that experience to this seminar is based on the extensive use by Community Research Associates of methods and concepts borrowed from public health. In a paper for our 1960 Annual Program Meeting, Bradley Buell explains the underlying concepts of the experiment:

> At the outset of our projects therefore, CRA adopted a *therapeutic* concept of preventive programing. This concept assumes that the systematic organization and application of the community's therapeutic resources at different stages *after* pathological symptoms are detected can result in delaying, halting or curing the repetitious course of the disorder, and that this can make a measurable impact upon the community's total problem.
>
> Prevention in this context depends upon the reduction of the multiple causes that result in the measurable breakdown of functional self-sufficiency. We all have had experience showing that the results of deteriorating family situations continue into a second and third generation; and we have known it could have been prevented if appropriate measures had been applied at critical points along the way.[7]

He goes on to say in speaking of the concept of control:

> In times past, social welfare often has regarded "control" as a nasty word. It has been assumed that the term, as a program objective, referred to physical control over the person and, therefore, was an "undemocratic" concept. The contrary, of course, is the case. "Control" in public health refers

---

[6] Workshop on Use in Curriculum of the Concepts of Prevention and Control, New York, N. Y., March 29-31, 1961.

[7] Bradley Buell, "Implications for Social Work Education of a Conception of Prevention," in *Education for Social Work; Proceedings of Eighth Annual Program Meeting, Council on Social Work Education, Oklahoma City, Oklahoma, January 20-23, 1960* (New York: Council on Social Work Education, 1960), p. 143.

to the control of the incidence and prevalence of a disease. Three reasons for linking it with prevention apply logically to preventive programing for the control of psychosocial disorders.

First: The term brings in a community-wide connotation. That is, it implies a concern about the spread of the disease or disorder throughout the entire population, not just about the cases that may come to the attention of a particular agency. The implication is that a preventive program should attack the community totality of the problem or disorder, not just pieces of it.

Second: It introduces the concept of the modern science of epidemiology. In public health this means the study of the frequency and distribution of disease, but the concept is also applicable to social welfare problems. The facts revealed by CRA's original St. Paul study about the heavy concentration of psychosocial disorders in a relatively small group of families with a multiplicity of problems were significant "epidemiological" facts. The term also has a more comprehensive connotation and implies a scientific approach to the synthesis of all knowledge practically applicable to the community-wide prevention and control of a given problem. Social welfare research will not achieve full utility to preventive programing until it produces trained scientists broadly competent to pursue this epidemiological goal.

Third: Finally, it introduces the concept of statistical measurement of community-wide incidence and prevalence and other demographic data. The fact that the rate of a particular disease or problem is going up or down is not, of course, proof per se that the results are due directly or solely to the control program. But it is the absolutely indispensable base from which to make such an analysis and judgment.[8]

To us, the two most challenging ideas CRA is testing, by applying the principles of epidemiology, are these: Can social work develop a workable classification of social pathology and

---

[8] *Ibid.,* pp. 143-44.

procedures for the continuous collection of facts about the frequency and distribution of social problems? And how can social work measure accurately the results of its efforts to prevent and control these problems?

Our attempts to ascertain the implications of prevention and control have taken considerable time and have resulted in two Council publications.[9] In the second are significant recommendations, the last of which I quote:

> The concepts of epidemiology should be studied in connection with social policy and the profession. There may be implications for new approaches to fields of practice which eliminate some of the distinctions such as child welfare, mental health, public assistance, and family welfare.

I should mention, as further evidence of our desire to work with the health field, a project carried in our work program for a number of years, and approved by our Board, but requiring special funds before it can be initiated:

> **Special project on social work education in relation to the broad health field.** Financing will be sought to support intensified educational activity for the purpose of utilizing the full potential of the broad health field in the generic program of social work education. The health field, in this context, includes medical care programs, rehabilitation, public health, and community planning for health and medical care. A special project, including consultation service, committee and workshop activity, would embrace the identification for use in the curriculum of concepts pertinent to social work drawn from the health field, the development of content in field instruction, and the improvement of field placements. The project would contribute to the study of the educational climate and standards necessary in a training center. It might serve as a pilot project in the long-range consideration of the

---

[9] *Memorandum on the Implications for Social Work Curriculum of Community Research Associates' Materials* (New York: Council on Social Work Education, 1960); *Concepts of Prevention and Control: Their Use in the Social Work Curriculum,* Report of Workshop (New York: Council on Social Work Education, 1961), p. 32.

appropriate utilization for field instruction of programs and agencies other than social agencies.[10]

We hope that eventually we can undertake this project.

I want to conclude these remarks by indicating why I have titled them "Great Expectations." Let me recapitulate our stated objectives for this seminar:

To stimulate within the field of social work a better realization and understanding of the dynamic aspects of what the field of public health can contribute to the well-being of the individual and the community.

To promote within social work education better understanding of the field of public health and to encourage working together in developing ways in which this content may be incorporated in the social work curriculum.

I have an additional objective:

To develop among social workers a greater familiarity with such concepts as diagnosis, prevention, control, community, and client as they are used in public health, and with the methods of classification, systematization, and measurement and their optimum utilization in social work. The paper on "Concepts of Prevention as Applied to the Practice of Social Work" by Elizabeth P. Rice is a notable contribution.[11]

Finally my hope is that the public health personnel at this seminar will grow in knowledge of social work education and practice and will find added reasons why collaboration between our two fields is worth-while and should be encouraged.

I am grateful for this opportunity of welcoming you here. I hope that by the end of the week all the great expectations for this meeting will have been fulfilled.

---

[10] *Work Program for 1961-62 and Report of Progress for 1960-61* (New York: Council on Social Work Education, 1961), p. 10. Mimeographed.

[11] Elizabeth P. Rice, "Concepts of Prevention as Applied to the Practice of Social Work," in *The Significance of Health in the Child's Growth and Development,* Tulane Studies in Social Welfare, No. 3 (New Orleans: Tulane University School of Social Work, 1961), p. 87 ff.

Public Health Goals[*]

by JOHN D. PORTERFIELD, M.D.

Our Common History

This morning I offer you two case histories—yours and mine.

More literally, I want to talk about the case histories of our professions—social work and public health. For the physician, as for the social worker, the case history of a group can be as revealing as that of an individual, as vital to diagnosis, as essential to prognosis.

"History" is the key word here. The historian is not, despite his detractors, a man who roams among the gravestones of the past; rather is he a man who climbs a mountain the better to trace the road he has traveled, and the better to discern the long road ahead.

The psychiatrist who grows to understand his patient becomes the historian of that individual. What do the case histories of our professions teach us? Let us go back together, as the psychiatrist might urge, to our childhoods.

We began together. Both public health and social work grew out of intolerable conditions in the great cities of this country three-quarters of a century ago. If this were a documentary film, the screen would now be showing a public health officer and a social worker, in the costume of the period, meeting in the doorway of a Chicago slum dwelling in the 1890's.

Poverty and disease in the huge industrial communities of the late nineteenth century posed a crucial challenge to our civilization; social work and public health were twin responses to

---

[*] Paper delivered March 5, 1962.

this challenge. The times called for action, and we were action people.

We began by working together. But the very existence of this seminar (so long needed, and from which so much is expected) suggests that our professional growth patterns have differed, and that now we must meet to compare notes on our goals. Frankly, I don't accept this hypothesis. I believe we have always followed parallel paths. If we pause a moment and push aside the underbrush that separates these paths, we'll find, I am certain, that we're as close together as we were seventy years ago.

Of course, we are both now mature professions, which means we have provided ourselves with impenetrable vocabularies, those tribal totems of contemporary professional recognition. Let us communicate the way we did when we were both young, idealistic occupations, eager for work to do rather than for recognition for having done it.

We have assembled here in this beautiful village one hundred of the best brains of our two trades. We plan to spend one full day discussing each of three important terms—"epidemiology," "prevention," and "community planning."

These three terms—explained, amplified, and understood—contain all that modern public health is striving for; they outline all our goals. Let us glance briefly now at the three ideas we shall be spending the rest of the week analyzing and discussing.

Theme 1: Epidemiology

Epidemiology is the basic, the central, the controlling concept in public health; it would almost be fair to say that the profession developed to practice epidemiology. In the twentieth century man has learned to conquer his ancient enemy—the epidemic—and the application of the scientific method to this warfare has properly been called "epidemiology." Once bacilli had been observed and recognized under the new microscopes of the later nineteenth century, the detective-story technique for the pursuit and destruction of disease germs was written within one generation, and the classic triad of the "agent," the "host," and the "environment" became enshrined in public health textbooks. All modern progress in public health methods has consisted of applying this triad to new problems; thus we have moved from the study of the mosquito, the swamp, and the malaria victim to research concerning the automobile, the highway, and the accident victim. But it's still epidemiology, and if it were not it would not be public health.

And yet, to reveal a well-kept secret, the term actually belongs to the social work profession rather than to public health. It derives from three Greek words which may be translated as "knowledge about people," or perhaps "the science of people." If that is not a sound description of social work, I have yet to hear a better one. While it may be too late for you to recover from the public health profession this excellent word, through legal action, still the etymology should be instructive for all of us at this seminar. Epidemiology, what we in public health have always said we do, turns out to be what you in social work have always done. The parallel paths have been closer than we suspected.

Since our sessions this week will be devoted to bridging whatever gap remains between our professions, let me point out some of the bridging we in public health have done, under the pressure of the revolution in medical science which this generation has experienced. With World War II we passed out of the era of infectious disease and into the era of chronic disease. This truism has been repeated so often by public health spokesmen that others must be as bored with the expression as we are, but it is a simple, sober fact that we shall all be struggling with the implications of this idea for the rest of our professional lives. And our success in achieving the transition from the era of infections to the era of chronic ills will determine whether public health continues to contribute to the welfare of society on into the twenty-first century.

The straight question is, "Can the detective-story technique that defeated smallpox, yellow fever, typhoid, and the rest cope effectively with cancer, heart disease, and the other killers of the present day?"

We can prove on paper that the answer is "yes."

But the practice, as usual, goes harder than the theory, and the old, reliable tools of the period of contagion—inoculation, quarantine, and sanitation—have to be stretched almost out of shape to adapt them to the problems of chronic illness.

Led by Los Angeles, this country has awakened in the last dozen years to the realization that air pollution may be as great a national challenge as water pollution. The latter job is far from finished in the United States (it is, indeed, a present crisis), but we do possess the technical knowledge for assuring our population a pure water supply. Do we know that much about "air sanitation"? What sources of air pollution should be "quarantined"? It's all easier said than done.

One extreme of the life-span we deal with competently: today's babies are protected from most of the health hazards that earlier generations had to accept as the rigors of fate. The greatest single factor in the prodigious increase in life expectancy of our day is the decrease in infant and childhood mortality. But, at the other extreme of the life-span, we deal less competently and far less successfully with the health problems of the aged. The very extension of life expectancy in which public health takes such pride presents us with ever-growing multitudes of older people and with an ever-growing proportion of chronic disease conditions that, as I have admitted, we are imperfectly prepared to combat.

We are trying to prepare ourselves more effectively; hundreds of millions of dollars are spent each year for research in cancer, heart disease, mental illness, and other chronic disease areas. No nation has ever endowed medical research so generously, and I am proud to report that a large share of this expenditure is co-ordinated by the Public Health Service.

Working with state and local health departments, we seek constantly to put research results to work, through field studies, demonstrations, pilot projects, and the support of health activities throughout the country.

But it would be misleading to imply that we have yet achieved the precision of prediction, the inevitable sequence of deduction concerning the causes of heart disease and cancer that we long ago reached in the field of communicable disease. If, however, we cannot yet speak of a classic epidemiology of chronic diseases, we are faithful to the epidemiologic approach; we know that eventually this application of the scientific method will bear fruit.

We work with our traditional tools on this latest frontier, this frontier of chronic illness. Our goals are to learn, to understand, to predict, and thus to cure and to prevent. Our goals were never more vital to human welfare, because this is perhaps the ultimate health frontier for mankind.

Theme 2: Prevention

When I use the word "prevent," I am introducing the second theme of this seminar—prevention. Again, if public health had not been able to prevent disease it could never have come into existence as a profession. Epidemiology demonstrates the chain of circumstances leading to the spread of communicable diseases; prevention cuts that chain, stops the spread, makes epidemics impossible. The world looked to public health for prevention as far back as the turn of the century. In many parts of the world this cutting of the chain of contagion is still the major public health task, and even in this country thousands of local and state public health workers labor to maintain the traditional safeguards against infectious disease, supported now by the finest of modern laboratory resources (such as those at our Communicable Disease Center in Atlanta).

But how do we prevent these chronic conditions, these chief enemies of today? Until we have solved the riddle of the etiology (or causation) of chronic diseases we cannot achieve primary prevention; our work in this field must at this time concentrate on what we call secondary prevention—the prevention of disability and deterioration resulting from disease.

Early detection of diabetes makes possible timely treatment that retards or minimizes later consequences of this condition. Early detection of glaucoma makes possible the prevention of blindness. Early detection of certain forms of cancer makes possible highly effective therapy.

"Early detection" is the key phrase, the motif, of much of contemporary public health practice. Through a great variety of testing and screening techniques we are constantly checking millions of apparently well people throughout the country for evidence which, if confirmed by a physician's diagnosis, indicates the presence of a chronic condition that will benefit from early treatment.

You perceive that, whereas formerly there was a clear-cut distinction between prevention and treatment, we now live and work in a world where we prevent by treating, prevent many types of suffering and disability.

The idea of secondary prevention must, of course, be viewed with a due sense of proportion. All medical care is designed to alleviate pain and ameliorate the course of disease. Let us not wax so enthusiastic in our logic that we include the setting of a broken arm in our definition of secondary prevention. But let us clearly recognize the value of this concept as a workable expression of what public health and medical science can accomplish today, in the light of existing knowledge, in managing the chronic diseases.

Thus, while we cannot prevent the chronological phenomenon of aging, a truly immense national research effort is daily uncovering possibilities for mitigating what we once thought the inevitable degenerations of the aging process. For the first time in history we are approaching the prediction that eventually "a happy old age" will cease to be a sentimental wish and become an attainable goal.

Right now the grave problem of chronic disease is compounded by the rapid increase in the number of old people, more prone to such disease—but remember that we are fighting this war on both fronts simultaneously, and victory on either front will mean total victory.

Theme 3: Community Planning

This two-front war might also be thought of as amphibious, since it includes both research and community activity; it is waged in great laboratories and in your home town and mine. Despite our impressive investment in medical research, the prime mission of the Public Health Service remains the serving of the *public*. History will judge us not as pure scientists but as workers in the vineyard, and our vineyard is the American community. Thus, our third theme for this seminar is "community planning."

No phrase is more deceptively simple than this one—for surely everyone knows what a community is and what planning is. But *do* we know?

This charming town of Princeton is famous throughout the world as the seat of a great university; it is a model university community. But, even if the Governor did not live here, there would also be a political Princeton. There is a commuter's community, too. There is a religious community, a commercial community, a scientific community. There are many more Princetons. For which one, then, shall we plan? And what is planning? The Brink robbery was well-planned—probably we don't mean *that* kind of planning. Nor do we mean the Russian kind.

Two of the occupational sins of professional groups in contemporary America are glibness and provincialism; let us pray to be delivered from these sins. Some of us are sorely tempted to let vocabulary solve all our practical problems. We say things like "Public health planning is voluntary planning," and relax in contentment, unaware that all we have done is pose a paradox. Again, because we live in a world of public health departments, hospitals, clinics, medical and nursing societies, and health associations we are tempted to invite all these groups to a luncheon, and once more relax in contentment, saying, "The whole community is here."

I shall not shock you if I mention that social work, too, has its vocabulary and its provincialism. This week we must do more than superimpose our vocabularies and our provincialisms.

The American community we both serve exists. It is real. Its boundaries may vary with the context of each problem we tackle, and our planning must take this into account, but we *can* help communities to plan, and we *can* help each other to get this done.

If you and I were to descend from a bus in a typical American community of, say, 30,000 population near the geographical center of the United States, and launch a joint community planning project, we'd find that our two specialized professional universes had a large overlap. The most important one would be, of course, the city government, from whence cometh, so often, our salaries. The schools, the churches, the men's clubs, the women's clubs, and all the myriad groups Americans love to join, the newspapers, and the radio and television stations, even the public transportation system—we may like to call them "resources" or "facilities," but we are jointly concerned with them, and we hope they are interested in *us*.

Let us not say—please, let us not say—we are going to "organize" this hypothetical community; it is, as a typical American town, already organized within an inch of its life. Its streets are lined, figuratively, with poles carrying the transmission lines of local power. What we really do is to hook onto these power lines and divert some electricity to operate our own joint planning "equipment."

Then, when our equipment is whirring and buzzing away, how do we manage it?

This is where the goals of public health and the goals of social work meet. Here, at the local level, in the act of "community planning" we understand and help one another, because we face, cope with, live with, and *do something about* the same reality.

Here on Main Street, U.S.A., it is clear we both seek to help people lead healthier, more enjoyable, more useful, more confident lives. If we can't contribute to gaining these goals on Main Street, then all our conferences and all our learned publications are vanity. Both our professions should in that case disband.

In the broadest sense our planning takes account of the circumstance that American society is a unique blend of "public" and "private"—unmatched anywhere on earth—and the community, as a microcosm of that society, is a similar blend. Whether we speak of health or of welfare, our planning must merge the public and the private sources of strength in the community to further the general good of all.

Despite the newspaper cartoonists, neither of us demands an always-increasing flow of taxpayer's gold to achieve our ends. Rather, in the old Yankee phrase, we labor to help communities "make do" with what they already have. The public health worker functions much more often as a guide than as a boss; he tries to help a community give maximum health service to people through the most efficient use of its hospitals and clinics, physicians and nurses, and all the other "health facilities and resources." If we change the phrase to "welfare facilities and re-sources," I'm sure the social worker's pattern is the same.

Only a community which has thus "co-ordinated" itself is pre-pared for the health challenges of the present day—chronic dis-ease, mental illness, the infirmities of old age. Only thus is it pre-pared for the welfare challenges of this era of automation in in-dustry, social ferment, a mobile population, and the fading away of old standards and customs.

I spoke of the overlap of our professional universes. The greatest overlap is, of course, the people we serve—not patients, not clients, not cases, but people.

Only together can we serve them well.

This speech will end without supplying any of the official information you may have been braced to hear. I completely for-got to provide you with a history of the last 170 years of the Public Health Service, decade by decade. Nor was I thoughtful enough to describe for you the dozen or more pieces of major federal legislation upon which the Public Health Service depends or may depend in the future. From others you will have to glean the statistics of mortality, morbidity, life expectancy, prevalence and incidence of disease, and similar facts of public health life. I have even withheld from you the details of the Public Health Service budget for fiscal years 1962 and 1963. Worst of all, although I was asked to speak about public health goals, I neglected to present a proper outline of those goals, broken down by "primary" and "secondary," and arranged by Roman and Arabic numerals, large and small letters.

All I intended to do was to skip from mountain peak to mountain peak. In the days ahead, we shall push through many valleys, climb many steep slopes. It seemed a good idea to begin by reminding ourselves that the mountain peaks are there.

Programing—Principles and Elements*

by LESLIE W. KNOTT, M.D., M.P.H.

When I first began to think about the subject of programing, I consulted an Oxford Universal and a Webster desk dictionary to check my understanding of the word. I soon found myself in the rather interesting position of having to develop a talk around a word that apparently was nonexistent. It gave me the feeling associated with preparing a review of a book whose cover is gone and leaves torn out! Nevertheless, I proceeded, thinking that this probably would not be the first time you had heard a marvelous talk on nothing. But later I consulted a Webster's unabridged version and found that the word, "programing," does exist and is defined.

One definition of program, in antiquity as well as now, is a public notice. Although this is not the meaning that specifically applies to our discussion today, it is an important element to keep in mind. For, as we shall see later, success in programing often depends in part upon letting people know what we hope to do or are about to do.

When it comes to the process of programing, there is nothing strange about it although at times it can be a complicated procedure. Each of us tends to begin the day with some program in mind, especially those who have to earn a living. It consists of planned actions on what we hope to accomplish in the next 24 hours. Behind this plan are reasons, likes, dislikes, methods of proceeding, and a host of factors, conscious and even unconscious, that influence our actions toward one or more desired

---

* Paper delivered March 5, 1962.

ends. Although events that could not possibly have been foreseen may upset the day, our success depends largely upon the reality of our goals, the motivations in seeking them, the thoroughness with which we have considered related factors, and the manner in which we move toward our objectives. How keenly we feel over success or failure at day's end depends upon how important and timely those goals are.

As we move from the individual to various organizational units of society—for example, the family, the industry, the service agency—the business of programing becomes more complicated and far more essential. But the general principle is the same, namely, determining what is to be and can be done and how best to do it. In short, programing for the purpose of our discussion is nothing more than the sound planning and implementing of action with realistic ends in view. This, I am sure, is no great revelation to you, for as administrators of curricula and planners of careers you are keenly aware of "programing."

The specific technique of programing, however, and the elements involved differ depending on the end in view. My responsibility is to explain how we in health go about programing. Because of the close relationship between health and welfare, I am sure you will find a number of points in common with the field of social work.

Defining the Problem

A first and most essential step in formulating health programs is to determine potential and existing health problems of the community. To the public health physician the community is his patient; it is subject to the risk of disease; it is afflicted with illness; prevention and treatment are as applicable to the community as they are to the individual. Although the method of examining the community may differ from that used for the individual, the principle is the same. Just as the physician must review the patient's medical history, examine him carefully, and come to an appraisal before developing preventive and treatment objectives, so must the health authority study the community—city, state, or nation.

He must know the nature of illnesses that prevail or threaten and the extent to which they cause or may cause impaired health, disability, and premature death. Mere reports of communicable disease and mortality, once the traditional bases for public health programs, are no longer sufficient. The modern public health officer must diligently seek to learn, for the past as well as for the present, the major causes of ill health and disability, the non-infectious as well as the infectious maladies. This search has assumed increasing significance over the last two decades as the number of cases of communicable disease has declined and as chronic illness has affected more and more lives, particularly among the ever-growing number of our older citizens.

With the basic data on morbidity and mortality translated into crude rates—that is, cases per thousands of population—for the area as a whole and for its subdivisions, the health officer begins to formulate some concept of the health of his community, its progress for better or worse, and the nature of its symptoms and signs—the diagnosis, if you please.

I emphasize this step as a beginning—this is the raw data, the foundation of programing. As this information is classified and arranged in order of magnitude, the major areas of concern become more clear. This step gives preliminary indication of where effort should be directed.

Analyzing the Problem

The problem, however, does not rest with its gross definition. A mere inventory of morbidity and mortality, basic and valuable though it may be, requires considerable analysis before it can serve as a solid basis for programing. This is the second step in the programing process. Foremost in the mind of the public health official is the matter of cause. What the causal factors? Are we dealing with disease of bacterial origin? Are external physical or chemical agents involved? Is there a metabolic phenomenon within the individual? What is the relationship of the problem to social, economic, environmental, or personal elements such as age, race, sex? In other words, what is the natural history of the illness?

Even when all causal factors are not known, as in the case of so many chronic diseases, we can frequently prevent the complications and disabling effects of illness. Through rehabilitation and restorative techniques we can often reverse disability despite our inability to cure the disease.

The point to be emphasized is that programing for any given illness or disability depends on what is known about the factors related to cause and the possibilities for prevention, treatment, and rehabilitation. Although we may succeed in diagnosing the community's ills, the planning of our course of action—that is, programing—rests on the available knowledge concerning them. In each, is the end in view realistic? Do we have the knowledge to accomplish it?

The "stethoscope" used for examining our community patient, in defining and analyzing its problems, is epidemiology. This, in modern terms, is the scientific study of all factors relating to health, illness, and disability in groups of individuals. I shall not enlarge upon this technique and its uses—that is the subject of another session in this conference. I do wish to emphasize, however, that the appraisal of community health as a basis for program is a continuous, or at least a periodic, process, not a one-time affair. Physical ills, like social ills, are affected by community change. Nor do I wish to leave the impression that the defining and the analyzing of health problems are accomplished with ease. The lack of meaningful past data, the development of effective methods for collecting current information, and the cost of conducting such studies on a continuing basis are significant items. Epidemiology, nevertheless, is the fundamental process for assembling and analyzing the information so essential to the wise selection of the objective and to the planning of the course to achieve it.

Developing and Implementing a Course of Action

This brings us to the third step in programing—developing and implementing a course of action. With knowledge of our community ills and the risks to health, and with awareness of what can be done to prevent, control, or ameliorate illness and disability, we can proceed with program planning.

Success in planning frequently depends upon recognition of

the principle that the public health agency is not an independent, free-wheeling organization, even though it may be so established by law. Its effectiveness depends upon the understanding of its goals and programs by such community groups as the medical profession, official and voluntary organizations having an interest in health, and finally the general public. The intelligent health officer may devise sound, effective measures for control of disease, but if these efforts lack the cooperation of other interested groups or are not understood by the public, the end results are friction, achievement short of the goal, or complete failure.

Wisdom, then, calls for consulting with or including in the planning representatives of key interested groups. This may be accomplished in a variety of ways—by meeting with individual organizations, developing an advisory committee of representatives of selected groups and lay community leaders, or working through an existing body such as a community health and welfare council. Wisdom also dictates the manner in which the health officer seeks to obtain desired action. He may lay before the group a completed program and ask for review, comment, or approval. The alternative is to state the problems, explain their extent and severity, and with the group jointly build up ways and means of solving them. This latter course may be the wiser even though the health agency may be fully competent to devise its own plans.

Community participation in planning is likely to pave the way for community participation in action. It also provides the opportunty for developing agreement on needs and priorities. Establishing priorities is essential to placing major emphasis on major problems and to the appropriate utilization of resources, particularly if they are limited. This is to be guided by tradition. The alert health agency not only needs current basic information about its community "patient"; it also needs the stimulation, the views, and the assistance of others who are concerned with and who work toward the community's well-being.

Whatever approach is adopted, program development and implementation call for adequate consideration of eight elements vital to its success.

Objectives

I have already mentioned several points about selection of objectives—the need for basic information, their feasibility, and viewing their importance in relation to community needs. For programing purposes, objectives should be stated in language that can be understood by health and related professions, by appropriation bodies, and by the lay public. To the extent possible, they should be expressed in such a way that progress toward achievement can be measured. This calls for specificity rather than broad terminology. The conditions, the segments of the population, and what is to be accomplished are parts of the overall target that should be clearly defined.

In diabetes control, for example, we know that early detection and prompt medical attention can prevent or delay complications and disability. Our broad objective is to find all undetected cases of this disease. But we also know from epidemiological studies that the most likely suspects are adults over 40, those who are obese, women who have given birth to progressively larger babies, and persons having diabetic relatives. Thus our objective becomes clear as to the groups of individuals on whom we should concentrate our efforts.

Procedures

Along with objectives, of course, we must consider procedures. The two obviously are interdependent. Given the natural history of a disease, we must select from our available knowledge those measures which offer the best possibility for control.

Our foremost hope always is to prevent the occurrence of illness. For the infectious diseases we have a number of vaccines to confer immunity; these are fairly well known. In some instances good sanitation can eliminate the need for vaccines. As an example, immunization for typhoid fever is not generally recommended now except where questionable sanitation or other hazards exist. Preventing the occurrence of disease or injury by eliminating hazards or by immunization is known as primary prevention.

In chronic and degenerative diseases, we know little about

cause and must rely on what is termed secondary prevention. Early detection and prompt medical attention, as described for diabetes, is typical of this approach. It is applicable to other conditions such as glaucoma—an important cause of blindness—cancer, and certain forms of heart disease. The prophylactic use of drugs, another secondary line of defense, may eliminate the recurrence of acute episodes and damaging effects of disease already established, as in rheumatic fever, gout, and epilepsy. These are examples of diseases that cannot be prevented in a primary sense, but their progress and complications, or premature death, can be checked by secondary means.

Even in the face of disability we are not entirely helpless. Arthritics, stroke victims, those disabled by other diseases or by injuries can in many instances be restored to a high degree of independence through appropriate rehabilitation. As an illustration, the stroke patient not so long ago was regarded more or less as a hopeless case. Experience has shown, however, that 80 per cent of those who survive can be brought back to useful living if restorative measures are applied.

Selection of procedure, then, depends upon our knowledge in regard to preventing the occurrence of disease, halting its progression, or reversing its effect. We have not fulfilled our mission until we have explored and applied all that is known about each of these approaches in the order in which they have been described here.

Community Organization

Determination of objectives and of the most effective control measures are preliminary to the next step: the organizing of community resources for implementing a program. As indicated earlier, the probability is that more than one agency has an interest or concern in a given health problem. The primary purpose and scope of authority of each agency are, of course, among the first factors to be considered. With these points clarified, it is then possible to consider which agency (or agencies) has the greatest capability of implementing the program.

Perhaps a visiting nurse association rather than the health department is best able to render a particular service; or perhaps

a combination of services, one supplementing the other, would
be best. A stroke rehabilitation program, for example, may involve a practicing physician who prescribes treatment, a hospital
in which certain procedures and services must be established, a
health agency to provide follow-up services in the home, another
—or the same—to provide over-all administration, maintain records, and assume responsibility for evaluation. Non-health agencies may be involved in such matters as payment for care, provision of suitable housing, or inspection and licensure of facilities
related to the program.

The over-all purpose is to place major responsibility in that
organization which can best serve the target population. Where
responsibility is divided—and this is frequently the case—efforts
must be directed to the creation of good working relationships
through agreed-upon delegation of functions and measures for
co-ordinating operations.

This consideration emphasizes again what has been said
earlier. Health agencies have a responsibility for leadership in
solving health problems, but their success in planning and implementing frequently depends upon the degree to which they include other key community groups that have an interest or active
part in the program operation.

Organization within the Health Agency

It is hardly necessary to mention that once the health agency's responsibility for a given program is defined, the internal
assignment of responsibility and tasks becomes of prime importance. Reorganization and change in the functions of its personnel
may be necessary. Participation of staff members or their representatives in discussions of objectives, procedures, and their roles
in implementing them can certainly lead to a greater appreciation
of goals, to the contribution of ideas, and to a far greater sense of
security in adjusting to new programs.

Evaluation of the agency's personnel resources—those necessary and available—is an integral part of this process. What are
the kinds and numbers of personnel required to carry out the
program? Can personnel be diverted from other activities with
lower priority? Is training necessary to equip personnel in meet-

ing any new roles? If additional staff is needed, what are the recruitment potentials? Can less highly trained personnel be utilized under professional supervision? These are very practical questions that must be answered, particularly in this day when shortages of qualified manpower seem universally acute.

Information and Education

To what extent will the rank and file of the health and related professions and the laity understand and appreciate program goals and operations? Inclusion of key representatives on an advisory council is helpful in promoting such understanding but does not assure widespread support and co-operation. Workshops, seminars, meetings of various disciplines, and journals are well-known means of developing understanding among those in professional life. Stimulating teaching centers to provide postgraduate courses is helpful in disseminating new knowledge and updating services for the control of illness.

Informing the general public may be accomplished in a variety of ways and is an essential part of program planning.

One aspect that cannot be overlooked is the quantity and quality of professional manpower required for the continuation of an essential program. Just what can be accomplished hinges on the size and financial resources of the agency. Providing opportunities for students to gain meaningful experience in a program may stimulate interest in future employment or at least can lead to better understanding of agency function. Professional personnel of local organizations can participate in the teaching programs of professional schools and thereby familiarize future practitioners with the community aspects of health. Teaching grants and traineeships have long been used to help strengthen curricula and to attract more students to the various professions.

The point I wish to emphasize in regard to information and education is that programing must take into account the necessity of informing the professional and lay public. Where necessary, it should provide for the improvement of professional knowledge. When feasible, it should also provide for meeting future needs for qualified manpower to implement or support essential program activities.

Research and Studies

My frequent use of the term "available knowledge" implies many unknowns, and such is the case in regard to the natural history of many illnesses and to the most effective means of controlling them. In program development, gaps in knowledge and doubts about methods will appear. Depending on the available competencies and other resources, program plans might well include research and studies that will attempt to eliminate the unknowns and the doubts. Needless to say, such efforts should be well designed and provide for sound methods of evaluation. Research and studies, however, should not overshadow service objectives but should, when possible, supplement them.

Evaluation

In discussing objectives, I briefly mentioned the need to express them in meaningful terms that could be measured. The future of any program depends upon how well progress toward our objective can be demonstrated. All too often we in health, like those in other service agencies, merely enumerate activities without showing whether or not we are making any impact on a problem.

In health our ultimate goal is to eliminate or at least minimize morbidity, disability, and premature mortality. Counting patients, clinic sessions, and nurse visits to the home is important and provides helpful data, particularly for appraising costs. But totals alone tell us nothing about those denied help, for example, or about the extent to which those served have been restored to maximum function. Even when morbidity and mortality figures show progressive decline, we cannot always be sure that our actions have been responsible.

A good example is tuberculosis; we believe public health measures have helped to bring about a reduction of cases and deaths but we also recognize that higher living standards, better education, and social improvements in general have also had considerable impact upon the disease. To distinguish between fact and fancy is a task fraught with difficulty, but this does not lessen our responsibility for making an earnest effort to gauge the effectiveness and efficiency of program activities in relation to realistic objectives. Here again epidemiology is our most valuable tool in defining our problem and in measuring progress toward its solution.

Financial Resources

In reviewing the various elements of program development, the lack of consideration of financial resources up to this point has probably been obvious. Although finances are a basic element, human needs and methods for meeting those needs are our prime considerations and our justification for obtaining the required funds. The preparation of budgets that clearly show a proper relationship to program elements is part of informing and educating the public, especially the appropriating body.

It is assumed that before presenting the budget for approval, the health agency, preferably in co-operation with its advisory group, has scrutinized the financial request to assure itself and others that cost estimates have been kept at a minimum without sacrificing program effectiveness. Where it is at all feasible, the budget justification should point out what preventive measures may accomplish: improved health, fewer unnecessary deaths, less drain on private or public funds, by reducing the need for more costly types of care.

It is well to bear in mind that those responsible for appropriating funds, particularly legislative bodies, are quite sensitive to public interest and demand. This again brings us back to the need for a well-informed citizenry, including the professional groups with an interest in health.

Implementation of program rests on this final resource—money. If budgetary reductions are imposed, program elements must again be reviewed with an eye to priorities. Certain objectives and procedures will be amenable to limitation; others may have to be postponed. It is hoped, however, that funds are well justified and are appropriated in accordance with the major health needs of the community. This depends on how well the health officer has diagnosed his community and convinced his "patient" of the need for prevention, the maintenance of good health, and proper care in the event of poor health.

Summary

    To summarize the principle and elements of our subject, programing is the process of sound planning with realistic ends in view. The process in the health field, although specialized techniques are involved, is similar to that in other fields of endeavor.

    Through the epidemiological approach we seek to define problems of health and to learn all factors pertaining to the natural history of a disease and practical measures for its control. Applying all available knowledge and well-known principles of community dynamics, we develop a course of action, establishing priorities and feasibility. During this process we seek the answers to a host of practical questions in developing and implementing a program of optimum value. This may also provide for exploration of what is not known. The long-range success of our ventures depends upon appropriate evaluation, always in relation to our initial objectives. The immediate success is subject to the skill and care that are directed toward convincing appropriations authorities of the effectiveness of proposed measures.

Effective Community Health Services*

by GEORGE JAMES, M.D., M.P.H.

The Challenge of Change

The rapid expansion of knowledge and the public's growing sophistication make one fact clear to those in the health and social service fields. As professional workers, we must concentrate on services for the individual which meet his particular needs. We were not hired to plan and execute programs, develop agencies, stimulate co-ordination among agencies, improve teaching programs, or develop new tools, except as these activities may be useful in serving people. The effect, immediate or ultimate, on each citizen is the measure of our effort, and the only measure by which we will eventually be judged.

In this light one can discuss public health or social work with a minimum of slavish adherence to traditions, charters, laws, and agencies. One can give maximum attention to epidemiologic questions: what are the needs of our population, the resources available to satisfy these needs, and the modifying influences on community attitudes. We must develop effective services for the citizen while we continue to improve present resources and community attitudes.

This emphasis upon service to the individual, against the backdrop of his particular family and community environment, assures a tailor-made approach to local health services. It means that no two communities will need or should have identical health programs. It means that no person in the community need have exactly the same services as another. It means that with the rapid

* Paper delivered March 5, 1962.

changes in the social, economic, and scientific life of our time no single community can keep exactly the same pattern of health services for two consecutive years. Hence, all who practice public health are students. All of us are floating on seas of change, driven by variable main currents, tossed in swirling eddies. All our programs on behalf of health are adaptations. True, many of them have been devised and pretested in stable laboratories. But until they are tried in one's own community, upon each person in need, their real value in any particular area cannot be accurately assessed.

I am reminded of a personal experience in a southern state which was attempting to build up its child health services. Each local health officer was urged to obtain more funds for child health clinics and immunization programs. In one county roads were so poor that neither families nor clinic teams could reach any central service point during the rainy season of each year. Strange as it seemed to some of our public health colleagues, we made no request for special funds for child health services; instead, we urged increased expenditures for local highways. In terms of real and meaningful health resources, better roads were more useful in that area at that time than more doctors, nurses, social workers, vaccines, clinic quarters, health education, or anything else.

An important principle governs the development of local services, including health services: for the foreseeable future the needs of our citizens will remain insatiable. Under our present value systems, there are not sufficient resources to satisfy all human needs for housing, health, welfare, highways, education, museums, recreation, and those other community services we have come to believe essential. That human needs are insatiable means that communities must develop priorities for service. These will depend greatly upon human values, upon the specific crises and enthusiasms that develop, and on new scientific discoveries. Since each factor which will modify and affect priority is itself greatly subject to change, it is evident that a community's priorities for the various services will also change. Current program emphases on air pollution, radiologic health, and case-finding in diabetes and glaucoma were generally unknown two decades ago, although from a strictly scientific viewpoint the needs existed to approximately the same degree as now.

One cannot predict today exactly what will be tomorrow's major health priorities. It is essential that each community be so organized as to maintain constant contact with and understanding of the factors influencing change in community and health priorities. This organizational structure need not follow any fixed pattern. One has only to look around the nation to see many patterns and to realize that dogmatism in the organization of health services has no place in our 1962 plan of action. The test of any organization must be its effectiveness in meeting the needs and priorities for each community.

Diseases That Kill

Any discussion of local public health services must therefore start with the needs of the local population. We use the normal epidemiologic principle of stressing those conditions which do or can affect the most citizens. First come the major causes of death.

HEART DISEASE

The leading cause of death, by far, in all areas of this nation is "diseases of the heart." They kill at least 40 per cent of those who die each year. Although the group includes rheumatic heart disease and syphilitic heart disease, both now increasingly well controlled, the greatest killer is disease of the coronary arteries. Long-term prospective studies seem to indicate that coronary heart disease occurs more often in obese individuals who have high blood pressure, a high serum cholesterol level, and a generally sedentary occupation. The serum cholesterol level seems to be related to the amount of dietary saturated fatty acid, a food element commonly supplied by animal fats. Several important scientific groups have recommended that these individuals reduce obesity, eat food lower in saturated fat, and increase their routine exercise. It is true that our civilization devalues exercise as a daily component of life; transportation is the rule, and walking almost a lost art. Commenting on our present retreat from exercise in a recent television broadcast entitled "The Fat

American," Dean Mayer noted a high school near Boston which has made half its athletic field into a parking lot for the students!

While we are not yet prepared to make firm recommendations for the prevention of heart disease in adults, it looks as if some of the ideas arising from recent research on exercise and diet must be tested in demonstration programs, for eventual practical use. In the meantime, a huge number of patients with heart disease require medical care and present a host of major social problems to the community.

CANCER

The number two cause of death in this country is cancer. Cancer is responsible for about one in every seven deaths. No discussion of this health problem can be meaningful unless we categorize our remarks according to cancer sites. Man has made his greatest progress in controlling cancer of the cervix. It is believed that fully two-thirds of those now dying from this disease could be saved if early detection programs were developed. Each physician can check for cancer of the cervix as part of a routine examination program, or we can use mass methods by taking Papanicolaou smears on all women admitted to general hospitals and outpatient departments. It has been estimated that a single case of fatal cervical cancer costs the City of New York $10,000 from the time of discovery to the time of death. In our experience half the patients with cervical cancer would not have been detected without the smear, and of these more than two-thirds can be saved at the time of diagnosis. In New York City, therefore, the screening of 75,000 women at each of the two hospitals where we now have active programs is expected to save as much as $2,750,000 per year—$2,750,000 saved every year by a program estimated to cost less than a tenth of that.

The story of cancer of the lung is a dismal one because our biologic knowledge offers us highly effective techniques which our social sophistication cannot accept. By itself cancer of the lung is about number eight among the causes of death. In New York City it kills 1,600 persons per year, more than twice the number of those who lose their lives in automobile accidents.

Among men it is a leading cause of deaths from cancer. The most serious epidemic disease in our civilization, it sharply increases year by year among both men and women. Fourteen retrospective and three large prospective studies during the last 15 years have indicated an association between this disease and the habit of cigarette smoking. Although other factors such as air pollution may be significant, epidemiologists believe at least three-quarters of all deaths from cancer of the lung could be prevented if the cigarette-smoking habit were stopped. Despite these facts, no community to my knowledge has been successful in decreasing the number of cigarette smokers. On the contrary, cigarette sales continue to increase year by year in complete disregard of the risks involved. Faced with this gloomy picture, health departments have decided to concentrate on the youthful smoker, hoping to prevent the habit in those beginning to experiment with it.

Other cancers present other problems. Cancer of the stomach is decreasing as a cause of death; no one really knows why. Studies are attempting to ascertain the reason for this decrease in the hope that the downward trend might be accelerated if we knew the factors responsible.

Cancer of the breast still has not responded as well as expected to health education aimed at early case-finding. Although there are some small indications of progress in the saving of life, these at best are minors; there is much more we must learn about this condition if we are to bring it under control.

Cancer of the gastrointestinal tract is diagnosed in its early stages more often now than formerly. Health educators have stressed the significance of bleeding from the gastrointestinal tract and the importance of proctologic examination, which can detect small cancers and precancerous polyps of the rectum.

Leukemia, still a mystery, is invariably a fatal condition. The association of an increased incidence of leukemia with undue exposure to x-rays underscores the need to protect operators of x-ray machines from overexposure and to avoid the use of intensive radiation in certain therapeutic procedures for the very young.

STROKE

The third large category in the causes of death is stroke. This condition is responsible for about 7½ per cent of all deaths. Although there are obvious epidemiologic differences between this disease and coronary heart disease, it is generally believed that many of the same factors obtain in both. High blood pressure seems to play a definite role, and elevated serum cholesterol may be of some significance. At present there are no clear-cut recommendations for prevention of stroke, even for use in a demonstration program. Moreover, the stroke patient who recovers presents an enormous community problem in rehabilitation. Most of the local health departments have begun programs in this field.

RESPIRATORY INFECTIONS

In New York City the fourth leading cause of death is the influenza-pneumonia group, which is responsible for about 4 per cent of the deaths each year. Many occur among the old, and chronically ill, who lack the stamina to withstand an acute respiratory infection which settles in their lungs. It is known that old people readily lose their immunity to influenza; if this immunity can be maintained by booster doses of influenza vaccines, however, they may be in a better position to withstand an attack of disease. Development of the sulfa and antibiotic drugs has improved the patient's chances against pneumonia, even those of the very aged. In general, health departments maintain services for the influenza immunization of old people and other high-risk groups such as pregnant women. Moreover, the care of persons ill with such respiratory infections comes under the general heading of medical care services.

DISEASES OF EARLY INFANCY

The fifth leading cause of death is a general category called "certain diseases of early infancy." Most are not now amenable to either treatment or prevention. On the other hand, as obstetrical and early infant care improve we can expect further progress in this field. Proportionately, there are four times as many non-whites in this group as there are whites. This certainly seems to indicate that the lower socio-economic status of non-white parents is a major influence in many of the deaths among their off-spring. Although these diseases are fifth among the causes of death for all persons in New York City, they are sixth for whites and third for non-whites. Local health services providing early prenatal care for the mother, the best hospital delivery care, and prompt and adequate child health clinic services for the infant are essential.

ACCIDENTS

Sixth among the leading causes of death are accidents. Health departments have done a great deal to prevent death from poisons by poison information centers. Day or night, anyone in the world can call the center in New York City and find out exactly what chemicals are involved in any material. A large library contains information on a whole host of household substances never meant to be ingested, so that a physician can be told what hazardous chemical is involved and what treatments might be effective if some child should swallow one of them. Improperly operating gas appliances also caused some deaths from carbon monoxide poisoning in New York City until health education, combined with inspection and regulation of appliances, relegated this problem to minor status.

Even after these hazards have been checked, the largest group of accidental death remains: automobile accidents and most home accidents from falls and fires. Although obvious measures can prevent each such occurrence, it is extremely difficult to develop effective programs of prevention in the community. Recently the relationship between alcoholism and auto accidents has become increasingly certain. What is not certain, however, is whether stringent punishment or any other so-called deterrent to drunken driving is effective. Using the experience of our Scandinavian friends as an example, we first must deplore social drinking before driving and incorporate this attitude in our values system. Although falls in the home can be minimized by meticulous attention to slippery rugs, lack of hand-holds in bathrooms, and faulty appliances, health department efforts in these fields are still halting, tentative, and experimental, and they have not yet been shown to be effective.

CIRRHOSIS OF THE LIVER

The number seven cause of death is generally believed to be associated with alcoholism. It is estimated that there are over 300,000 alcoholics in New York City, a truly staggering proportion of our 7,700,000 inhabitants. Many communities have devoted much effort to the prevention and control of alcoholism. Although several studies show dramatic improvement in individual patients, no one claims that any major impact has been made upon the total community problem. At least we have come to recognize that alcoholism is a complex problem, and have attempted to provide medical care and mental health care for the alcoholic.

DIABETES MELLITUS

The eighth leading cause of death is increasing in importance despite the availability of insulin as a therapeutic agent for over 40 years. Although concrete proof is lacking, most medical scientists believe insulin and diet, by which the patient keeps his diabetes under control, effectively inhibit serious complications. These complications, which relate to atherosclerosis of coronary, renal, cerebral, and peripheral blood vessels, are responsible for most loss of life from diabetes. Most health departments, believing adequate control is essential to avoid complications, have begun diabetes detection programs. These are aimed at finding the disease in its earliest stage, when it can cause abnormally high blood sugar without necessarily producing symptoms. If the diabetic then receives good medical attention and cooperates by regulating his diet and taking prescribed medications, it is hoped that we can add immeasurably to his survival and continued self-sufficiency.

In addition, health departments are now becoming interested in another group: those who have a small distortion of blood sugar without presenting enough evidence to warrant a diagnosis of diabetes. These potential diabetics or "prediabetics" are now being studied to see whether special treatment might prevent their developing diabetes altogether. Screening would thus be a way of locating the individual at risk of developing diabetes so that measures could be taken to keep him free of the disease.

Certain additional groups are particularly prone to diabetes: individuals with a family history of the disease, the obese, and women whose infants weigh more than ten pounds at birth. Epidemiologic efforts are aimed at locating these individuals and seeing that they receive annual tests for diabetes. So far, although many communities have these programs, none has been able to demonstrate a major decrease in deaths chargeable to diabetes through these efforts.

GENERALIZED ARTERIOSCLEROSIS

Pathology in blood vessels, probably similar to that in coronary arteries, is the ninth cause of death. We know very little about the causes of atherosclerosis in other than the coronary arteries; there may well be influences other than diet, lack of exercise, and high blood pressure. Moreover, many deaths charged to this condition might have been charged to heart disease if the patients had been more thoroughly studied.

CONGENITAL MALFORMATION

At present our effort to prevent the tenth leading cause of death lies in instituting the best rehabilitative and medical care. Research now under way should help us understand the genetic mechanisms in these conditions. Much has already been discovered, and some day we may be able to prevent congenital malformations. With gamma globulin, health officials can now prevent German measles in pregnancy and thus prevent malformations in many fetuses.

OTHER CAUSES OF DEATH

Tuberculosis, eleventh cause of death in New York City, dropped in 1959 for the first time from the list of the top ten. Although tuberculosis decreases year by year as a cause of death, there is still a large reservoir of undetected cases in most urban centers in this country. No longer a major disease of young women, its primary target is now older men of the low socio-economic class, whose rehabilitation is often complicated by the need for total social rehabilitation. Alcoholism, poverty, homelessness, physical defects, and other chronic diseases make social rehabilitation difficult.

Cases are found in mass surveys or in routine x-raying of admissions to the general services of hospitals or outpatient departments. It is standard epidemiologic procedure to x-ray families and contacts of known cases. The tuberculin test is used to measure the prevalence of the infection among various age groups, and to find cases among the young. It is now recommended that very young children with positive tuberculin reactions receive isoniazid treatment as a preventive measure.

In New York and other large centers tuberculosis must be continuously sought among non-whites, Puerto Ricans, and inmates of homes for the aged, nursing homes, correctional institutions, and shelters for homeless men. Whereas the prevalence of tuberculosis in mass surveys is now well below one per thousand in New York City, the rate has been as high as 16 per thousand among admissions to a welfare shelter for homeless men.

Suicides, number twelve among causes of death, and homicides, number eighteen, represent groups in the community who are suffering from various social and emotional diseases. To prevent these deaths the health department must act in close association with many other community agencies. An interesting development in suicide control has been undertaken in several areas, where 24-hour counseling and guidance is available to the individual who feels he needs support. At present much more epidemiologic knowledge is needed about suicides. It has been suggested that persons who attempt suicide and fail are particularly in need of mental health services.

To prevent most of the other causes of death—ulcers, number thirteen; hypertension, number fourteen; other diseases of circulatory system, fifteen; chronic nephritis, sixteen; hernia and intestinal obstruction, seventeen; benign and unspecified neoplasms, nineteen; and hyperplasia of the prostate, twenty—the major resource is good medical care. This means prompt diagnosis of the condition, effective treatment, and follow-up care.

Priorities for Prevention

In summary, we can make a few general comments about the

20 leading causes of death as public health problems. Public health can do a great deal to prevent two of the 20. Although some mysteries still exist, we can save a significant number of those suffering from the influenza-pneumonia illnesses. With influenza vaccine and prompt, adequate treatment of pneumonia we prevent many deaths. State and federal laboratories can isolate new forms of influenza virus which appear in the community and promptly prepare vaccines for widespread use. We still have undiscovered cases of tuberculosis and our present methods of control could be applied more thoroughly.

We are essentially powerless, however, against 18 of the 20 leading causes of death unless we can discover new and potent weapons. Although the biologic facts may be known—as for the prevention of deaths from lung cancer—we have so far been unable to apply them in any community to any measurable degree. Insulin for the diabetic, and diet low in saturated fat for the heart patient may some day offer promise, but research and demonstration are needed now to indicate that this is really so.

Cancer of the cervix and certain conditions of early infancy are amenable to control, and effective measures should be taken by local health officers. The exact nature of the programs will depend upon many factors, but in nearly every community an effective start can be made.

Nevertheless, it is not yet possible to prevent most of the major causes of death in our present civilization. Our priorities must be:

1. Research to discover new resources which might be effective.
2. Demonstrations of promising new approaches to see if they are truly effective and acceptable to the population, and to ascertain their impact upon other programs.
3. Medical care to ameliorate the condition, postpone its degenerative aspects, and rehabilitate the patient to the highest possible degree of self-sufficiency.

Diseases That Disable

In addition to the major causes of death as determinants of the health program, there are a number of major non-fatal causes of disability. Leading the field are the mental diseases, which are responsible for half the patients in hospital beds in this nation. Most communities have mental health clinics; their over-all effectiveness is as yet largely unproved. Nevertheless, we must continue to offer mental health services in order to learn more about the mental illness and in the hope that our services will be somewhat effective.

Non-fatal stroke is another condition of importance; since World War II an enormous amount of attention has been devoted to the rehabilitation of stroke victims. Glaucoma, number one cause of blindness in this country, is detectable in its early stages; if treated early, most patients can be helped and blindness prevented. Arthritis, a rather mysterious condition, is being attacked by research in both laboratory and epidemiologic studies; present rehabilitation efforts show some good results.

A number of infectious diseases, such as the common cold, hepatitis, and measles, are major causes of temporary disability. The search continues for a greater understanding of these conditions and for effective vaccines. We may be on the threshold of effective vaccines for hepatitis and measles and for some, but by no means all, of the common respiratory diseases.

Dental caries is another significant condition which results in disability. We know how to prevent two-thirds of the dental caries by fluoridating public water supplies. Although nearly one-fifth of the U.S. population is now consuming fluoridated water, many large urban centers have not seen fit to adopt fluoridation. It has been estimated that one engineer responsible for the fluoridation of the public water supply in New York City could prevent more cavities in children's teeth than the city's 8,000 dentists could fill, even if they worked at the problem full time.

Accent on Rehabilitation

Rehabilitation has meant much to public health in this decade. Ingenious new techniques have made rehabilitation services more effective; the concept of rehabilitation itself has led to a major shift in public health philosophy. Whereas in the past we emphasized prevention and cure as major parts of a public health program, today we begin our rehabilitation programs with a frank admission of our inability to prevent and cure. We emphasize that despite his disease the patient can be brought to a greater degree of self-sufficiency if we apply special varieties of medical care. Hence, we can have two individuals with the same degree of arthritis, the same degree of farsighted vision, the same degree of high blood pressure, and yet one may be confined to bed and the other be a relatively active and productive citizen. We cannot find the difference between them by minutely assessing physical condition organ by organ, but by studying the total adaptation each has been able to make between his physical and mental status on one side and life's challenges on the other. Patients must be helped to adapt and thereby increase their level of activities of daily living.

The concept of rehabilitation has led us to accentuate the positives, not the negatives, in mental and physical health. Instead of stressing what is wrong with the patient, we stress what is right. It is not important in daily living that he can bend his knee only a little; the important thing is that he can bend it enough to walk and go up and down stairs. It is not important that he has lost 40 per cent of his vision; what is significant is that he can read effectively with strong spectacles. In New York City it is usually not enough that a disabled man be able to hobble around a little on crutches; until he can walk fast enough to cross a New York City street in 45 seconds, before the traffic light changes, he cannot ordinarily move about in our community. In a less hectic place, the demands upon him would be far less and he could be more self-sufficient. The concept of rehabilitation is geared to the individual in the particular situation in which he finds himself or in which we place him. Rehabilitation, more than anything else in public health, has made us concentrate upon the individual and forced us to plan each man's program in terms of *his* locus, abilities, goals, and potentialities.

There is a huge cost factor in rehabilitation. With an adult we are often working against time—time which seems to degenerate our patient faster than we can rehabilitate him. Rehabilitation has a practical goal—to return the patient to the activities of daily living—and we must be equally practical in deciding how much rehabilitation care we can afford to invest in each patient. In

New York City we are studying the dimensions of the problem through a community-wide program in one section with a 200,000 population.

I predict that rehabilitation services will take on increasing importance as the years go by. No matter what happens to our list of the 20 leading causes of death, there will always be patients needing rehabilitation. With each we must weigh the cost of improvement against the ultimate social and economic value of the improvement.

Five Criteria of Good Medical Care

No matter how we look at the health problems affecting large numbers of our people, the importance of good medical care is paramount. We recognize five criteria of a good medical care program. The first is *comprehensiveness*. A program is comprehensive when it makes available to each patient all the techniques and services he requires for adequate medical care—doctors, hospitals, vaccines, drugs, speech therapist, psysiotherapist, dentists, etc.

The second principle is *continuity of care*. Each patient should be cared for by a single physician or team of physicians through his entire medical care program. If this is impossible, the next best thing is to send his new physician or team an up-to-date, complete, and accurate medical and social record showing exactly what has already been done for him. This is not done routinely, as it should be; in many parts of the country it is actually easier to repeat complicated x-ray and laboratory procedures on a new patient than to obtain his record from another institution. Moreover, many of our major social welfare programs are geared to destroy continuity of care by forcing patients to change physicians and institutions when the patients are shifted from one type of assistance to another.

The third criterion is that medical care should be *family-centered*. Instead of fragmenting the family among many different clinics and physicians, there is much to be gained by centering the care of the entire family in one medical group. Not only is disease often a family phenomenon, but certainly its effective treatment and rehabilitation should make use of any community strength which may exist. His family is still a major source of community strength for any individual. Removing him from his family, ignoring other family problems as we plan his care, often leads to defeat for health workers. For example, recently we had proof that a child is far more likely to smoke when both parents smoke; any attempt at educating him in school to avoid the habit seems doomed to failure if he returns home to see parental smoking.

The fourth criterion of a good medical care program is that it should emphasize *preventive services*. Many hospital patients could be offered such preventive services as diabetes, glaucoma, cancer, and tuberculosis detection if such programs were available. Many go routinely to specialty clinics such as those limited to ear, nose, and throat, but may have other significant medical conditions, such as cervical cancer or tuberculosis, of which the specialty clinic is quite unaware. Every patient receiving care from any medical group is a candidate for comprehensive care, including the full range of preventive services.

The last criterion is that all medical care should be of the *highest quality*. Surgery should be performed only by competent surgeons, hospitals should meet full accreditation standards, and all the benefits of the teaching hospital should be available to the community. Although 90 per cent of medical care takes place away from the hospital bed, most of our high-quality physicians spend the greater portion of their time working with patients in teaching-hospital beds. The benefits of this high-quality care must be extended to outpatient departments, home care programs, home visiting, nursing homes, and homes for the aged.

In general, then, medical care must be oriented to the patient, not to the treatment facility. As Dr. Breslow says, "The right patient must be in the right bed at the right time and must be receiving the right treatment." This should be true for all, rich or poor. Many of our poorest, most fragmented medical programs are all that are available to the well-to-do. The practice of fragmenting programs by organizing them around the agency which pays for them is highly reprehensible. In most cases this results in episodic medicine, in purchasing a given piece of medical care of a certain category permissible under federal, state, or local legislation.

A study now under way in New York City highlights many aspects of this problem of fragmented medical care. For example, it has demonstrated that 80 per cent of those on our welfare rolls go off the rolls in any given year; sooner or later, most of them return to welfare. But during the time they are not receiving public assistance, their medical care is handled in an entirely different way by different groups of physicians. Recently we found that one man with six children, each of whom was going to a different outpatient clinic, was spending his entire day sitting in clinic waiting rooms. When his children were brought together in a family-centered program, the man went back to work and the entire family was removed from the welfare rolls.

Types of Service

OUTPATIENT CARE

The outpatient department is an important element in the scheme of medical care activities. Fragmentation of services by specialty, an outgrowth of the past, must give way to an integrated, family-centered approach. Outpatient care must become part of a continuum with hospital and home care. Visits to emergency rooms in New York City's municipal hospitals have increased 74 per cent in the last six years; visits to outpatient clinics have increased only 26 per cent. Patients have learned that the wait in emergency rooms is shorter, that they will be cared for any time, day or night. Emergency rooms give the most fragmentary kind of episodic services, of course. To correct this problem in New York City, we are trying to establish branch clinics of overcrowded institutions either in other hospitals or in health department facilities; here physicians of the home hospital operate the clinic in cooperation with the agency owning the structure. This brings clinic care closer to the patient's home and high-quality medicine to a wider area of the community, maintains continuity of care, avoids overcrowding.

New York City is also expanding its day clinics for mentally ill patients. We have found that these patients, who might otherwise have to be hospitalized, can be treated effectively during the day and returned home for evenings and weekends. The program is family-centered. Often the psychiatrists find that the patient under treatment at the day clinic for hallucinations and delusions is not the only mentally ill person in the family, but simply the one with overt symptoms. Sometimes a strong-willed and seemingly well-integrated person is really the sickest member of the family and the major cause of the patient's disease. The day hospital program gives the psychiatrist an opportunity to work with the whole family, often with startling results.

Home-care services are an important addition to the armamentarium of medical care. At first it was believed that a strong home was essential for the maintenance of home-care services. But we have found that a single person can be given home care when the community will add homemaker or housekeeper services. The total cost is much less than the cost of hospitalization, and the patient can be helped more readily toward self-sufficiency. The New York City Department of Health, in cooperation with other community agencies, is undertaking a number of programs in housing projects that will offer tenants improved health maintenance and home-care services. It has been surprising to us how many of these people had never received adequate medical care for the many conditions with which we find them suffering.

Nursing homes are another important part of the medical care program. It is essential that a nursing home be affiliated with a medical center so that the highest quality of medical care can be offered to the patients in the home. With rehabilitation the goal, the nursing home is part of the complex of medical care along with the hospital, the clinic, and the home-care program. A patient can be moved between nursing home and hospital to assure the best care at each stage of his illness, convalescence, or relapse.

GENERAL MAINTENANCE OF HEALTH

So far I have discussed the major causes of death and disability and the ways that health departments seek to prevent or ameliorate disease and otherwise care for the sick. Most health departments also provide a number of *general maintenance services*. One relates to the control of communicable diseases. Many of these diseases, once major scourges, are now largely controlled. The health department must maintain this control and keep the diseases from increasing in significance again. Smallpox reappeared in 1947; this year it appeared in India and Pakistan, whence it spread to England, Germany, and Switzerland. All port cities have been urged to step up their routine vaccination programs of hospital employees because most smallpox in western Europe and the United States in recent years was transmitted by undiagnosed cases in hospitals. There is also an extensive program of surveillance of those who have been in infected areas to see whether any develop smallpox after arrival in this country. Control of diphtheria and whooping cough must be maintained by ensuring that immunizations are up to date.

We are concerned about certain groups in the community who do not take advantage of the widespread polio immunization services available to them. Our efforts in these fields must continue and all promising leads must be explored. For example, we have given public health nurses syringes of polio vaccine so that when they visit a home they may immunize children on the spot. In most cases we find no resistance, just lethargy about taking advantage of the immunization procedure, which is widely available in clinics throughout the city.

Typhoid, cholera, plague, and rabies have essentially been wiped out as major threats to our population, but we must keep on the alert to prevent their recurrence. A few cases of typhoid continue to appear, spread by carriers in our community. Dog bites are frequent and rabies always a fear; with the recent discovery of rabies in bats in various parts of the country, this disease has taken on added significance. We now realize that there is an ever-present reservoir of rabies infection in our midst.

Another general maintenance service is the control of nutritional diseases. Although most major diseases born of malnutrition have been conquered, there are still groups in the population who are not receiving optimal amounts of common nutrients. Pregnant women must pay careful attention to their diet. The aged, because of low income, general lethargy, or cultural diet patterns, often do not maintain an adequate diet; lack of teeth and particular disorders of the gastrointestinal tract in this age group also add to the problem.

PRENATAL SERVICES

The provision of adequate services for pregnant women is a program of the highest importance in every community. Even in New York, replete with facilities, about one-fifth of the pregnant women have no prenatal care at all or receive care late in pregnancy. A recent study gave us the reasons: ignorance, a false sense of security because they had already had children, difficulty in getting away from the family when there are small children at home, and inadequate attention in clinics often not geared to their particular needs. Efforts are now being made to have prenatal clinics in the evening or to invite patients to bring their preschool children to daytime child health clinics. The Department of Health has developed a number of prenatal clinics in cooperation with hospitals to give more family-centered care. Most health departments have dropped isolated prenatal services in the belief that a woman should be cared for in the clinic of the hospital which will deliver her baby. This good arrangement is bettered when the hospital operates a branch clinic in the health department, thereby bringing services closer to the home.

SERVICES TO MOTHERS AND BABIES

The importance of continuous follow-up of infants and preschool children in child health conferences is well-known. All need immunizations and many require treatment because of physical defects. In addition, behavior problems evidenced during the preschool period can prove serious in later life if help is not given to the family. In New York City we study the attitudes of the mother toward the child, and, in the child health clinic, attempt first to discover what troubles her and take steps to be of assistance. On the other hand, if she has no particular difficulties and her child is well, the clinic team does not spend as much time with her. This is another indication of our attempt to gear the service to the patient. A problem that disturbs us in child health clinic care is the large number of "drop-outs"—children who come for a while and then stop coming. This is being studied to discover why it occurs and to take steps to correct it.

SERVICES TO THE CHILD IN SCHOOL

The health of the school-age child requires the full use of all community resources. In some areas this health program comes under the auspices of the health department, in others under the department of education. In either case no one department can do the task alone; in fact, many community agencies must take part. The school is a convenient place where children can be studied and followed with a minimum of administrative difficulty. Those with chronic rheumatic heart disease can be supervised to see that they take their daily penicillin tablet. At school we have an opportunity to study a defect and the effect of corrective measures. School is also an excellent place to observe early manifestations of diseases which if untreated, would become significant in later life. Among these is obesity, since it has been shown that the obese child is apt to become the obese adult. Dietary habits can be established in these children which will have great importance in their later years. It has been shown that many children establish the habit of smoking between the ages of 11 and 14; it may be possible to prevent this habit in many by working with children in this age group and with their parents. Habits of physical exercise should be inculcated in this group if we want them to maintain an exercise program when they are adults. The emphasis upon interschool athletics should not distract us from encouraging each child to develop his own physical exercise program on a permanent basis.

Nor should we lose sight of the enormous educational importance of demonstration during the school years. A hasty, ill-conceived, poorly done physical examination of a high school student merely leads that student to believe little can be expected from a physical examination later on in life. It is important that we show the school-age child only the highest quality of health services, including counseling and mental health services.

SERVICES FOR ADULTS

General maintenance services for adults are receiving greater attention now than ever before. In our early industrial hygiene programs we attempted to assure the continued health of the worker. Soon we discovered that many of the major conditions affecting the American worker were directly traceable to the home. For example, industry made great strides in preventing factory accidents but not in reducing worker absenteeism caused by accidents at home. Instead of providing clinic service only in illness, we now try to attract adults to clinics for general health maintenance. Some areas provide clinic services for the aged, since they suffer from a large number of physical and mental defects. In several New York City housing projects, health services are offered to aged tenants in an attempt to maintain them in their homes in maximum health, and to prevent disease from advancing to the point where hospitalization is the only hope. Although it is too early to report tangible results, we know that these health maintenance programs are extremely popular and that many patients are receiving necessary medical care for the first time in years.

Most health departments provide laboratory services: performing actual tests, training local laboratory scientists, developing new tests, inspecting and consulting with local laboratories. Again, in keeping with the desire of modern public health workers to be coordinators, it is not necessary for the health department to perform each service itself if it can help to raise the quality and ability of others and thereby ensure the adequacy of essential laboratory services.

HOUSEKEEPING SERVICES

These health services maintain the cleanliness of the community as a means of preventing disease and providing an esthetic and attractive environment. In insisting on sanitary food and milk, health departments not only prevent the spread of diseases such as typhoid, paratyphoid and dysentery, but also provide a wholesome, palatable product. It is important that the taste and odor of a water supply be inoffensive, even if they are not significant in preventing disease.

In our major cities, pollution of harbor waters has recently received greater attention. Unless pollution can be reduced and controlled, the recreational use of waters for bathing may be seriously impaired. General environmental sanitation—adequate housing, rat control, sufficient heat in apartments—is also a program that citizens have come to demand. It is obvious that the urban apartment-dweller cannot handle these problems by himself.

Other housekeeping services relate to environmental problems of increasing importance—radiation and air pollution. Although there has been much in the papers recently about radioactive fallout, by far the greatest source of unnecessary human exposure to radiation comes from the improper use of x-ray machines. A recent survey in New York City found 90 per cent of these to be defective, either in construction or operation. Most health departments are undertaking major programs of radiation control to prevent unnecessary dosages of radiation. When properly used, x-rays, a very potent device for the detection and treatment of disease, need give us no concern. On the other hand, it is unnecessary to spray portions of the population with scatter radiation which serves no useful purpose in medicine and can cause ultimate genetic damage to the human race.

Although the health implications of air pollution are not entirely known execept in major disasters such as occurred at Donora and London, the citizen demands a clean atmosphere for the enjoyment of life and property. Studies are under way to elucidate the importance of air pollution to chronic pulmonary disease and lung cancer. That air pollution plays some role in the development of these diseases seems fairly certain, but the exact relationship and the relative importance of air pollution requires much further study.

Finally, the health department provides certain services largely because they are socially desirable. Certification of births and deaths is one such service. The collection and tabulation of vital statistics enables us to analyze various facets of the public health situation and to derive new approaches to old problems. For example, several years ago we began to look to the birth certificate for information on congenital defects in newborn infants, and this has been helpful in planning rehabilitation programs.

Avenues to Public Health

What approaches are used by health departments in offering service to people? One is *direct service* by physicians, nurses, dentists, and social workers to prevent and treat disease. Another is *service on behalf of people*. For example, sanitation inspections of restaurants and public water supplies and the introduction of fluoride into a water supply system are services which aid people, often without their being aware of them.

A third approach is *health education* to stimulate greater use of health services. Health education is often aimed at special groups, subcultures in a community. For example, one study in New York City discovered that people from Czechoslovakia were twice as willing to accept medical care when symptoms of illness occurred as were those from Ireland. Such a cultural difference in the acceptance of medical care is extremely important, if we wish to emphasize early diagnosis and prompt treatment for chronic disease.

Health education has its limitations, and it is important that health departments realize this. Recently social scientists studied whether health education techniques were useful in persuading patients to get tuberculosis chest x-rays during a mass survey in the Bronx. Repeated studies of this population failed to reveal that health education techniques were effective. Of far greater effectiveness were (a) a loud-speaker at the site of the x-ray unit blaring forth Calypso music, (b) good weather, and (c) location of the x-ray bus where large numbers of people congregated, such as shopping centers. Another example of health education which failed was Edinburgh's extensive effort to point out the danger of lung cancer. Despite an amazing amount of community cooperation, no change occurred in the smoking habits of Scotsmen.

One of the approaches used by local health departments is *coordination*. Because of its broad mandate, the health department is often in the best position to take leadership among many agencies and bring them together on behalf of a given health program. The Queensbridge Housing Project program, organized by a district health officer, has five city agencies and several voluntary agencies working together for 1,000 aged persons who live in the project. The Department of Health has not determined the roles of these agencies, but has brought them together to concentrate on the specific problem; and in working together each group defines its own role. There are other examples in our area where the Department of Health has taken the first step in working with voluntary and municipal hospitals to develop joint programs for continuous, comprehensive, and, we hope, eventually family-centered care for groups in the population.

A health department can play a major role in *research and demonstation* for health. Research is essential if we are to provide new services to fill gaps. Although much research is undertaken by medical schools and other institutions, many major problems in chronic disease lend themselves to the epidemiologic approach. Health officers have the opportunity to study large numbers of presumably well people and to observe them when they develop the earliest signs and symptoms of disease. These prospective studies might give us much information about the development of disease, enabling us to take steps to control it.

Research is also needed if we are to streamline existing services. We can no longer continue to pour men and materiel into traditional programs when these resources are desperately needed for new programs. For example, a few shots of penicillin cure venereal disease better than a year and a half of arsenic and bismuth, and free a large amount of manpower for new services. Likewise, development of the three-in-one vaccine cuts the number of clinic visits for infants and preschool children, and frees clinic time and personnel for other activities.

If we are to bring more services to people who are not taking advantage of those now available, we may have to *redesign the package.* If all the polio vaccine in the world were on top of Mount Everest, few cooperative persons would come for vaccination—Tensing and Hillary and the four who followed later. For many, perhaps, the health services now available are really on Mount Everest. Let us bring them down. Let us find out how to locate and package our services to make them immediately available to all our people. Perhaps some do not take advantage of them because of ignorance, cultural blocks, inconvenience. Giving polio vaccinations in homes is a different way of packaging services. Bringing medical care into a housing project for the aged is another. The usefulness of any package depends upon the total problem, the local value system, and the particular group we are trying to serve. We must become involved with the specific problems, and keep an open mind about alternate solutions, if we are to achieve success.

Another approach is *evaluation*. Whenever we undertake a health program, we arrange for feedback of the results so that we can make indicated modifications. Periodically we become dissatisfied with a program and try a new approach, as we did in the control of cancer of the cervix in New York City.[1] We began in 1947 with a cancer detection clinic in a teaching center. Most of the patients were Jewish women, the group with the lowest incidence of cancer of the cervix in our city. Non-whites and Puerto Ricans, whom we wanted to attract, did not come to the clinic. Result: we found very few cancers of the cervix. We then opened a cancer detection clinic in East Harlem, heart of the Negro and Puerto Rican area, and still had a clientele composed mostly of Jewish women; only a quarter of the patients were in the high-prevalence risk groups. Noting that our social hygiene clinics served many in the high-risk groups, we began taking Papanicolaou smears along with gonorrhea smears and cultures. Although we found a high yield of cancer of the cervix, we still reached only a fraction of the New York City women who were developing the disease. We therefore extended the detection service to all women admitted as outpatients or inpatients to two large municipal hospitals in the area of highest prevalence. This resulted in the detection of an appreciable number of cancers of the cervix. Eventually we shall expand the program to the remainder of the city.

The information fed back to us from each clinic spurred the Department of Health to change its approach and modify its

[1]George James, "Program Planning and Evaluation in a Modern City Health Department," *American Journal of Public Health*, 51: 1828-40, December 1961.

program. Once we thought we would have to blanket the city with cancer detection clinics; now we know this would be an inefficient way of finding cancer. Instead, routine screening of general hospital admissions in areas of high prevalence is now the method of choice.

Organization of Local Health Services

More than twenty years ago Haven Emerson studied the pattern of local health services in this country and recommended the creation of a finite number of county and district health departments. His blueprint, based largely on recommendations from state health departments concerned about jurisdictional limits and home rule, was then used as a basis for the creation of new local health departments. To some degree his recommendations were accepted, but frequently they were ignored.

Local health departments expanded after World War II, but now seem to have reached a plateau. A study of Kit Carson County, Colorado,[2] shows that many citizens are receiving adequate services without an organized local health department. Elsewhere, communities with organized health departments are known to receive inadequate services. Our emphasis therefore has shifted from organization to service. The National Advisory Committee on Local Health Departments, formed in 1940 to implement Dr. Emerson's report, now recommends that we work toward the goal of adequate community health services, not toward the creation of a fixed organizational structure.

It is obvious that much is done to improve the nation's health by other than official health agencies. Nearly every governmental program has some health component. The police are concerned about safety, alcoholism, juvenile delinquency, narcotic addiction, and the enforcement of some Health Code provisions for cleanliness. Fire departments are interested in safe construction. Education departments are interested in school health, health education, and vocational rehabilitation. Welfare departments are often responsible for medical care of welfare recipients. Labor

---

[2] Donald Harting and Others, "Public Health Needs in a Great Plains County," *American Journal of Public Health,* 49: 1591-95, December 1959.

departments are interested in industrial hygiene. Departments of parks are interested in recreation and exercise, departments of markets in the cleanliness and wholesomeness of food, mental health departments in a significant part of the total health picture.

Voluntary agencies also carry on many effective health programs. Some have specific health goals: control of cancer, heart disease, muscular dystrophy, venereal diseases, tuberculosis, polio and birth defects. For others, the health goal is not paramount, though important. For example, Lions clubs are concerned about the problem of blindness; Boy Scouts, Girl Scouts, and Camp Fire Girls stress health and safety; and Kiwanis clubs and the Junior and Senior Chambers of Commerce frequently sponsor specific health projects of significance nationally or in particular areas.

There is no automatic, sure way of ascertaining which agency, public or voluntary, is best able to accept responsibility for a particular health program. Organizational patterns differ widely from locality to locality, and a given health program may be sponsored here by one agency, there by another. Nor is there a rule which says this category of personnel must be governmental or voluntary. Even sectarian personnel—chaplains, for example— are found on government payrolls in state and municipal hospitals.

Today we see the emergence of new patterns in health programing. New Jersey's Hunterdon County is showing how a large county hospital can detect chronic disease and raise the level of medical care for an entire county, with results far superior to those obtained in most communities with organized local health departments. Northern California's small counties buy their health services from the state health department. Labor's health centers are delivering adequate health services to union members, and certain industries have developed health programs of note.

To reiterate, it is not important that a particular local health structure meet a given organizational criterion. It *is* important that the health service received by our people be of excellent quality. That is the true measure of success. Is the service adequate, effective, efficient, comprehensive, family-centered? These questions must be answered as we evaluate a health program and seek to improve it.

Conclusion

How does one steer a course through this maze of organizations, policies, goals, disciplines, techniques? In the interest of efficiency, we must argue for some coordination of effort. Although research may require many different approaches and thrive on competition, service programs generally are injured by competition because it inhibits free communication and concentration upon all aspects of the changing problem. Competition and lack of coordination fragment services for individuals who were never created to be served in a fragmented fashion and whose needs are not fragmented. Fortunately, affiliations are developing between health centers and hospitals, child health clinics and hospitals, school health programs and hospitals. The child whose defects are detected in a school health program can now be treated in the hospital by the same physician who serves the school. Our welfare recipients would benefit from a similar liaison between the health and medical care programs in the community. One cannot buy medical care for welfare recipients as one buys a pound of spinach; spinach is generally as good in one store as in another. We will never have comprehensive, continuous, preventive, high-quality, family-centered health care so long as we think of it as so much spinach.

In New York City the director of welfare medical care is an employee of the Department of Health on full-time loan to the Department of Welfare. He calls upon the full resources of the Department of Health and of other city and voluntary agencies which can be useful in developing a program that works. In addition to the welfare medical director, the Department of Health has assigned several other employees to other agencies. One physician is developing a home care program in a city hospital. Another is developing a program of research and demonstration in community medical care for a voluntary hospital. We have a separate Department of Mental Health, although the Department of Health operates many programs with mental health implications. To handle these properly, we have requested the Commissioner of Mental Health to assign a psychiatrist with public health experience to the Department of Health. In developing the mental health programs, he will look to the Department of Health for administrative supervision, to the Commissioner of Mental Health for technical guidance.

I end this paper as I began—by emphasizing the individual's need as the proper point of reference and evaluation. I have mentioned the Queensbridge Housing Project, where five municipal and five voluntary agencies cooperate in bringing health services to 1,000 needy aged tenants. Once a month representatives of these agencies meet to hear the medical staff discuss problem cases. Recently I heard three cases, each offering the array of difficult problems peculiar to the economically depressed aged and neglected person. Each agency representative remarked at least once when a particularly difficult problem arose, "We can't do anything about this particular problem. Our agency doesn't cover this sort of thing." Before the discussion was over, however, each was suggesting how his agency could be of help after all. Something upsets our cherished notions when we leave our desks and face a person in need.

The road to success in community programs is not paved with agency policies, principles, manuals, and regulations. These are necessary, of course. But when there is human need, when resources are at hand, precedents, traditions, rules must bend before the appeals for help. The impact of a small discrete demonstration on the agency's over-all program is not immediately drastic. There is time to modify, slowly and methodically. In this way the new service can develop within the agency without disturbing the integrity of normal, routine programs.

If we believe we can solve health problems by evolution rather than revolution, then let us arrange ourselves so that we can respond to these pressures for service. Let us cooperate with all others who can help. Let us learn to work together as we learn how best to serve people in need.

Cooperation and co-ordination are not merely desirable principles, signs of an advanced civilization. If we could be successful working alone, then by all means let's stop this infernal round of committees, conferences, communications, and interagency discussions. But we cannot. The problems of medical care, rehabilitation, health maintenance, and health inspection are too complex to be solved by any single agency. Man's present health problems cannot be solved by fragmented approaches. "Unite and conquer" is the slogan of this age of ecology. The insatiable social and health needs of our many different populations demand this of us. The least we can do is meet each other halfway, flexible of mind, dissatisfied with current methods, continuously aware of the problem itself. A real willingness to work with all useful individuals and agencies will come. It *must* come if we are to succeed in local public health service during this present era.

Potentialities and Limitations of Epidemiology*

by JOHN M. CASSEL, M.B.B.Ch., M.P.H.

To gain some understanding of the contributions that may legitimately be expected from epidemiology, it is first necessary to define what is meant by epidemiology and briefly trace the development of this scientific discipline.

To a newcomer the term "epidemiology" would seem most logically to be concerned with the study of epidemics, and epidemics are usually thought of as outbreaks of infectious diseases. Consequently, epidemiology is frequently considered as a science restricted to the study of outbreaks of infectious diseases. Historically this would have been an adequate formulation since, at the time of the development of this discipline, infectious disease epidemics were the most important and terrifying of the health problems afflicting mankind. These diseases therefore commanded practically all the attention and interest of all the health disciplines, including epidemiology. Today, however, as I hope to indicate, this would be inadequate as a definition.

Hippocrates and the Four Humors

The origin of the science of epidemiology can be traced to the Hippocratic era in the Golden Age of Greece. Hippocrates was one of the first physicians to recognize that disease outbreaks were not happenstance occurrences, attacking unfortunate individuals at random. Different populations were subject to different types of diseases, and these occurred at different seasons. Furthermore, within any population were various subgroups with different degrees of susceptibility to these diseases. For example, some

---

* Paper delivered March 6, 1962.

diseases attacked children primarily, others adults; some were most prevalent among the poor or among those who lived in a certain sector of the city.

From these beginnings two cardinal principles evolved which characterize and are central to the science of epidemiology. These are, first, that the unit of study of epidemiology is the group rather than the individual. By this we mean that the epidemiologic method is not the most appropriate technique for discovering why any particular person became ill when he did. More appropriately, epidemiology answers why people with a certain set of characteristics are more or less likely to become ill than other people without these characteristics. The second point central to epidemiology is that its major contribution has been in identifying those reasons for illness in aspects of the environment or way of life of the group under study.

As mentioned previously, the diseases of most concern to the Hippocratic physicians, and indeed to physicians for the next 25 centuries, were the infectious diseases. Furthermore, in this same period the aspect of the way of life of people of most concern to epidemiology was the relation of men to their physical environment. Thus, for example, in Hippocratic times the occurrence of disease was explained by the strength and direction of prevailing winds, the amount of rainfall and sunlight, the height above sea level, or the nature of the soil.

It is most important to recognize further that the particular aspects of the physical environment that were selected as explanations of disease were determined by existing theories concerning the causation of disease. This relationship between variables selected for study and prevailing theories of disease causation is equally true today and must be fully understood to appreciate the potential contribution of modern epidemiology. In Hippocratic times disease was thought to be caused by a disturbance in the balance of the four humors—blood, phlegm, black bile, and yellow bile—in the body. The proportions of these humors was in turn determined by the distribution of various attributes of living matter. These were categorized as wet or dry, hot or cold. The amounts of wetness or dryness, heat or cold were themselves determined by the proportions of what were considered to be the four elements making up the environment: earth, water, fire, and air. Thus, according to these concepts, the explanation for the occurrence of disease should be sought in those aspects of the environment which might influence the exposure of people to these four elements. It was therefore perfectly logical, given this theoretical framework, to search for an explanation for disease in the strength of winds or the amount of humidity.

Medieval Miasmas

This concept of disease remained almost unchanged for more than a thousand years. The next major theory about the cause of disease occurred in the Middle Ages when the idea of miasmas was introduced. Miasmas were foul odors, or gases. According to this new theory, it was thought that many diseases, in addition to being produced by exposure to different proportions of the elements as defined by Hippocrates, could be caused by exposure to these miasmas. Many of our modern terms for disease derive from this theory. For example, the word malaria comes from "mal" (bad) and "aria" (air); originally it was thought that malaria, or the fever of malaria, was caused by exposure to foul air or gases. As the idea of miasmas as a cause of disease became more accepted, the variables in the physical environment used to explain the occurrence of disease changed. Thus, many diseases were thought to be due to living in low marshy places or in areas of the city where excreta was thrown indiscriminately into the street. As you might expect, many people living in those circumstances did have high disease rates, but the reasons for the occurrence of such diseases given by the physicians of that day would be very different from those given today. Thus, once again the variables invoked as causes of disease were determined by existing theories.

Pasteur, Koch, and the Germ

The next major advance in our ideas about causation occurred with the discovery of microorganisms at the turn of the last century. The classical findings of Pasteur and Koch ushered in a new and very important era in medicine which led to far-reaching results. On the one hand these discoveries led to tremendous improvements in our ability to treat many diseases and to a marked change in the factors in the environment studied to explain disease. Under the influence of the new microorganismal theory epidemiological inquiries were now directed towards those aspects of the environment which might be envisioned as breeding places for bacteria. Thus, attention was (and still is) focused on exposure to contaminated water or food or polluted air.

Simultaneously, however, these discoveries tended to blind medical thought to other ideas about causation of disease. The new findings were so exciting that for many decades it was thought that knowledge about these microorganisms and how man came into contact with them was all that was needed to understand the cause of disease. This view is still widely prevalent in medical thinking, but gradually the realization has developed that the presence of a microorganism is at best only a partial cause and sometimes not even the most important cause of a disease, even an infectious disease. This point of view can perhaps be best illustrated by some examples.

About the turn of the century the specific microorganism responsible for cholera was identified and it was found that people who had this disease excreted large amounts of the cholera bacillus in their stools. Despite this it has never been possible to produce cholera in human volunteers by feeding them cholera bacilli no matter how large a dose is given. At most a transient diarrhea occurs, but usually there are no symptoms at all. Apparently other factors besides the cholera bacillus have to be present before cholera can be produced, and these are sometimes more important for our understanding of the disease than is the bacillus. In fact, even with our extensive knowledge of the cholera bacillus today we cannot explain why cholera becomes transformed periodically from a minor pestilence in some oriental bazaar to a raging epidemic, and it is unlikely that further study of the bacillus alone will provide us with the answers.

As a second example we might think about tuberculosis. The cause of tuberculosis is said to be the tubercle bacillus. In a certain sense that is a useful formulation, but in another sense it is not very useful. It is rather like saying, "The cause of automobile accidents is the automobile." This is undoubtedly true, but the automobile does more than cause automobile accidents, and accidents can be caused by more than the automobile. Intensive study of the tubercle bacillus does not tell us why it is that of a hundred people exposed to the bacillus in the United States only about three develop tuberculosis. Why do not the other 97 develop the disease? How do they differ, these 97, from the three who do get it? Why is it that in other countries of a hundred people exposed to the tubercle bacillus 10 or 20 or 30 will get tuberculosis? Why is it that in more and more people who are developing tuberculosis today we cannot find the tubercle bacillus? We find some other bacillus which we call "atypical" tubercle bacilli, but the disease seems to be the same. Thus, to consider the tubercle bacillus as "the cause" of tuberculosis is useful up to a point, but beyond that point it is not very useful.

Limitations of the Germ Theory

To understand the limitations of the microbiological model of the cause of disease it is necessary to realize that the science of bacteriology, and from it most of the science of medicine, has developed in a very peculiar fashion outside the mainstream of development of other sciences. Specifically this is the only science which classifies the object of study, bacteria, as good or bad. No physicist classifies his atoms as good or bad, nor do chemists classify their elements as good or bad. But we physicians classify bacteria as "good" (that is, bacteria that do no harm or are beneficial) or "bad" (that is, pathogenic).

One of the most eminent microbiologists in this country, Rene DuBos of the Rockefeller Institute, has advanced a rather ingenious theory to explain why this is so. He suggests that in nature man occupies the pinnacle of the pecking order; that is, he can eat anything on this earth and not be eaten by any other animal. In this he is different from all other animals who can eat some and be eaten by others. The one living species over which we have no control, however, are the microorganisms. In DuBos' view this lack of control has been responsible for microbiology's developing this pattern of classifying bacteria as good or bad.

Whether this explanation is adequate or not, it becomes necessary to consider the question of what makes a microbe good or bad. The particular bacillus that sours the French peasant's milk and makes very delicious cheese is a good bacillus without which he could not make his cheese. That same bacillus sours your milk here in the refrigerator and therefore is a bad bacillus, an evidence of unsanitary habits. A hundred years ago tulip growers concentrated on a mottled red and white variety of tulip that was the most prized type. This mottling occurred when a particular virus lived in association with the tulip. A number of years later mottled tulips were no longer the fashion and people demanded solid colors—reds, whites, yellows, and so on. Suddenly then this virus which had been eagerly sought after became a "bad" virus, and tulips were sprayed to get rid of it. The virus had not changed, but our ideas of what was good or bad had changed.

Or consider the virus which "causes" poliomyelitis. A hundred years ago it was neither good nor bad. Although people were exposed to the virus, poliomyelitis occurred very infrequently and paralysis was very rare indeed. In the course of a hundred years the virus so far as we know has not changed, but polio has become a major crippling disease of young adults and children. We have changed, not the virus. The same may be said of infectious hepatitis. Man has probably been exposed to the virus for many centuries, but only in the last ten to fifteen years have we started seeing major epidemics of this disease. We will not be able to explain these phenomena by studying only the virus concerned.

The development of the germ theory of disease had a further unfortunate consequence for epidemiology. Believing that the answers to the causation of disease had been found, epidemiological investigators restricted their studies. Before this, epidemiology had sought to identify those factors in the way of life of people which increased their risk of developing disease. After the discovery of bacteria most studies sought only to identify the means and vehicle of infection in a specific outbreak in an attempt to control that outbreak. Epidemiology thus changed from a research or investigative science to an applied technology. As such, it performed some very useful functions and doubtlessly was responsible for saving many lives, but it ceased, for a number of decades at least, to add to our knowledge of the factors responsible for disease. Unfortunately it is this infectious disease "epidemic fighting" function of epidemiology that has become the prevailing concept of the discipline. In my opinion, this is one of the least important of its potential contributions.

Over the last 20 to 30 years there has been a resurgence of interest in the contributions that epidemiology, as an investigative science, can make to an understanding of the disease process. Through such an understanding it is hoped that rational leads for intervention can be developed.

This reawakening of interest has occurred simultaneously with a growing realization of the limited utility of the rigid microorganismal model of disease causation. In addition to the factors mentioned previously that tend to cast some doubts on the usefulness of this model, two further developments in the field of health have occurred which make a more sophisticated theory imperative. The first has been the dramatic increase in the noninfectious chronic diseases as major causes of death and disability in modern industrialized society. This change in the nature of our major health problems has occurred over the last 40 to 50 years. During this period diseases which for thousands of years have been cripplers and killers of mankind have decreased to their lowest point in human history, and have been replaced by new diseases. Coronary heart disease, lung cancer, diabetes, arthritis, and mental disorders may have occurred before, but never to the extent that we are seeing them today. The microorganismal model of causation gives us very little help in suggesting the factors we must search for to explain these modern "plagues."

The second development is that it is becoming increasingly clear that we cannot explain the occurrence of disease solely in terms of man's relationship to his *physical* environment. A very important factor is his relationship to other people; that is, to his *human* environment. Here also the theory which postulates that exposure to a microorganism is the cause of disease is of very little use in determining what social or cultural factors—that is, *human* environmental factors—need to be studied to understand disease occurrence.

Theory of Multiple Causes

How then does this microorganismal theory need to be modi-fied to make it more useful for our purposes; that is, for the pre-vention and treatment of disease? First, it is necessary to recog-nize that inherent in the microorganismal theory of disease is the idea that there is a *single* cause—a microorganism or some other agent—for each disease, that each disease has its cause and each cause has its disease. This concept of a single cause we no longer find at all useful in any disease.

The lack of utility of any single-cause theory can easily be illustrated with such a disease as cancer of the breast. This is a useful disease to study in terms of "cause," because we can pro-duce it very easily in certain experimental animals—mice. Breast cancer occurs very infrequently in mice under normal circum-stances, but by selective breeding a strain can be bred in which 60 to 70 per cent, sometimes as high as 80 per cent, of the off-spring will develop breast cancer. Thus it is possible to postulate a genetic factor, something passed down through the genes as a "cause" of breast cancer.

It has also been found that if these genetically susceptible mice are taken from their mother's breast at birth and allowed to suckle from a mother who is from a nonsusceptible strain, they will not develop breast cancer. The explanation is that the sus-ceptible mothers excrete a virus in their milk which has to be present for breast cancer to develop in their offspring. So a virus is implicated in the cause of breast cancer.

However, baby mice born of nonsusceptible mothers and allowed to suckle from susceptible mothers (that is, fed milk con-taining this virus) do *not* develop breast cancer. Furthermore, not all mice born of susceptible mothers and suckled by these mothers from birth develop breast cancer. This develops only in female offspring, not in males. If estrogen, the female sex hor-mone, is injected into these male offspring shortly after birth, however, they too will develop breast cancer. Thus a third factor, a hormone, may also be thought of as a "cause" of breast cancer. Finally, mice in which all three factors are present—that is female mice bred and suckled by genetically susceptible mothers and then placed on a restricted caloric intake—rarely develop breast cancer.

Now in terms of a single-cause theory, what is "the cause" of breast cancer in mice? Genetic transmission? A virus? A particular hormone? Diet? Obviously no single factor is the cause; all four factors have to be present for breast cancer to develop. Any attempt to say *the* cause of breast cancer in mice is genetic or viral is not very useful.

Thus we have to change our thinking from a single-causal theory to a multicausal theory. Many factors can cause any particular disease, and what may be causal under certain circumstances may not be causal under others.

Questions of How and Why

Even the acceptance of a multicausal theory, however, is not sufficient for our purposes in trying to understand the causes of any disease. We have to pose the further question: why do we want to understand causes? Are we concerned with the causes for the onset of the disease or with the causes for recovery? These factors, those causing onset and those causing recovery may be, and frequently are, very different.

An elementary illustration may make this clear. We have many theories about the causes of coronary heart disease: the amount of fat in the diet, the amount of exercise taken, the number of cigarettes smoked, the level of blood pressure, genetic factors, and so on. Whatever the particular causes, let us consider two men each of whom has a heart attack as a result of the same causes and let us assume that each suffers the same amount of damage to his heart. Despite these similarities, we know from clinical experience that one of these men may be an invalid the rest of his life and the other may be like former President Eisenhower, completely capable of undertaking the strenuous task of directing a country. Although identical conditions may have led to the onset of their disease, very different conditions determine their recovery.

One further aspect of "cause" must be taken into consideration for a fuller understanding of the disease process. For both types of causes, those responsible for onset and those responsible for recovery, we should be concerned with questions of "how" and "why." *How* does a person develop diabetes? "Some disturbance in insulin metabolism" would be the answer. *Why* does a person develop diabetes? Our knowledge of the relationship between disturbed insulin metabolism and the disease we call diabetes does not tell us *why* this patient at this point developed this disorder. If, however, in addition to knowing about the relationship of insulin metabolism to diabetes, we knew that immigrants develop the diabetes rates of their new country to the same extent that they absorb its customs, and if we knew what these customs were, we would be getting some clues that could help us answer these "why" questions. These customs might bring changes in diet and exercise and in the amount and types of emotional strain. These causal factors would tell us something about why or under what circumstances people develop diabetes and thus increase our knowledge about what needs to be changed to prevent new cases from occurring. In the identification of this category of causes epidemiology makes, in my opinion, its major contribution.

Modern Epidemiology

Perhaps the relevance and importance of these points can be made more clear by an illustration. To do this I would like to present data from a modern epidemiological study of a disease traditionally explained on the basis of one cause. It will become evident how much more can be learned about this disease if the questions are posed and the results interpreted within this broader theoretical framework.

The disease is tuberculosis and the "cause," using the traditional model of causation, would be the tubercle bacillus. Knowledge of the role of the tubercle bacillus has been very helpful in telling us something about how people get sick—they get sick because of the tubercle bacillus—but it tells very little about how they recover and nothing at all about why they get sick. As indicated above, the vast majority of people exposed to the tubercle bacillus do not develop tuberculosis. To determine why some do, it is helpful to know how people who do get tuberculosis differ from those who do not.

One relatively recent study in Seattle gives some clues. This study started by dividing the city into four economic areas. Area 1 was the poorest, with the worst housing and the most over-crowding. Area 2 was a little better but also poor and over-crowded. Area 3 was about average for Seattle. Area 4 was the richest part of the city. The investigators examined the distribu-tion of tuberculosis by area. As might be expected, the rates were highest in Area 1, lowest in Area 4, for both males and females. Examining the distribution by race, they found the same relation-ship for whites—but for nonwhites the pattern was almost re-versed. The highest rates for nonwhites, both male and female, occurred in the richest area. The nonwhites in this area were not domestic servants but professional people—doctors, lawyers, busi-ness executives, and so on. The lowest rate for nonwhites oc-curred in Area 2, which in addition to being one of the poorer areas was that part of the city in which nonwhites lived in com-pact neighborhood groups and had many opportunities for inter-personal contact and friendships. The highest rates for nonwhites thus occurred in the area where they were a distinct minority without opportunity for warm personal contacts with other peo-ple. Conversely, for whites the rates were highest in those areas in which there were high proportions of nonwhite neighborhoods and where the whites had little opportunity for social interaction.

The next characteristic examined was residential and job mobility. Unlike the nontuberculous, those who developed tuber-culosis had been highly mobile. They had moved from home to home about five times more frequently than does the average per-son in the United States, and they had changed jobs very fre-quently. The third characteristic was marital status. Fewer of the tuberculous had been married and far more had been divorced or widowed than is true for the population as a whole. Finally, the fourth distinguishing characteristic was that a large propor-tion of the tuberculous lived alone in one room.

To summarize: At this point in time we find that the tuber-culous are strangers in the neighborhood where they live; they often move and change jobs; if they marry, their marriages are frequently broken by death or divorce; and they live alone. People with these characteristics have been referred to by sociolo-

gists as "marginal men." They do not belong, they have few
friends, few neighbors that they know well, no kin, and very little
contact with fellow human beings.

To determine whether the findings of this Seattle study had
been observed elsewhere, I attempted to review as much of the
recent literature as possible. No study was found that had specifically addressed itself to the question, but one accidentally provided corroborative evidence. This was a study done in Britain
in which the investigators addressed themselves to the relationship between overcrowding and tuberculosis. The authors selected
some 14,000 or 15,000 families living in a city and used the living
arrangements (less than one person per room, one person per
room, or more than one person per room) as an index of crowding.
All family members were x-rayed to find out if those living in
houses with more than one person per room had more tuberculosis than those who were not crowded. (Before analyzing the
data, all lodgers in these homes were eliminated from the study
because the authors believed they would weight the one-person-
per-room category.) The families were also categorized by social
class, since it is known that tuberculosis occurs much more frequently in the lower classes. The findings indicated increased tuberculosis rates in family members as social class declined—but
no relationship between tuberculosis and overcrowding in any
social class.

Fortunately the investigators included, as an appendix, their
findings on the lodgers in these families. Although the lodgers
lived under the same general conditions as the families, their
tuberculosis rates were almost twice as high, particularly in the
low social classes. The major difference between lodgers and family members, of course, is that the lodgers are more likely to be
people without families or kin, living alone, often single, and
lonely.

Stress and the Social Isolate

If the findings of these studies are accepted, they pose a number of further questions. How is it possible that these factors can
increase the chances of getting tuberculosis? Obviously not all
people who are isolated develop tuberculosis even when they are

exposed to the bacillus; therefore, what are the differences between isolated people who develop the disease and isolated people who do not? What else needs to happen?

A study of tuberculosis hospital employees sheds some light on these questions. Each employee who had developed tuberculosis was matched with a nontuberculous employee of the same race, age, sex, date of employment, type of work, tuberculin test result at the beginning of employment, appearance of the first x-ray, presence or absence of any other significant disease, marital status, income, and history of alcoholism. So far as possible, the two groups were identical except that those in one group had developed tuberculosis and those in the other had not, although both had been exposed to the tubercle bacillus as a result of working in a TB hospital. In each group the number of situations likely to produce stress during the previous ten years was measured. These included economic factors such as financial worry and loss of job, and social and personal factors such as marital stress, social withdrawal, and personal crises.

The actual number of stressful situations did not differ in the two groups, but the distribution of these stresses over time differed very markedly. In those who did *not* develop tuberculosis the stressful situations were distributed randomly, some years being relatively free of stress and some years having multiple stresses. In the tuberculosis group, however, the stressful situations mounted in a crescendo, each year being worse than the previous one. These situations reached a peak about one to two years before tuberculosis was diagnosed.

Thus it appears that people exposed to mounting life stress who are deprived of help and support from society, who have no friends or kin—that is, no one interested in them—have to handle these threats unaided. One of the consequences is the disease we call tuberculosis.

Hormone Balance in the Tuberculous Patient

A question that would follow from such a formulation might be this: Why tuberculosis? There is evidence to show that tuberculosis is not the only deleterious consequence of such a set of circumstances. People who develop schizophrenia or who commit suicide, for example, have very similar characteristics to those who develop tuberculosis. When a person develops tuberculosis, additional factors must therefore be present.

Some of these have been tentatively identified in yet another study from Seattle. In this, a group of tuberculosis patients in a hospital were investigated to determine the relationship between their hormone balance and their recovery from tuberculosis. The hormone measured is produced by the adrenal gland and called the 17-ketosteroids. It was found that the level of this hormone fluctuated widely from patient to patient, and that there was a close relationship between the emotional state of the patient and the level of his hormone. Those who had very low levels of hormone tended to be apathetic, depressed, withdrawn—to feel hopeless. The closer the hormone level came to the normal for their age and sex the more the patients tended to be calm, contented, and well adjusted to their situation. Those who had very high levels tended to show the classical signs of anxiety, restlessness, aggressiveness, hostility, fearfulness, and to refuse to stay in bed. Under adequate therapy those whose levels were nearest normal tended to recover the fastest. Those whose level was lowest tended to die and those whose levels were highest tended neither to recover nor die, but become chronic. If a patient's emotional state was changed, his hormone level would also change as would the response to tuberculosis. Thus, if an apathetic, withdrawn patient was made more calm and contented, his hormone level tended to rise and his chance of recovery from tuberculosis improved.

The Causes of Tuberculosis

It is now possible to reformulate our concept of the causes of tuberculosis. Exposure to mounting life stresses in people deprived of emotional support from society will lead to their being overwhelmed, with a resulting increase in depression and apathy. This emotional state may lead to an alteration in hormone balance, which increases their susceptibility to the tubercle bacillus. If any of these factors are missing, tuberculosis is unlikely to occur. For example, people similarly exposed to mounting life stresses who are well integrated in society, who can get support from a wife or a husband, or from neighbors or kin, are not likely to become so depressed and apathetic and withdrawn as are the lonely, and thus would not have the alteration in their hormone level. Exposure to the tubercle bacillus would therefore not be followed by tuberculosis.

Tuberculosis was deliberately selected as a disease of traditional concern to epidemiology, namely, an infectious disease. I wanted to indicate, as dramatically as possible, that if modern epidemiology can increase our understanding of a disease about which so much is already known, it can make an even greater contribution to the study of conditions about which little at present is known. Not only can all diseases, noninfectious chronic diseases as well as infectious, be studied by epidemiological methods, but many other states of health are amenable to such investigation. For example, epidemiological studies have been conducted on accidents, industrial absenteeism, fetal survival, and growth and maturation. In addition, there is growing realization that various psychological factors, including behavior development, emotional states, and intelligence, can be studied in a similar fashion. Finally, it is our belief that increased understanding of the various manifestations of social maladjustment—for example, delinquency, chronic dependency, and criminality—can also be gained through epidemiological investigation. For all such conditions the major contribution of epidemiology will derive from its ability to elucidate the role of environmental factors, particularly factors in the human environment, in the causal chain.

The most important single factor which up to the present has limited the intelligent application of epidemiological techniques to such problems has been our inability to develop an adequate conceptual scheme indicating the relevant social and cultural processes. Whatever the present limitations of the bacteriological theory of causation, for a time it provided a useful model which led to an intelligent selection of relevant variables in the environment. To proceed further and gain understanding of the impact on health of social and cultural processes we need a new model which takes into account the modern view of causation and indicates the types of social and cultural variables we need to study. To devise such a model requires the closest collaboration of the social and the health sciences and is a task of central concern to our Department of Epidemiology.

Summary

Epidemiology is one of the sciences concerned with the study of the processes which determine or influence the physical, mental, and social health of people. It is with their health in relation to their behavior in social groups that epidemiology is primarily concerned.

Up to this point I have been concerned solely with the theoretical basis upon which epidemiology is, or should be, founded. Without such a basis epidemiological investigation is sterile. The theoretical formulations should not be confused, however, with the methods and techniques by which epidemiological investigations are carried out. These methods, requiring considerable skill in execution, can be simply stated. Epidemiology is an observational science. The essential element in observation is comparison. In epidemiology we compare the characteristics of a group having a specific condition with the characteristics of a group without the condition. From our knowledge of the similarities and differences between the two groups, we derive hypotheses as to the processes which caused the condition. To carry out such studies, we collect facts concerning the state of health or condition being studied, the nature of the group in which the condition is being studied, and the habitat or environment of that group. Groups may vary in size from a single family unit to a whole nation; they may also differ in kind. But whether it is an informal, relatively intimate group or a formal organized group, the same general principles apply. Special indices, such as incidence and prevalence rates, have been developed to quantify these data and describe their distribution, taking into account the differing numbers of people at risk in various groups and the differing lengths of time they are observed. Various statistical procedures are required to determine the strength of any associations found to exist between the characteristics of the group or habitat and the state of health under study. Formal rules have been developed as to the generalizations possible depending on the nature of the sample and the way the data were collected. All these factors bear the same relationship to epidemiology that laboratory techniques bear to, for example, bacteriology. They are essential tools without which scientific epidemiological investigation is impossible. A knowledge of these tools without any grasp of the basic theory leads, however, to pedestrian studies of very limited usefulness to investigation.

If social workers decide to apply epidemiological methods to the study of social problems, I hope they will address themselves not only to the scientific techniques required but to an even more challenging requirement: the development of meaningful conceptual models which can be made operational and tested. In this latter area I see great opportunities for fruitful collaboration between social work and epidemiology.

Applied Epidemiology and Its Use in the Control of Mental Illnesses*

by ROGER WILLIAM HOWELL, M.D.

In describing the basic principles which underlie modern epidemiology, Dr. Cassel was careful not to overstate the significance of this approach to an understanding of how illnesses develop and can be managed. Nevertheless, he was able to point out a number of ways in which the science of epidemiology has had to change to deal with new public health problems. It is important to keep in mind his descriptions of how and why these changes occurred, as they definitely relate to many problems considered in this presentation.

There are a number of reasons why a sharper focus on mental illnesses extends even modern epidemiology beyond traditionally accepted scientific limitations. In the first place, there is considerable question as to what is a case of mental illness and what is not. Even if we can identify a case in one sociocultural group, it may not be regarded as one in another group. In certain circumstances behavior may be completely abnormal, while under different conditions the same behavior may be quite normal. Most explanations of why behavior occurs as it does must still be regarded as theoretical rather than scientific. Questions can be raised about even the most plausible explanation, such as the relationship between an infection by the organism responsible for syphilis and the occurrence of paresis. These problems, and

* This paper, delivered March 6, 1962, is based largely on information derived from *Causes of Mental Disorders: A Review of Epidemiological Knowledge, 1959; Proceedings of a Round Table Held at Arden House, Harriman, New York, 1959* (New York: Milbank Memorial Fund, 1961).

many others, tend to complicate an exact application of epidemiological methods to the control of mental illnesses.

Epidemiology and Social Problems

But we are not here to belabor problems of applying sound methods to currently challenging situations. Rather, we are here to discuss ways in which epidemiological methods might prove useful to social work, and this suggests that this paper should concern itself with possible, or even probable leads, rather than with proved facts. Dr. Cassel has already hinted that epidemiology is changing and will continue to change as changes occur in the nature of the challenges it faces. It therefore seems appropriate to extend scientific limitations a little for the purpose of indicating what may be the future applicability of epidemiology to diverse problems with which society is and will be faced.

Two introductory comments are indicated. First, social work has used epidemiological methods; they are not new to the field. The appearance of group workers in community settlement houses resulted from the finding that certain neighborhood groups seemed to need special services. Mothers deprived of necessary income were recognized as special persons in need of extra funds to permit them to continue to care for their children. Other susceptible groups in our communities, such as the elderly, have been identified as needing special attention and services. These and many others have been identified as needy persons as a result of epidemiological investigations, and services designed to meet their special needs have been offered. We may question the effectiveness of the programs developed to meet the needs, but the method of discovery has been sound.

Second, I would like to re-emphasize three major points made by Dr. Cassel:

1. A change has occurred recently in our thinking about the factors which produce illness: We have replaced our mono-etiological theory with a multicausal theory, and now hold that a number of factors, rather than a single factor, contribute to the development of a disease.
2. Factors responsible for the onset of a disease may not be those which contribute to recovery.

3. Etiological agents in human cultural, social, and psychological environment are as important as agents in the
   physical environment, both in producing the condition
   and in contributing to its proper management.

Disease and the Genetic Factor

The first point suggests that a disease results from a number
of different factors in the disease-producing agent, the environment, and the host. Let's look at schizophrenia, for example.
There is pretty reliable evidence that an individual who develops
schizophrenia has an hereditary predisposition to develop the
condition. This may be more pronounced in some than in others.
Geneticists refer to this power as being related to the penetrance
of the gene which carries the predisposing factor. It is possible
that this hereditary predisposition could be so strong that it
would most likely cause the development of schizophrenia. But
it is also possible that a completely normal intrauterine developmental experience plus a nontraumatic delivery plus a completely
satisfying relationship during the early years of development
after birth plus a life comparatively free from stressful events and
full of supporting and gratifying interpersonal relationships would
counteract the hereditary tendency to the extent that the disease
does not develop at all. Any of these other factors may also contribute to the appearance of a disease which resembles schizophrenia. Thus the actual causative agent of the disease is difficult
to isolate in any one case, let alone in a group, which is, after all,
the principal focus of the epidemiologist. The same sort of listing
of factors might be possible for the other functional disorders—
juvenile delinquency, alcoholism, and psychoneuroses.

Dr. Cassel's second point suggests that factors which contribute to the onset of the condition may not be involved at all in
influencing recovery from the disease. An excellent example can
be seen in the way the mentally retarded child is treated today.
Without knowing the cause of the disease, we carry out successful treatment by providing the child with special educational experiences; they do not change his basic learning handicap but
do make it possible for him to develop somewhat, in spite of his
handicap. The same approach to other conditions, such as senile

psychosis, schizophrenia, and epilepsy, has also been tried.

Cultural, social, and psychological factors contribute to depressions which occur at the menopause, accompanying obvious physical change. These factors, which are considered in treating the condition, seem also to contribute to recovery. This example tends to support Dr. Cassel's third point.

With these points in mind, let us look at some of the problems which beset the epidemiologist as he attempts to study mental illnesses. All authorities seem to agree that the most troublesome feature is the vagueness of psychiatric diagnosis. As most diagnostic categories describe a pattern of behavior, which is then judged as appropriate or not, considerable variation in clinical judgments is not surprising. Moreover, the descriptions of the conditions rarely consider any of the possible etiological agents which contribute to their onset. Even in conditions which follow actual physical damage to the brain there is such variability that one frequently wonders just how much the damage has to do with the condition. This bewilderment, however, should not keep us from trying to do everything we can to protect the brain from damage, as there is reliable evidence that damage to the brain results, in many instances, in disturbances in behavior. Nor should this lack of definitiveness keep us from doing everything we can to minimize the effects of brain damage once it has occurred, and to engage in active rehabilitation along modern therapeutic lines.

Some infectious diseases seem to produce damage to the brain. Many of them have decreased in frequency as a result of epidemiological studies and procedures derived therefrom. They include infectious meningitis of several different types, virus encephalitis, polio, measles, and toxoplasmosis, a disease resulting from an infestation of the nervous system by a parasitic organism. All these have been studied intensively, and many have responded favorably to control of the disease process itself.

The same can be said about syphilis of the central nervous system, which used to contribute rather extensively to the population of our state hospitals. Fewer cases of paresis are seen now than previously, not because fewer cases of syphilis occur but because we are using better case-finding and treatment methods today than in the past.

A number of other conditions create organic abnormalities in the brain which may or may not be related to disturbances in behavior. Some of these conditions we understand fairly well, while others we do not. Also, many influences contribute to disturbances in behavior which are not directly referable to injury to the brain tissue. Most of these are poorly understood, and a clearer understanding of them must await further advances in the basic sciences as well as in the behavioral sciences. For example, we do not know why comparable degrees of cerebral arteriosclerosis produce variable patterns of behavior. It is obvious that the resultant disturbance in cerebral circulation is not the only factor contributing to the behavior.

Mental Illness and the Environment

With these comments about organic conditions which predispose toward abnormal behavior I should like to pass on to a more meaningful discussion, from the point of view of this conference. Mental diseases seem to be related to factors in the cultural, social, and psychological environment. The exact way in which the relationship exerts its influence is not clear, but evidence of the significance of these factors is strong enough to warrant their consideration as areas for epidemiological investigation.

The rest of this presentation will be devoted, then, to a discussion of factors which seem to need further examination as to their role in contributing to mental illnesses. Certain logical hints will be discussed, and some attempt will be made to elaborate upon their relationship to human behavior. (This following through on hints is a tried and true public health procedure. It is based on the thesis that when one doesn't know for sure what to do about a problem, one tries to make an intelligent guess about what should be done, and then proceeds to do it. Obviously, mistakes occur, but every now and then answers result that would otherwise not have been revealed.)

Mental illnesses seem to be characterized by an inability of the sick person to adapt successfully to the ongoing processes of life. It has already been mentioned that hereditary tendencies may predispose the individual to this difficulty. One is inclined to think that if a thing is inherited, it's inherited, and that's all there is to it. But studies have shown that when certain inherited conditions are expected, or at least suspected, and early tests confirm their existence, steps may be taken to interfere with the natural course of the handicap and to inhibit its most drastic effects.

An example can be found in phenylketonuria, a metabolic disturbance which results in the excretion of an abnormal substance in the urine about three weeks after birth. If this condition is allowed to pursue its normal course, it will eventually result in brain damage. This course can be averted, however, by a special diet and other procedures, and thus damage to the brain may be prevented. In other words, here is a disease that we know to be hereditary. Individuals whose ancestors had this disease should have the advantages of counseling, even before marriage and certainly before having children. If children are born from this background, they should be examined early, so that procedures to control the condition can be instituted.

Other conditions merit greater consideration, just as does phenylketonuria. If we consider other types of factors which tend to predispose individuals toward inability to cope with life's stresses, but which are not related to genetics so much as to other observable influences, we might develop quite a list of suspected agents of disease. Should an obstetrician be concerned when an emotionally disturbed woman becomes a mother? Should he at that point think of the infant as someone who immediately has become susceptible to an unhealthful growing-up experience, which may result in his becoming a mental case himself? If so, what kind of services will the infant and his parents need to alleviate the conditions which predispose toward the development of illness? These questions come immediately to mind when one realizes that obstetricians see evidences of unhealthiness in some of their patients. There is certainly some evidence that disturbed mothers bring up disturbed children—although this evidence exists largely in case records rather than in well-developed epidemiological studies. Here, perhaps, is an area that needs further study.

One might also wonder if the unmarried mother might not be regarded as a sort of double-barrelled problem. Certainly she herself is, in many instances, under extra stress. Case records suggest that many of these mothers have difficulties; if they decide to keep their children, it is quite likely that it will be difficult for them to maintain a healthy relationship with their children.

One wonders about the possible significance of early marriage on the capability of younger women in mothering their children in as healthy a way as might be desirable. This is not an attempt to suggest that nineteen-year-old girls cannot be good mothers. It is merely another question which might be raised, an area of research which might be indicated.

There are countless other factors which might be pursued as to their effects on the kind of relationship the infant is able to establish with his mother. Since this is an important relationship, studies designed to help us discover potentially poor mothers might lead to programs in which they would be treated as people in need of special services. Again, these ideas are based on the concept that one learns to cope with stresses partly by how well one is taught to do so by one's mother in the very early months of life.

And we shouldn't leave out the father in these considerations. It should be possible to develop a long list of things we would like to know about him too. One very obvious question comes to mind with respect to both parents. A good many parents learn to do a pretty good job of child-rearing, even if they didn't want the child before it was born. I know of no evidence that parents who don't want a child do a poorer job of child-rearing when it comes along than do parents of the wanted child, but it is possible. It does seem that there are quite a few children who get born to parents who openly say they don't really want this child right now!

The Promise of Epidemiology

A number of these questions seem amenable to observations of an epidemiological nature, and with this thought in mind I have pursued them. Epidemiological studies do not have to be any more complicated than some of these questions would indicate. A great deal of effort has gone into studies of the whole process of socialization of the child in the family, but there doesn't seem to be any consistency in findings that would be helpful in answering any of these questions. There does seem to be fairly good agreement that there is such a thing as maternal deprivation, and that its effects can be measured in different ways. But there is also incomplete evidence of striking cultural differences among various groups throughout the world.

If we are concerned about those factors which tend to improve the early life experiences of infants, we need also to take a look at those in a position to assist in bringing this to pass. Every community has individuals who indulge in helping young mothers, but there are also some in every community who consistently relate to new mothers in a helping way. The social worker is one who is in a position to support and otherwise assist young mothers, and she may also be in a position to pursue some leads deriving from her contacts with parents. One would certainly think of the obstetrician, pediatrician, and family doctor, the public health nurse, the clergy, and perhaps some others, as being involved in the early months of an infant's life. But how well prepared are these persons, even though they are professionals, to do the kind of a job that we hope they could do? This too should be a subject for research, so that feasible answers can be worked out for the question which asks, "What is needed, and how can it be obtained?"

There are other periods in the normal life span of an individual when unusual stress is encountered. Many of the questions about maternal-infant relationships could be raised about the first few weeks of school, the onset of adolescence, the early adult years when serious plans for life are being made, the involutional period, and the period of retirement and old age, to mention only the major ones. Each period seems to have its own set of factors which should be investigated. There would be the constant question about the personality make-up of the individual which predisposes him to adapt or to fail. There would be the same questions about social factors which contribute to success or failure in adaptation, about cultural factors, and about environmental factors as well. Of particular interest would be the patterns in which new helping persons, such as the visiting teacher and the school counselor, are introduced to the individual.

So much, then, for the approach to an understanding of mental illnesses through utilization of our knowledge of the growth and development pattern, and of rates of illness at various ages throughout the life span. Much more work will have to be done before any very clear leads emerge from this broad area of study, but it is encouraging to know that some have already appeared in the literature. These comments have been made in the hope that a comprehensive view of possible epidemiological approaches to the mental illnesses would be more stimulating than a mere repetition of what is actually known about the various illnesses, which really isn't very much.

New Epidemiological Approaches

Another approach to the epidemiology of mental illness has been the attempt to discover correlations between various patterns of behavior, healthy or not, and identifiable social or cultural factors.

There is conflicting data about the effects of social position and of changes in social status upon the mental health of people. There seems to be evidence that schizophrenics are more commonly found in the lower strata of society than in the upper strata; the exact meaning of this, however, is not at all clear. There is also some evidence that the effort to improve one's status makes for stress and might produce symptoms of illness. The comments about this in the literature seem to suggest that some kinds of social mobility may be beneficial and some may not. It has been suspected that migrant people would show more signs of mental illnesses than do nonmigrants, but this has not been substantiated at all; the findings are ambiguous.

Industrialization has come in for its fair share of study. There seems little doubt that some increase in stress can be attributed to the rapid growth of industry, the increasingly complicated way of life, and other changes in our society as a whole which have occurred as part of our becoming an industrial society. These changes, however, so far as has been determined by a number of studies, do not produce an increase in the major mental illnesss, the major psychoses. It is suggested that they may be responsible for some increase in anxiety states, mild depressions, other neurotic illnesses and perhaps alcoholism.

Interesting attempts to find differences in the rates of psychoses in the various races have not presented us with any clear-cut evidence one way or the other. It has been noticed that there is less alcoholism among Jews, but this seems to have been replaced by a greater propensity for psychosomatic disturbances. Other social relationships have been investigated, but they show very little, if any, suggestive evidence. The point must be made that there is a great volume of literature on the mental illnesses, and it is not surprising that in attempting to cover it all one encounters conflicting reports. This probably is a result of the multivariance of factors which contribute to the occurrence of these diseases, to the extent that it is almost impossible to get an accurate picture of what any one factor is likely to do.

Several quite well-recognized phenomena in history seem to be related to behavior symptomatic of mental illness. Suicide, for example, has shown several epidemic-like increases. Of note is the increase which resulted from the depression of 1929. In contrast to these findings, however, there seemed to be a decrease in suicides during World War II.

The obvious factors which might contribute to the development of depressions at the time of retirement have been well delineated many times. The question can be raised, however, whether or not any of the evidence permits the institution of preventive programs which work. Not enough solid experimentation with programs which seem to be preventive has actually gone on. One gets the feeling that a number of leads which already exist in the data gathered from epidemiological investigation could be tested—but they have not been, probably for many reasons. Although one should be quite careful not to jump to conclusions not merited by the data, it seems to me that we should be equally diligent in our attempts to utilize whatever leads we have.

Epidemiology and Social Work

What might this discussion suggest for social work? Many of the questions raised here about mental illnesses are questions that social workers raise as well, for they work with the mentally ill and are interested in controlling these diseases as much as is possible. More than this, however, social workers are interested in the behavior of human beings as individuals and members of groups. The epidemiological method, especially as it attempts to discover leads which will influence mental illness, is interested in the behavior of human beings also.

Although there is much yet to be learned about the use of epidemiology in controlling mental illnesses, we do have a few leads. These leads should prove equally helpful to social work and to public health.

In thinking of problems which might lend themselves to an epidemiological approach and are usually of concern to social workers, we might begin by asking ourselves: What are the factors which contribute to indigence? Possibly so many are already well known that a further pursuit of them is not indicated. And yet, have we any good leads which might suggest what we should be trying to do about it? Other areas of interest to social work which might benefit from investigation along these lines would include, it seems to me, the factors influencing the effectiveness of adoption and the factors related to illegitimacy, delinquency, alcoholism, and neglect. All of these are dependents of human behavior, and as such should probably be studied epidemiologically as well as clinically.

These few examples from the field of mental illness and from the field of social work show what one can hope for in using the epidemiological approach in an attempt to understand more about how we can possibly interfere with undesirable patterns of behavior. No attempt was made to cover the many epidemiological studies carried out in an attempt to understand illness more fully. This paper is intended to show in a little detail the way leads obtained from epidemiology can help one to think about approaches to controlling conditions. It is obvious that there are no striking clues as to what has to be done to control any one mental illness, even those we know the most about. For the present we need only make sure we are using every bit of the scanty information we have.

Epidemiology—Its Application for Social Work[*]

by MAURICE B. HAMOVITCH, PH.D.

Definitions

Epidemiology has been defined as "the study of the distribution of a disease or condition in a population, and of the factors that influence this distribution. Thus, the epidemiologist is interested in the variation in frequency of diseases or conditions by such characteristics as age, sex, race, social class and occupation."[1] Paul refers to modern epidemiology as "the study of the ecology of disease."[2] He defines it further as the study of *"the circumstances under which diseases occur, where diseases tend to flourish, and where they do not . . .*; they may be based on genetic, social, or environmental factors; even religious or political factors may come under scrutiny, provided they are found to have some bearing upon disease prevalence . . . all human blights . . . have their epidemiology. . . ."[3]

Others, however, point out: "While there has been repeated expression of faith in the applicability of the principles of epidemiologic investigation to non-infectious diseases, there is no doubt that the transfer of epidemiologic concern from the in-

---

[*] Paper delivered March 6, 1962.

[1] Herman E. Hilleboe and Granville W. Larimore, eds., *Preventive Medicine; Principles of Prevention in the Occurrence and Progression of Disease* (Philadelphia: W. B. Saunders Company, 1959), p. 663.

[2] John R. Paul, *Clinical Epidemiology* (Chicago: University of Chicago Press, 1958), p. 7.

[3] *Ibid.*, p. 9.

fectious to the non-infectious diseases has necessitated appreciable modification of methods, if not of principles."[4] Dr. Cassel, in his paper, indicates further that this modification must recognize that inherent in the classical approach to epidemiology, based mainly on the microorganismal theory of disease, is the idea that there is a *single* cause for each disease. This theory, he says, has little or no utility in understanding noninfectious, chronic diseases. Dr. Cassel goes on to say that epidemiologists have to change their thinking from a single-cause theory to a multicausal theory; they have to recognize that many factors can cause any particular disease and that what may be causal under certain circumstances may not be causal under others. Even the acceptance of this, however, is not sufficient for our purposes, he maintains. We have to pose the further question: For what purpose do we want to understand causes? Are we concerned with the causes responsible for the onset of a disease, that is, the causes responsible for making a person sick? Or are we concerned with the causes responsible for recovery from this disease?[5]

Review of the literature of epidemiology, including the papers by Dr. Cassel and Dr. Howell,[6] render very apt an observation made by Dr. Alfred Katz:

> Molière's character had been "talking prose" for forty years but did not know it. We in social work have for decades been employing aspects of an "epidemiological approach" without any conscious reference to its analogues in medicine and public health. Yet in the same fashion as M. Jourdain's increased self-consciousness resulted in greater attention to his grammar, it may pay us to examine explicitly and consciously what we may usefully borrow and apply from public health. Not only might our use of an epidemiological approach gain in logic and consistency; what

[4] Brian MacMahon, Thomas F. Pugh, and Johannes Ipsen, *Epidemiologic Methods* (Boston: Little, Brown and Company, 1960), p. vii.

[5] John M. Cassel, "Potentialities and Limitations of Epidemiology," paper presented at Public Health Seminar (Princeton, N. J., March 6, 1962).

[6] Roger W. Howell, "Applied Epidemiology and Its Use in the Control of Mental Illnesses," paper presented at Public Health Seminar (Princeton, N. J., March 1962).

we do might be more easily explained and taught; one worker's approach might be more readily reproduced by others.[7]

Shifting Emphases in Social Work

Examination of the history of social work and social welfare
reveals that we have gone through a number of phases. During
some of these we approached problems in ways not too dissimilar
from those of the epidemiologist; during others, we approached
from the opposite pole. Prior to the twentieth century and even
into this century, the spirit of social work studies was very much
in line with the prevailing epidemiological approach. A great deal
of attention was devoted to ascertaining the "causes" of dependency and crime. Many theories were developed and many
studies were undertaken to "prove" one cause or another for
these social ills.

Following World War I social work turned to Freudian psychology and the clinical frame of reference. The major concerns
became the individual case and the acquisition of skill in dealing
with the individual client or patient. While during the depression
there was considerable ferment in the realm of social policy, the
trained social workers sought professional satisfaction in clinical
practice, and little research was undertaken. This persisted into
the post-World War II period.

In the last ten years there has been a resurgence of interest
in research generally and in research designed to investigate the
etiology of social ills and emotional disturbances. We are fum-
bling with inadequate tools, however, partly because we are not
clear about the appropriate questions to ask, partly because we
have inadequate theories to test or on which to build, and partly
because of a certain amount of resistance to modifying the notion
that "every case is unique" and a fear that emphasis on epidemiologic methods will lead to an anticlinical bias. This is linked
to the fact that epidemiologists generally deal with circumstances
involving more than one person. Paul, however, points out that a
clinical epidemiologist "can start with a single patient and his

---

[7] Alfred H. Katz, "What Can Social Work Learn from Public Health Methodology?" (ms.)

family and branch out cautiously into the community. His efforts are to discover patterns of disease similar to those of the original patient, which can be associated with the patient's genetic background or his ways of living."[8]

One of our problems in social work research is that our professional journals have inundated us with descriptions of single cases leading to generalizations without adequate evidence. As a result, some in the field have turned to statistical studies, using tools which may be appropriate in other fields but not necessarily in our own. There has been the curious result on the one hand of studies utilizing sophisticated statistical devices inappropriate to social work data, and on the other of studies which ignore the theoretical and methodological contributions available from other disciplines.

Objectives of Epidemiology and Relationship to Social Work

What are the objectives and methods of epidemiology? In what ways are they similar to those of social work research, and how might they be used in social work?

MacMahon *et al* state: "The most challenging purpose of epidemiology is that of identifying those components of causal mechanisms that enable the formulation of effective preventive measures. This aim encompasses a number of subsidiary, more specific purposes:

"1. Formulation, selection, or rejection of hypotheses that explain disease distribution in terms of specific characteristics or experiences of affected persons.

"2. Testing hypotheses of disease origin through special surveys or other observational studies.

"3. Testing the validity of the rationale on which control programs are based, by the use of epidemiologic data collected in conjunction with the programs. A control program may be considered as an experimental design, the subject of the experiment being the knowledge of causal mechanisms which gave rise to the program.

---

[8] Paul, *op. cit.*, p. 11.

"4. Distinguishing entities of disease and disability through knowledge of disease distribution and of causal factors."[9]

These purposes are clearly in line with the objectives of social work research. Are we not just interested, or should we not be, in the "formulation, selection, or rejection of hypotheses" that explain the distribution of social problems "in terms of specific characteristics or experiences of affected persons?" In juvenile delinquency, in unmarried motherhood, to some extent—as pointed out by Dr. Howell—and in mental illness, we have undertaken a considerable amount of research, but we are a long way from the answers. As Dr. Cassel pointed out, the epidemiologist is also still looking for breakthroughs in research on noninfectious chronic diseases and even in some aspects of infectious diseases—tuberculosis, for example. Where we in social work have lagged behind is in attempting to develop and test hypotheses regarding such problems as marital conflict, parent-child conflict, child neglect, discharge against medical advice, and failure to follow through on medical recommendations. Here we have done little research which might be considered epidemiologic in nature. There have been some attempts in recent years, notably by Community Research Associates and the St. Paul Family-Centered Project, to examine the multi-problem family epidemiologically, and this may mark a positive trend.

Social work has been singularly remiss in failing to validate the rationale on which control programs are based. Characteristically, new programs have been developed out of the conviction of a number of professional and lay leaders who have persuaded enough people in the community to found voluntary agencies, establish new tax-supported agencies, to expand existing agencies. As a social worker I share the conviction of most of my colleagues that family service agencies are worth-while and that the welfare of the community is enhanced by their existence. I believe, too, that child guidance centers serve a useful purpose, as do child welfare agencies, licensing divisions of

9 MacMahon *et al., op. cit.,* p. 7.

welfare departments and medical social work programs. As researcher, however, I confess that we have done little toward testing the validity of the rationale for these programs. True, we have a more difficult task in this connection than do public health epidemiologists in demonstrating the effectiveness of vaccines and sanitation measures in the control of epidemics. But, as both Dr. Cassel and Dr. Howell pointed out, our problems are not too dissimilar from theirs as they test noninfectious disease control programs. The difference is that they attempt to examine their problems systematically. We have been reluctant to do so. We shall never find the answers to social questions if we do not attempt to formulate and examine the questions. One must grant that our present tools are rudimentary, perhaps even inadequate. If we address ourselves to the problems, however, we may be able to develop more adequate tools.

For a long time a major limitation on the contribution of epidemiology was the lack of knowledge about disease entities; many entities were submerged under umbrella-like categories, making it difficult to distinguish one disease from another. It is virtually impossible to develop control programs when it is not clear what is to be controlled. If, however, patterns of distribution can be ascertained, it may be possible to isolate the disease entities and to develop control programs. Similarly, until we in social work are certain what we mean by juvenile delinquency and recognize that the term may subsume a number of different social problems, it will be difficult to develop adequate control programs. This is equally applicable to parent-child problems, child neglect, etc. These may not be single entities but several, and first it is necessary to isolate the specific entities.

Methods of Epidemiology and Relationship to Social Work

As MacMahon *et al.* point out, epidemiology is essentially an applied discipline, and its methods are primarily observational rather than experimental. The goal is to discover a causal association "between two categories of events in which a change in the frequency or quality of one is observed to follow alteration in the other." MacMahon *et al.* postulate two major types of association:

1. Independent—in which there is no statistical association between the categories of events.

2. Statistical—in which there is a statistical association between the categories of events.[10]

These need to be examined more closely, MacMahon and his co-workers note, to determine the nature of the association. There may be a secondary association that is noncausal or one that is directly or indirectly causal.

These authorities point out that "it is never possible to determine whether two single events are causally related; such determination can only be made with respect to categories of events."[11] This has special meaning to social workers because it is the basis of conflict between the social work practitioner and the researcher. The practitioner fears that the researcher's findings of a causal relationship between two events would hold in *every* case. This is not so. To use an illustration from the previous reference: If 100 individuals are inoculated against a certain disease and 100 are given a placebo, and if 20 of the vaccinated and 50 of the controls contract the disease, a statistical association is found between vaccination and freedom from the disease that is probably causal. But 20 of the vaccinated contracted it, implying the presence of other factors that would need to be examined in specific situations.[12] Dr. Cassel's illustration also makes this point. From the standpoint of public health a control program might be in order, including vaccination, although other factors would need to be considered in determining cause and effect in each case.

The same is true in social work. For example, if a study showed that children placed through licensed adoption agencies had a significantly lower rate of emotional disturbance than that of a matched group placed independently, there would be evidence to support a policy of licensed agency adoptions. However,

---

10 *Ibid.,* pp. 9-12.
11 *Ibid.,* p. 13.
12 *Ibid.,* pp. 13-14.

this would not mean that all or even most licensed adoptions would work out successfully or that all or most independent adoptions would fail.

MacMahon *et al.* describe two methods of epidemiologic investigation: prospective and retrospective studies.[13] Retrospective studies search backwards from effects to causes in primary samples of affected and unaffected population. Prospective studies look forward from causes to effects in exposed and unexposed populations. MacMahon *et al.* refer to prospective studies as cohort studies—that is, "investigation over time of an identified group or cohort of individuals." Retrospective studies, referred to as case history studies, are based on investigation of histories of individuals affected with a disease.

Advantages of Cohort Studies

Cohort studies have certain advantages over case studies, according to MacMahon *et al.* Direct estimates can be made of the risks associated with the causal factors. If, for example, we start with two matched groups of children placed for adoption—in one group those placed by a licensed agency and in the other those placed independently—we can follow them long enough to determine the frequency of disturbance in each group, and estimate the incidence of risk associated with each method of placement.

A second advantage of the cohort method noted by Mac-Mahon *et al.* is that "spurious relationships resulting from bias in data-collecting procedures are somewhat less likely"[14] than in case history studies, because it is not necessary to rely so heavily on the memories of informants. If we had to rely on adoptive parents' recollections for information on the five years following adoption, we might have problems in assessing the reliability of the data.

The major disadvantage of the cohort method is that it is "laborious, time-consuming and expensive."[15] Furthermore, loss of informants because of mobility, lack of interest, etc., may result

---

[13] *Ibid.*, pp. 45-48 and 211.
[14] *Ibid.*, p. 47.
[15] *Ibid.*, p. 47.

in a biased sample. If the population we wish to examine is rather small—for example, children hospitalized with a mental illness— it would be necessary to follow many thousands to assure having a final sample large enough to be meaningful statistically; the cost might well be prohibitive. The more common the condition, however, the easier it is to locate cases and the more feasible is the cohort method.

The cohort method is also feasible when the interval between the suspected cause and the end result is short. A cohort study of the influence of counseling services to unmarried mothers during pregnancy on the decision to place or relinquish their babies might well be feasible, because the time span is relatively short.

On the other side of the coin, the more objectively the history of a suspected cause is recorded, the more satisfactory is the case history method, as has been pointed out. Where case records are known to contain the type of information desired, this retrospective method may be useful and certainly more economical. In social work, however, we tend to be overly optimistic about the nature of our case records. Before embarking on a case history study it is important to examine the records very closely as to their appropriateness and completeness for a specific piece of research.

Summary and Conclusions

This paper examined the epidemiologic method and its applicability to social work. Although this epidemiologic method is not altogether foreign to social work researchers, until recently it has not been considered carefully by social work practitioners, including those in public health, and even by many faculty members of schools of social work. The committee responsible for this seminar is to be commended, for out of this discussion may come a wider recognition of the values inherent in the public health approach to social work problems.

We in social work have been talking for years about our services as preventive as well as remedial. We have done little to document this or to examine what we mean by prevention, primary or secondary. We need to be precise in our terminology. Exactly what conditions are we attempting to prevent? Can we identify the risk populations in relation to these conditions—that is, do we know who is susceptible or more susceptible? Where, in other words, should we concentrate our attention? Can we identify causes? What gives rise to the conditions we would like to prevent? Can we identify those services or programs which are effective in preventing these causes? Can we document the efficacy of these programs?

These are crucial and difficult questions. We obviously cannot answer all or even very many of them now. The epidemiologists have not answered them for public health either. The epidemiologic method, however, offers an opportunity and a hope of answering them as we learn the right questions to ask, in ways that can be answered. The tools of public health may need to be modified in the service of social work. But the important thing is to ask the questions, to refine them so that they are meaningful, and to *begin* to tackle them. Only in this way may we hope to develop a firm base on which to build our profession to the point where others view our contributions not on the strength of sentiment or tradition but on the strength of scientific evidence.

The Five Faces of Prevention[*]

by CLAIRE F. RYDER, M.D., M.P.H.

The previous papers in this collection acknowledged the importance of prevention—in relation to the goals of public health and social work, in programing, in the control of specific diseases. Mine will show the relevance of prevention to the social work profession and suggest specific ways that social workers can apply their knowledge and skills in preventive services and in support of their colleagues in the public health field.

Prevention has traditionally been so nearly synonymous with public health that I have ventured to apply the accepted public health principles to prevention in the title of this paper. I refer to the well-known five levels of prevention—promotion of health, specific protection, early detection and prompt treatment, limitation of disability, and rehabilitation. Those of us in the Public Health Service who are concerned primarily with chronic illness and the health of the aged find no difficulty in identifying these five levels of public health practice as they are involved in chronic disease and aging.

Prevention in Retrospect

Before spelling out the essential contribution that the social work profession can make in this field, let us glance at a few historical examples of the several faces of prevention. I should like to discuss these approaches to public health practice in social terms, that is, in relationship to the individual and to the community as a whole.

The earliest type of prevention was the isolation of the

---

[*] Paper delivered March 7, 1962.

patient having a contagious disease. When the U.S. Public Health Service was created at the end of the eighteenth century (in the presidency of John Adams), its special mission was to provide hospital care in ports for merchant sailors with yellow fever or some other scourge of the era. In these hospitals they could be isolated from the rest of the community until they either recovered or died.

From earliest times this separation of the patient from the community was based on fear and superstition (often disguised as religious dicta). To the caveman the action coincided with the survival of the fittest. From Biblical times down through the Middle Ages the "unclean" leper with his bell was not an uncommon sight on the highways. Many today can still recall wearing the asafetida bag, which isolated the patient if it did not always prevent an ailment. In Elizabethan times the hospitality of the pesthouse was extended to the insane and to the poor; they too were isolated from society. Gradually the concept of quarantine developed to include treatment as well as isolation, so that by the end of the eighteenth century, when our marine hospitals were founded, modern public health was beginning to emerge. Today, although we still isolate tuberculosis patients, modern therapy has steadily shortened the period of isolation and speeded their return to the community.

When isolation of the patient constituted all of public health practice, the program could be initiated in any community solely by the decree of a responsible official. The patient was not a target for health education; it was not necessary to motivate him. Isolation was ordered for the good of the whole community, and the individual was required to comply.

Later on, the idea of controlling the environment developed, and it is interesting to note that the effectiveness of environmental control measures became apparent before the reasons for them had been established. The Biblical food laws constituted perhaps the first sanitary code. Originating in the context of religion and culture, they were nonetheless based on sound observation and empiric knowledge. This early control of the environment was direct, straightforward, and dramatic; it brought prompt and tangible results.

Thus the value of a pure water supply, a pure milk supply, and other sanitation principles were accepted historically long before science provided a foundation of solid fact. Again the community acted through duly constituted authorities; early public health measures grew out of the community's exercising of its police powers. Only a small group had to be convinced of the need for them.

Similarly, immunization techniques, a later development in public health practice, were utilized by communities when local leadership recognized their importance. Slowly the whole population came to understand that epidemics could be prevented if potential patients were inoculated or vaccinated, and for the first time we began to see the need for personal acceptance of a preventive measure.

Immunization of the well required more than empiric knowledge; it called for isolation of the infectious agent. By adding individual participation to legal sanction, the practice of immunization moved public health into an era when individual attitudes, fears, and emotions had to be taken into account. Ultimately we have progressed to the point where the President can announce a contemplated plan for total immunization of the public.

Now where do we stand? We find ourselves living in the era of chronic disease. The great killers today are cancer and heart disease. Paramount problems for prevention are mental illnesses and accidents. And new problems such as radiation and air pollution are coming to the fore. How do the classic public health procedures fit into *this* picture?

First let me say that the time-honored procedures have not been abandoned simply because infectious disease in this country has been largely brought under control in our generation; public health departments in all our communities continue to perform their traditional functions. But superimposed on and intertwined with these established services—in response to the threat of chronic disease—are many new programs and procedures.

Our aging population has resulted directly from the successful control of disease and death in the early years of life. If we think of the full span of life as a bridge, we see that although the length of the bridge has not been extended many more people now reach the extreme end of the bridge that is old age. We have repaired the section that is childhood and youth, have replaced timbers and repaired guardrails, but the far end, old age, now calls for special effort on our part.

Again, modern public health is like a large mansion to which many rooms have been added over the years; all are still occupied but the most important family activities now take place in the new wing. Here we encounter the five faces of prevention, the five procedures which gear the public health worker's traditional philosophy of prevention to our two major problems—chronic disease and aging. Let me delineate what is involved in the prevention of disease, prevention of the progress of disease, prevention of disability, prevention of dependency, and finally promotion of health—the ultimate goal, the state of well-being in which the individual prevents disease by maintaining total functional fitness.

The five faces of prevention derive, of course, from Dr. Hugh Leavell's famous five levels of prevention.[1] They are not to be thought of as separate entities but as a continuum based on "points of intervention" in the natural history of disease. Since we do not abandon our old approaches to prevention as we develop new approaches, the points of intervention in this continuum apply to acute as well as chronic diseases, but my own interest naturally leads me to stress their application to chronic illness.

Prevention of Disease

It was once assumed that *primary prevention* of chronic diseases would have to await greater knowledge of the etiology of specific diseases, but breakthroughs are already observable. Fluoridation of the water supply achieves primary prevention of dental caries. Community effort can achieve primary prevention of accidental injury; safety devices such as seat belts can actually prevent deaths in automobile accidents. The onset of rheumatic heart disease can be prevented by prophylactic care of a child who has or who has had rheumatic fever.

---

[1] Hugh R. Leavell and E. Gurney Clark, *Textbook of Preventive Medicine* (New York: McGraw-Hill Book Co., 1953), pp. 31-32, and *Preventive Medicine—for the Doctor and His Community* (New York: McGraw-Hill Book Co., 1958), Ch. 2.

Further research will, of course, be required before we can give final answers to questions about primary prevention of the full range of chronic diseases, but we already have instructive leads and valuable suggestions about the course that present and future research activities can follow. For example, certain studies have indicated that control of weight helps to control heart disease and diabetes. It has been suggested that a fat-controlled diet may help to lower blood cholesterol in certain individuals.

The Preclinical Stage
in the Natural History of Disease

Prevention of the progress of disease, or *secondary prevention,* means the prevention of disabling aftereffects by early detection and prompt treatment. It must be admitted that the most fruitful way to prevent a chronic disease today is to detect it early, before complications occur and while the disease is most amenable to treatment.

Since a chronic condition often has an insidious onset, a disease may already have progressed significantly before symptoms (pain and discomfort) bring the patient to medical attention. The National Health Survey revealed that over a third of the elderly had not seen a physician for two years or more. Community programs to screen for hidden diseases are an obvious essential in dealing with the problems of the chronically ill and aging. In addition, the private physician plays a vital role in finding diseases early, by examining his patients periodically and by seeing others in "well-oldster" clinics.

It is estimated that there are almost 1,500,000 cases of undetected diabetes in this country now. Because undetected diabetes is a progressive disease, early diagnosis and treatment are important to prevent disabling complications.

It is estimated that roughly 1,200,000 undetected cases of glaucoma exist today in the United States. A simple screening test can reveal the possible presence of this disease, which causes perhaps one-seventh of all serious eye diseases in adults.

Prevention of Disability

The third face of prevention grows immediately out of the concept of secondary prevention; it is the prevention of disability. Much of the disability we see today among the chronically ill and aged might have been avoided if prompt, aggressive, suitable medical and nursing care had been provided.

Many complications arise not from disease itself but from immobilization of the patient at the onset of disease. It follows that mobilization of the individual can prevent such complications as atrophy of muscles, contractures, stiffness and soreness of joints, incontinence, and subsequent bedsores.

In 1948, Dietrick, Whedon, and Shorr demonstrated that immobilization of apparently healthy young men produces a syndrome with features much like those observed among patients confined to bed for long periods. Within six weeks, study subjects who were immobilized in bed by plaster casts covering the pelvic girdle and legs developed negative nitrogen balance and lost, on the average, the equivalent of four pounds of muscle tissue. There were other consequences as well: an obvious decrease in the girth of the extremities; development of negative calcium and phospho rus balance; disruption of creatine metabolism; deterioration of stance reflexes; decrease in blood volume; stiffness and soreness at the joints; general weakness; and identifiable emotional reactions. Furthermore, the stiffness and soreness persisted for three to four months following removal of the casts. If this can happen to healthy young men, consider the problem of older persons, whose resiliency is much less than that of young people.

The Public Health Service has developed two booklets—*Strike Back at Stroke* and *Strike Back at Arthritis*—to guide the patient and his family in mobilizing the patient wherever he may be, in his own home or in a hospital, nursing home, or other institution. These booklets, to be prescribed by the family physician, offer information on bed positioning, passive and active exercises, and techniques of ambulation. A third brochure will be directed toward the amputee.

No single challenge is greater than the prevention of disability in the chronically ill. Services must be provided to these patients wherever they are—in the home, the hospital, or the nursing home—and important services are often required by their families as well.

The Prevention of Dependency

The fourth face of prevention, the prevention of dependency, has only recently been considered to be within the realm of public health. Taking account of the "whole patient," it embraces physical, economic, social, and emotional dependency. Clearly, dependency in one of these categories tends to promote dependency in the others. Restoration of a formerly bedfast patient to some degree of physical independence, for example, has an immediate impact on his social and emotional dependency.

Although the older, chronically ill patient seldom regains the ability to be fully employed, even a partial return to independent living, to self-care, can mean a triumph in new self-respect, in enhanced human dignity.

Health Promotion

The first face of prevention, following Dr. Leavell's terminology,[2] would have been health promotion, that is, the achievement of positive health. I have chosen to discuss it last, however, since the previous four form a continuum in the avoidance of disease and disability. Health promotion, on the other hand, must itself be considered a parallel continuum accompanying each of the other aspects of prevention: primary prevention, secondary prevention, the prevention of disability, and the prevention of dependency. At each of these points of intervention positive action can be taken to maintain health, just as action can be taken to prevent or combat disease. In other words, the term "health promotion activities" means all measures brought to bear in helping the individual function at the highest possible level whether disease or disability exists.

At each point of intervention social work can take positive action paralleling the preventive measures of public health. In the same way that classic public health techniques prevent disease,

---

2 *Ibid.*

social work can develop techniques for analyzing and for coping with social problems at the level of primary prevention.

In secondary prevention the social worker may well study the feasibility of screening devices for the early detection of social disfunctions. Early detection of the problems which arise in stress situations—adolescence, retirement, the death of a spouse—makes possible preventive social measures that are similar to the secondary approaches of public health. If we equate counseling with therapy, we can visualize the potential contribution of social work to physical and mental health promotion at the secondary level.

The immobilization syndrome that public health seeks to combat in preventing disability has its parallel in the concept of social immobilization, a phenomenon familiar to social workers. A so-called "cardiac cripple" may be sound (or at least adequate) medically, but socially he may need rehabilitative social casework services. Here again, working in the continuum of health promotion (understood to include mental and emotional health), the social worker can help the individual to work toward a higher level of independence. And thus the prevention of disability leads to the prevention of dependency, the achievement of some degree of self-reliance by a patient who may or may not be susceptible to full-scale vocational rehabilitation.

We are plagued by many unanswered questions in the area of health promotion. Much research remains to be done before we can speak with confidence about the interrelationships of physical, social, and emotional health. We do know that positive health must equate with functional fitness, and we can proceed from this baseline.

Summary

I have attempted to suggest briefly the relevance of the five faces of prevention, as understood in the public health profession, to the resources and skills of the social work profession. I have found my best illustration of this relevance in the concept of the parallel continuum of health promotion, where social work already operates and where future victories for social work will be, I am sure, most significant.

The social worker can make many specific contributions to

public health, especially in facilitating home care, health maintenance, the successful functioning of clinics, and the like. Understanding and encouragement of motivation are vital to the management of patients in any setting—home, hospital, nursing home, or clinic—and the social worker is trained to use these skills. More and more health workers have grown to understand that the family of the chronically ill patient must be considered an important element in the treatment problem. Traditionally the family unit has always been the milieu of the social worker. Home-care programs that attempt to function without social work consultation and service face great difficulties. Progressive nursing homes are learning how valuable is the contribution social workers can make in facilitating the initial adjustment of patients to the nursing home environment. The social worker's understanding of family backgrounds can be brought to bear in improving outpatient service by clinics. And, of course, the social worker is accepted as a key member of the hospital team.

Here we join hands. In hundreds of communities throughout the country the total job can be achieved *only if* we join hands. For we have moved far beyond the early days of public health, when isolation, sanitation, and immunization could meet current needs under almost authoritarian auspices. Now we must deal with voluntary responses of individuals. And now we must deal with community action. Only by perfecting the educational, organizational, and motivational techniques that the situation calls for can we bring prevention up to date. Only this will bring public health itself up to date. And in this effort the social work profession is our most essential ally.

Programing for Prevention in a Rural Area*

by FRANK KIESLER, M.D.

Setting for Service

The Tri-County Mental Health Center, with headquarters in Grand Rapids, serves three northern Minnesota counties with a combined population of approximately 68,500 in an area almost the size of Massachusetts. Only eight towns in this whole area have more than 1,000 people; the largest, Grand Rapids, has 7,265. About 45 per cent live in small cities or incorporated villages. Except for a few relatively isolated families on small farms or in the woods, most of the rest live near the towns. For example, if suburban settlements and residents nearby are counted, the effective population of Grand Rapids doubles.

This is a land of lakes, forests, and summer tourists. The economy, based mainly on 75 years of open-pit iron mining and custom paper-making, recently passed its postwar boom peak and began to wobble as high-grade iron ore supplies neared depletion and as other areas of the United States developed competing paper industries. Citizens of towns where mining companies formerly supplied up to 90 per cent of the tax money to operate some of the best school systems in Minnesota now have to dig into their own pockets to pay the bills, and they don't like it.

In this time of crisis two patterns have emerged. One is an angry, stubborn, demanding stand-patism deeply rooted in labor-management struggles and embodied in the belligerent statement: "The mining companies can't do this to us . . . they owe us something . . . and they'll just have to stay here and come

---

* Paper delivered March 7, 1962.

across." The other is illustrated by the efforts of welfare departments, retraining and relocation agencies, area redevelopment groups, and individual businessmen to tide families over the period of economic reorganization, to reduce the serious amount of current unemployment, and to transfuse the economy with new business enterprises.

Although the Tri-County Mental Health Center, when organized by a local group in 1959, was envisioned as providing only general outpatient psychiatric services, the three professional staff members recruited during the ensuing year found the community willing to accept a quite different program. During the year and a half the center has been in full operation, professional time has become distributed as shown in Table 1, the pattern to be continued in 1962-63.

TABLE 1

PREDICTED AVERAGE DISTRIBUTION OF PROFESSIONAL TIME
1962-63

Clinical Functions		45%
Direct clinical services	30.0%	
Clinical consultations	13.0	
Clinical research	2.0	
Public Health Functions		35%
Community planning	12.5%	
Public health research	10.0	
Education for professionals	8.5	
Public information	4.0	
Management Functions		20%
Program administration	11.0%	
Staff development	4.0	
Miscellaneous activities	5.0	

(Percentages derived from tallies
of professional time during 1961)

The philosophy underlying this distribution of professional time is stated in the program plan of the center: "The energies of the board and staff of the Tri-County Mental Health Center are directed toward strengthening the efforts of the people of these three counties to improve their mental health . . . [because it is believed that] . . . the current and future mental health needs of [all of] . . . the people can best be served if all individuals and groups concerned with promoting mental health and with caring for the mentally ill assist each other . . . [and that] . . . the whole community will gain the greatest ultimate value from programs aimed at positive stimulation of mental health and at prevention and early interception of mental illness. . . ."

One Answer to the Manpower Problem

The reports of the Joint Commission on Mental Health and Illness have brought into inescapably sharp focus the alarming magnitude of the gap between the size of the mental health job to be done and the comparatively small number of mental health professionals to do it. To meet the nationwide need for mental health services, as currently defined and delivered, would require the availability of four to five times as many mental health professionals as now exist. Despite the probability that massive federal aid will be provided for training and research in mental health, we must face squarely the likelihood that neither expanded professional training programs nor technological breakthroughs will eliminate the handicapping effects of this manpower shortage within any reasonable time.

This does not mean, however, that we are doomed to helpless waiting. If the patterns of care supplied to all with diagnosable mental disorders in any population sample are closely examined, it is immediately apparent that even in communities without professionals explicitly concerned with mental health matters—without psychiatrists, clinical psychologists, or psychiatric social workers—mental health needs are at least partly met. Doing the job are the firing-line professionals—family doctors, social workers, clergymen, school people, lawyers, law enforcement personnel, and others having contact with troubled people. Mental health professionals can never be expected to take over the entire mental health job. Because they will for a long time be in short supply, we must rationally expect them to function only as additions to those in the total professional armamentarium of the community who are fostering mental health and combatting mental illness.

On the premise that neither adequate reduction in the incidence of mental disorder nor improvement of mental health can be accomplished in any community by mental health professionals alone, we in our part of Minnesota have designed a program which requires that firing-line professionals not only retain most of the direct responsibility for clinical work but also that they become more proficient in handling it. Furthermore, if more professionals should be needed to work on mental health matters, they will be recruited for other agencies and institutions of the community, not for the Mental Health Center. If, for example, the schools should need more psychological testing, psychologists will be hired by the schools. If more psychiatric services should be required, a psychiatrist will be encouraged to enter private practice in this district. The Mental Health Center staff will never consist of more than three professional people, as at present, and they will continue to function least as mental health clinicians engaged in direct diagnostic and therapeutic activities, most as highly mobile catalyzers and facilitators of many varieties of activity throughout the three counties.

Clinical Functions

Table 1 (see page 117) shows that 45 per cent of professional time is allocated to clinical functions; of that, almost one-third is assigned to clinical consultations, those sessions with other professionals aimed at assisting them in handling clinical problems in their own practices. Only 30 per cent of professional time has been reserved for direct diagnostic or therapeutic activities. In actual practice, however, these services to patients and their families occupy only half the time for direct services (or 15 per cent of total staff time); the other half is spent in administration, which includes such patient-directed activities as telephone calls, preparing for appointments, working on clinical records, collecting research data, handling correspondence, and other necessary activities on behalf of patients.

In handling our clinical work we have set up several procedural rules:

1. No one is seen for direct clinical services unless a responsible professional person or agency in his locality has evaluated the problem and talked with us. Thus, both the firing-line professionals and the clinic automatically pre-screen all potential candidates for direct clinical services.

2. Whenever feasible (and this is in about six out of ten cases discussed with us in clinical consultation) we help firing-line professionals carry out appropriate diagnostic and therapeutic procedures without ourselves becoming directly involved.

3. When in clinical consultation we find it necessary for us to provide direct diagnostic services in order to decide the nature of the problems, how they might best be handled, and by whom, the **whole** family must come for evaluation. Everyone living in the household at the time must be present for at least the initial diagnostic session. We subscribe to the principle that the person who first comes, or is sent, for help is actually the emissary of a troubled family. In our experience, seeing the whole family enables us to diagnose and suggest a form of treatment much more rapidly and accurately than if we saw only the emissary.

4. In supplying any kind of direct clinical services we always enter into a collaborative relationship with the local professional person who retains the primary responsibility. Consultation with us becomes only one part of a total process of evaluation and treatment under the general management of the local professional. Patients and their families are not turned over to the Mental Health Center. This is particularly well illustrated when the primary professional is the family doctor; he continues to retain all medical responsibility including the prescribing of any required medications. The response to this rule has been favorable. As we suspected, doctors like to keep their patients.

5. The Mental Health Center staff takes an active hand in

treatment only when the problem promises to respond to brief intervention of a kind we can supply and which is not available from firing-line professionals in this locality.

6. To allow the Mental Health Center staff adequate time and freedom for activities aimed at reducing the prevalence of mental disorder and at improving mental health in the whole population of these three counties, no long-term psychiatric treatment of any kind is provided at the Mental Health Center, and no inpatient psychiatric work is available.

7. Procedures for evaluating the family are sufficiently standardized so that systematic collection of research data is possible.

When we first enunciated our intention of operating the Mental Health Center with a public health rather than a traditional clinical orientation, the community accepted this statement as laudably pious and then, lacking a conceptual model for anything other than clinical expectations, went right on trying to use us almost exclusively as a clinical resource. We therefore concluded that the first phase of our program had to develop from a clinical base. Because the clinical door was the only one open, we used it, deliberately employing clinical services as the major available vehicle for establishing interprofessional relationships of the kind we wanted for the long haul.

We found it was a mistake to start by setting limits, spelling out what we would not do. Instead, it was necessary to demonstrate what we could best do. We at first made and enforced only one rule: we would consider no one for direct clinical services unless referred by a qualified professional person or agency.

Collaboration, Not Competition

As referrals came in, we immediately moved toward the referring professionals. We telephoned them, visited them in their offices, or saw them in any place convenient for them. We tried to show we wanted to join forces with them in understanding and dealing with the problems they were trying to solve, to enter into whatever kind of active collaboration was most feasible. In the process, most professionals began to perceive us as we wished them to do: as highly mobile facilitators and expediters eager to be educated in the practical realities of the communities to which we had come as strangers. We literally and sincerely asked referring professionals to be our teachers, to help us learn enough about the problems of professional practice and about each community to be intelligent co-professionals and assist with the many jobs to be done.

In the process we found ways to be directly helpful. At the appropriate time we were able to demonstrate the value of interprofessional clinical consultation, with the result that many referrals were tabled and problems were handled by the firing-line professionals. If it became apparent that we should accept a referral because of the nature of the problem or the discomfort of the referring professional, we arranged for direct evaluation. Immediately following evaluation we called on the referring professional to go over our findings and to join him in evolving a proper course of action.

As interprofessional acquaintance and respect grew, we were asked more and more often to confer about patients rather than to see them. Simultaneously, professionals began to move toward us. Even busy medical practitioners came to the center to see us about their patients. As the number of clinical consultations increased, our waiting list for direct services was eliminated; since the summer of 1960 we have had no waiting list. Concurrently, the amount of time spent in direct contact with patients and their families has dropped to about 15 per cent of total professional staff time.

Illustrating one effect of this shift are the figures in Table 2, which compares the impact of professional time spent in clinical consultations with time spent in direct clinical services during one three-month period, February-April, 1961.

On the average, nine times as much professional staff time was spent on each family seen for direct clinical services as on each family aided through clinical consultation. Except for an irreducible minimum of cases requiring explicit psychiatric opinion or intervention, there may be no essential differences between the families or the problems in the two groups. If further analysis of our data supports this preliminary estimate, the logical next step will be to restrict direct clinical services to the irreducible minimum, and to use clinical consultations as the vehicle for

TABLE 2

	Total Number of Families*	Total Number of Professional Hours	Average Professional Time Focused Upon Each Family
Clinical Consultation (Time with other professionals regarding families not seen by center staff.)	108 (410 persons)	93½	52 minutes
Direct Clinical Services (Time with and regarding families seen by center staff.)	73 (277 persons)	569½	468 minutes (7.8 hours)

* Average family had 3.8 members.

providing assistance to all others. Put another way, if through clinical consultation we can help nine times more families per unit of professional staff time than we can aid through direct clinical services, and demonstrate equivalent results, the population of this area will benefit more if we put as much time as possible into clinical consultation.

Public Health Functions

As shown in Table 1 (see page 117), 35 per cent of professional time is allocated to public health functions. Development of these functions constitutes the second phase of our program.

With the first phase well underway, preparations for the second phase were made more explicit. In the course of clinical interaction with all varieties of professionals we deliberately began to turn their attention, in terms related to their own concerns and competencies, to the necessity of utilizing other than clinical approaches if the mental health picture in the whole community were to change. We began to voice our conviction that mental health programs appropriately include more than concern with the already sick and handicapped, more than work with individuals or even individual families, but rather programs based on public health principles and carried out in the community at large.

Progress in the second phase has generally been slow, however. Within our general formulations of strategy and tactics, we continue to play by ear. Gradually new doors have opened and new key people have begun to understand our purpose. Of vital importance has been the fact that each of us is becoming a permanent citizen of this locality. For the most part each has left behind his previous identity as an outsider, a foreigner, and has become an insider. As this became our community, as our personal futures became visibly interwoven with the community's future, willingness to let us have a real part in the community increased.

Sometimes in appraising community readiness to accept the mental health program formulations that we consider of greatest potential value to the whole community, we encountered resistances which filled us with impatience. But when personal deadlines were eliminated as we and our families decided to stay here permanently, our impatience lessened. We learned to back up, wait, look for other avenues of approach, and in the process to persuade the community to help us become more useful.

In any community perhaps the most organized settings offering opportunities for preventive programs are the schools. In one key town we initially were flatly informed that there was no need for us in the schools in that district, that the schools themselves would take care of all their problems. Our assurances that we didn't want to be *in the schools* or to interfere with or take over school functions of any kind, and that we wanted only to become acquainted and explore possibilities for collaboration, were met with disbelief. In line with our strategy, we backed off and waited —and waited. Not until later did we realize how thoroughly threatened some key people in that community had been and how thoroughly convinced they were that we were a competitive danger. We were looked upon as foreign mercenaries attempting to gain a beachhead, and we were to be kept out, or at least under good control, at all costs. This stood in dramatic contrast to the reception we found in the rest of the district. Consequently, we have come to appreciate the unique intracommunity dynamics responsible for the fright of the key people in that one town. The last few months have seen solid progress toward allaying these fears.

Service to Other Professions Through Education

Organized education for professionals has been a natural outgrowth and extension of clinical consultations. As professionals were helped with clinical problems, they began to ask for more systematic presentations aimed at enabling them to become more proficient in diagnostic and treatment techniques. From the beginning, both in arranging consultations and in accepting referrals, our staff emphasized the desirability of focusing on the whole family rather than on individuals. When more systematic presentations were asked for, we continued to focus on the family. In this context we have fostered a transition from evaluation and assistance centered on disorder to activities aimed at the maintenance and promotion of health.

In consultations about families who sought professional attention apparently because they recognized disorder in one member, it has been possible to stimulate interest not only in planning how to correct or manage the disorder, but also how to protect and enhance the mental health of others in the family. These are concepts well known in both medicine and social work, but we have found they need restatement and reclarification in the mental health context. For example, professional staff members of the three county welfare departments in our area participate in a seminar on human development, a consequence of clinical consultations in which everyone realized caseworkers were using vague criteria in evaluating the adaptive health of children and their parents. Moreover, although the caseworkers could often define what had gone wrong and state why maladaptation was occurring, they had difficulty in defining health and in seeing what was responsible for it and what might foster it. As a consequence, they needed to sharpen their evaluations of adaptive assets and their plans for using strengths in the family and community. In addition, they needed to shift toward using brief techniques to assist those most capable of change, and only bolster those with unalterable handicaps, so that the total professional effect could be exerted over a broadened base.

Our thesis has been that if programs are to have an effect on populations, all possibilities must be considered. In trying to alter the mental health of the people in our three counties, we have based much of our strategy on the following premises:

1. Families are the population units most instrumental in determining the mental health of the community.
2. All families are in contact with doctors, particularly when children are young.
3. The system of compulsory education in this country subjects every family to some degree of official public scrutiny as soon as it has a child of school age.

Thus, if we assume that the mental health of any community is a function of the mental health of its families, programs designed to influence the mental health of a whole population must reach families as units, and the most likely way of reaching them is through family doctors and school personnel.

Measuring Change

But first, methodology must be clarified. Before we can intelligently plan for change and subsequently say that change was brought about, hopefully for the better, it is necessary to know something about the starting place. In our district, because the epidemiological study required to establish baselines from which to measure change was much too large for our Mental Health Center staff, we set up a parallel organization called the Tri-County Social Science Research Program. This organization, which is recruiting a staff of sociologists, has its own budget. Among several projects to be carried out during the next five years, a comprehensive mental health survey will have first priority in the program.

It immediately becomes obvious that if this survey is to have practical value, it is necesary to decide what criteria will probably be most useful so that the right things can be measured. For example, use of the base rate for schizophrenic reactions as a criterion in measuring the mental health of a given population is ruled out because of serious disagreements about criteria for the diagnosis of schizophrenic reactions. In searching for less equivocal items to count, certain phenomena, symptomatic in nature to be sure but reasonably countable, can be found. These are social phenomena to which the community attaches significance, generally because people think they are too numerous. Among them are marriage failures, school drop-outs, juvenile court hearings, mental hospital admissions, and accidents of various kinds. If we examine one of these—marriage failures, for example—we immediately see several kinds and many possible causes. In our district we are particularly concerned about a specific kind of marriage failure because of its apparently high frequency, and also because it provides an opportunity for demonstrating to the community one way in which preventive programs may be put into action.

Preventing Unstable Marriages

Early in the history of the Tri-County Mental Health Center we noted a rapidly growing roster of marriage failures among couples not yet out of their teens, or at most only in their early twenties. All these marriages had occurred because of pregnancy, and by the time they failed not just one child but usually two, three, or even four children had been born. The marriage partners were disillusioned, unhappy, bitter, and angry, and felt cheated of an opportunity to enjoy life before being tied down by responsibilities. They were completely fed up with marriage and children. We were concerned about these marriages not just because many pairs of teenagers had made a mistake in trying marriage and parenthood before they were ready, but because their children had started life with children for parents, consequently had known little but crises, and now faced still another, deeply serious crisis.

Our Social Science Research Program has been asked to obtain data on the incidence of marriage among teenagers, the incidence of failure, what happens to these families after failure, and what may be the differences between those that fail and those that do not. Meanwhile, however, preliminary to deciding what might be done about these families, we obtained estimates of the frequency of failure from those sources considered best able to provide this information: family doctors. We chose them because they diagnose pregnancy, deliver babies, and supply medical care to young families, and because they are generally in at both the beginning and the end of marriage. They estimated that the rate of failure of these marriages in this district ranges between 50 per cent and 100 per cent, with most doctors suggesting 80 per cent.

When this whole sequence is inspected for points at which preventive activity might be effective, it becomes obvious that the ideal solution should ultimately come from more adequate preparation of children for handling adolescent relationships, so that there would be fewer pregnancies propelling teenagers into premature marriage. In looking for a quicker solution, we concluded, however, that at one point the sequence of pregnancy, marriage, childbearing, and marriage failure might readily be interrupted. But a major shift in social attitude and practice would have to be stimulated. Invariably these marriages are arranged by parents to solve the problem of pregnancy, and practically all are performed by clergymen. Thus it occurred to us that clergymen might be convinced that the long-range results would be better if they refused to perform these marriages.

By not performing marriages which run such great risk of failing, clergymen could set in motion a train of preventive events. Instead of allowing marriage to be used as the only recourse, clergymen could offer to help teenagers and their parents work out plans that might correct rather than compound the mistake. If not permitted to marry, the teenager could be helped to grow up and prepare for mature marriage. If suitable for adoption, the children born of these pregnancies could have the opportunity to start life in stable families. Furthermore, second, third, and sometimes fourth children would not be born when their parents were least prepared to be adequate parents.

This is one preventive program we promote in the hope of reducing the incidence of disorder arising from too-early marriages. We were pleased to find that many clergymen had been thinking along these same lines. In one large town the Catholic priest put this policy into action in his parish the Sunday before the meeting of the Ministerial Association at which we first brought this subject to discussion. He simply announced from his pulpit that henceforth he would perform no more such marriages.

Doctors, welfare workers, school personnel, civic organizations, and parent groups have also been presented with this formulation. Their reaction has been relief that someone has finally talked about this in public. But more than that, the proposal seems to have mobilized serious interest in family and community responsibility for better preparation of all children for eventual marriage and parenthood. Thus far, the healthy families ask the most questions. We hope to identify the characteristics of these apparently successful families so that we can establish positive as well as negative mental heatlh baselines. We must describe health as well as disorder. As part of its first task, therefore, our Social Science Research Program will spell out the epidemiology of mental health, as well as that of mental disorder, in this district.

Secondary Prevention Through the Schools

In attempting to interrupt a sequence of disorder-producing events, it is not always possible to focus sharply on key factors. Often, although we understand a general problem, the most we can do to improve the situation is to increase our alertness and skill in working with other professionals. During the last year some schools offered us wider opportunities for interaction. In some instances we were invited to meet with school administrators, first as professionals wishing to know particular schools more thoroughly, and second as possible contributors to discussions of administration and educational policy. As we began to be unofficial program consultants, we made sure that we would continue to be looked upon not as part of the school but as guests invited to participate with school personnel. As guests we have a fluid responsibility which enables us to engage when appropriate and disengage when school people have no need for us. For example, during one consultation we saw that our hosts felt they had to have something for us to do every time we were in the vicinity to keep us happy and feeling useful. At once we said our feelings would not be hurt if they did not want to include us or had nothing for us to do. This cleared the air.

Preventive programs developed through the schools so far stress secondary prevention. In working with teachers we find that many children about whom the schools are concerned sent up distress signals at the point of transition from home to kindergarten or first grade. Because teachers often tend to be year-oriented, problems in a particular grade are commonly dealt with by stopgap methods which tide the child over until he can move to the next higher grade—and another teacher. (On one occasion a youngster was referred to us for assistance only because his teacher had also been transferred to the next higher grade. The referral said, "Something has to be done about this boy before the teacher will tolerate him for another year!") We have tried, therefore, to help teachers recognize the red flags indicating crisis or early signs of maladaptation. We regard as even more important the possibility of working with all levels of school people on the techniques of engaging families, so that they can take appropriate action before problems become severe.

How to help school personnel with their own anxieties about dealing with parents occupies much attention, particularly in schools which lack social workers or similar professionals to mediate between teachers and parents. During the first phase of our development we saw a succession of families referred by schools wanting to know whether psychiatric treatment might remove a child's "mental block." Quickly it became evident that in each of these cases the school people had found the child mentally retarded in some degree and were reluctant to report this to the parents. Instead, the euphemism "mental block" was offered, together with referral to the Mental Health Center. We were asked to tell the family the bad news. We have capitalized on this by opening up, with school people, the whole question of how to tell parents discomfiting facts, and by showing that crises, properly handled, lead to growth in adaptational skills for everyone concerned—for parents by opening up realistic alternatives, for children by tailoring parental demands to each child's capacity, and for school personnel by providing successful experience in handling recurrent situations.

Enhancing Mental Health

As can be seen, in most settings we have been shifting our focus from already existing problems to secondary prevention and then to the promotion of positive mental health. We take our opportunities where we find them, with the result that we usually begin with special situations which serve as demonstrations. Meanwhile, we continue to move into position as program consultants to key people and groups.

We are beginning to develop activities with industry. The point of entry here is the personnel department. Although management has been cordial in inviting us to observe its practices, organized labor remains distant and apparently fearful. One reason we are interested in working with key people in industry is our wish to study how the local patterns of shift work affect family life. Concentrations of some disorders in certain parts of this area may be importantly related to the fact that many men, to keep their jobs, have to work odd hours, thus they function largely outside the mainstream of family life.

By this time it must be clear that a most important segment of our professional time is allocated to research. Thus far, we have been developing designs and instruments. As the Social Science Research Program moves ahead, we should know more definitely into what kinds of baskets the community should put its preventive eggs, and how best to facilitate their hatching. The community is repeatedly reminded that these are long-range goals, that some eggs may not hatch for one or two generations. There continue to be scattered expressions of impatience. But money to keep the program going continues to arrive on time, proof that people have faith in our work and want us to go on.

Therapy, Prevention and Developmental Provision: A Social Work Strategy*

by ALFRED J. KAHN, D.S.W.

Prevention has always been a social work concern, despite the fact that there have been times when the premises of preventive activity may not have been adequately taken into account in the interpretations as to why specific individuals needed help. Although much remains to be accomplished in practice, this gap in thinking has been filled in the past several decades. We may perhaps now be entering a stage in which the prevention concept itself may be limiting. It is the thesis of this paper that while social work has a major preventive task on all levels, in the public health sense of the term, the profession should *also* address itself to developmental provision. The distinction between preventive activity and provision may have significant consequences for the public at large, for "clients," and for social work.

This thesis is best presented in a historical perspective and after review of social work thinking about prevention and the public health model.

Backgrounds

Social work's interest in prevention may be traced to its pre-professional days when middle-class humanitarianism, strongly motivated by a religious ethic, sought to combine moral reform and "good works." For example, in Boston the Unitarian clergyman, Joseph Tuckerman, whose activities in the 1820's were to predict the later course of the charity organization movement,

* The explorations of which this paper, delivered March 7, 1962, is a partial consequence were supported by NIMH Project OM-516, 1961-62.

combined individual work and visiting with a concern for the environment and opportunities of the poor: housing, wages, and education.

Before the Civil War, Robert Hartley of New York's Association for the Improvement of the Conditions of the Poor, who saw moral reform as a prerequisite to material improvement of the poor, nonetheless also carried on an energetic and successful crusade against "distillery milk" (which could be tied to infant mortality). He surveyed tenement conditions, was responsible for a legislative investigation of housing, and erected model facilities. He also founded public baths, laundries, dispensaries, and a hospital while supporting facilities for public sanitation and promoting personal hygiene. Hartley lectured the poor on their "idleness, improvidence, or intemperance" and said that the truly worthy would—in time of unemployment—go where there was opportunity. But he knew enough of social realities to seek to remove what he saw as causes of illness, degradation, and poor habits.

A few years later, in 1853, launching New York's Children's Aid Society and setting a pattern of foster home placement which was to be copied in major Atlantic seaboard cities and, later, in the midwest, Charles Loring Brace, a missionary to the "squalid poor," decided that the "best of all asylums for the outcast child is the *farmer's home*." He considered evangelical efforts inadequate and was convinced that "moral disinfection" demanded visits to a neighborhood, reading rooms, an industrial school, lodging houses—and eventually emigration and foster homes.[1]

It must be noted, of course, that most of these early reformers and their colleagues remained convinced that those who "failed" gave evidence of basic moral inadequacy and inferior endowment. This in turn affected the form and character of the help and services offered to individuals at the very time that environmental remedies were sought. The explanations lay in

---

[1] For elaboration and sources of quotations see Robert H. Bremner, *From the Depths* (New York: New York University Press, 1956), Ch. 3. Also, Frank D. Watson, *Charity Organization Movement in the United States* (New York: Macmillan, 1922). Also, Charles Loring Brace, *The Dangerous Classes of New York, and Twenty Years' Work among Them* (New York: Wynkoop, 1872). Also, Amos G. Warner, *American Charities* (New York: T. Y. Crowell, 1894).

Puritanism, evangelical Protestantism, and the nature of available opportunities in the era of the open frontier and considerable economic growth.

The selfsame dual alertness to work with individuals and to the potential for preventive action in relation to environmental forces characterized the charity organization societies of the 1880's—despite their original primary commitment to individual work. The societies did not begin with both concerns, but their experiences taught them that the social environment could be a "cause," not merely the consequence, of pauperism. From their very beginnings the settlement houses of the same period were vehicles for local self-improvement and tried to meet the basic social needs which blocked individual opportunity, contributed to social problems, and undermined family life.

It was during the Progressive Era (from the mid-1890's to World War I), however, that the process reached its full flowering. Shortly after publishing *Friendly Visiting among the Poor,* Mary Richmond was writing *The Good Neighbor in the Modern City.*[2] Charity organization societies and settlements participated in social investigations which contributed to the "discovery of poverty" as a product of the urban-industrial system where once, as Bremner notes, it was defined only as a moral phenomenon. The results are well known: housing and sanitation reform, consumer protections, educational facilities, new medical and rehabilitative services, child care resources, baths—and the general upgrading of public services which accompanied the attack on municipal corruption. A broader range of "causes" of poverty was recognized and revolutionized casework too.

This was the period during which social work was born as a profession: the first formulations of method on a scientific basis, the first publications, the professional associations, the educational facilities. But it was also the period when social work leadership was closely aligned with political action. In retrospect, social workers speak of the Progressive Era as the time when "social action" was important to social work. The objective was

---

[2] Mary E. Richmond, *Friendly Visiting among the Poor: A Handbook for Charity Workers* (New York: Macmillan Co., 1899); and *The Good Neighbor in the Modern City* (Philadelphia and London: J. B. Lippincott Co., 1907).

the attainment of "the good life" as depicted early in the twentieth century: protection against the major hazards, fluctuations, and inequities of modern industrialism. Factory legislation, workmen's compensation, child labor legislation, consumer protection would do much. Municipal reform and housing legislation would add even more. And, according to some, modest "pensions" (to widows, the blind, the aging) would begin to offer needed protection. At the same time, charity organization workers and settlement residents sought to strengthen their direct services—for problems *within* the individual were still of concern.

It will be noted that there is no great precision here in defining "levels" of prevention or in proving a one-to-one relationship between deprivation and pathology. The discovery that poverty and many attendant ills could derive from the social environment and not—as centuries of ideology had held—from moral inadequacy was enough to justify a wholesale attack on obvious evils in the environment in which families and children were reared. And because even a half-century of progress was still to leave much unconquered, the conviction remained that promotion of "the good life" through better housing, medical care, factory legislation, workmen's compensation, and income maintenance programs would certainly decrease the social evils of the day. Depending on the era, these were defined as intemperance, laziness, irresponsibility, delinquency, or mental inadequacy and illness.

One additional bit of history to bring us fully to the present: Social work has never again given so major a role to social action —and thus to prevention—as it did prior to World War I. In the 1920's we stressed the development of casework method and the introduction of psychoanalytic concepts. In the 1930's our "causes" grew out of depression-born needs. Our subsequent campaigns related to refugees, defense, and war. Despite many important exceptions, it may be said that for several decades we were *preoccupied with* method and its development, while we were *interested in* and supported social security, adequate income maintenance, public housing, better immigration policy, and improved services to the delinquent and the mentally ill. While public health practitioners tended to describe all of their interventions—even the care of the chronically ill—as "prevention," we saw almost all of ours, even in relation to community issues, as "treatment." The present period may be one of change, as we shall see following more precise discussion of social work and prevention.

Social Work and Prevention

The recent analyses serve to bring us up to date on social work thinking about preventions. In 1959 the Commission on Social Work Practice of the National Association of Social Workers issued a report entitled *Prevention and Treatment*. Early in 1961 both Rapoport and Wittman discussed "prevention" in the NASW journal, *Social Work*. A point of view is also implied in Boehm's analysis.[3]

Let us begin with the NASW statement. It confirms the view that social work traditionally has associated prevention with social change, but it goes beyond this view:

> Prevention in social work is, on one hand, therefore concerned with inducing social change so as to create communities conducive to healthy social and personal development.
>
> On the other hand, the preventative effort in social work is directed toward individuals, families, and groups who require attention because of problems induced by social change or because of conflict with social norms—even though it is recognized that sometimes it is the norms themselves that require change.

The statement then proceeds to consider how activities directed toward prevention *should* be organized in social work and it rejects both the public health model (primary-secondary-tertiary prevention) and the self-maximation objective. The public health model is set aside as including virtually all of social work and thus failing to guide a prevention emphasis. "Self-

[3] National Association of Social Workers, Commission on Social Work Practice, "Prevention and Treatment" (mimeographed working draft, 1959). Lydia Rapoport, "The Concept of Prevention in Social Work" and Milton Wittman, "Preventive Social Work: A Goal for Practice and Education," *Social Work*, 6:3-12, 19-28 (January, 1961). Werner W. Boehm, *Objectives of the Social Work Curriculum of the Future*, The Social Work Curriculum Study, Vol. I (New York: Council on Social Work Education, 1959), Ch. 3.

maximation" is not pathology-oriented and one cannot relate it to specific social ills—particularly, the report holds, since knowledge of etiology is so incomplete. The statement concludes that one should limit the prevention concept to those activities which may avert or discourage the development of *specific* social problems or which may delay or control "the growth of such problems after they have presented beginning symptoms." Criteria to implement this point of view are specified.

Rapoport makes a telling attack on this analysis. She notes that a concern with prevention is a natural consequence of an "institutional" view of social work and social welfare services as normal, basic, ongoing features of industrial society.[4] She quotes Boehm's listing of social work's functions: restoration (curative and rehabilitative services), provision of resources and prevention (early identification, control and elimination of potentially hampering conditions, and study of social infection). But she then adds, quite appropriately, that the NASW statement stresses "control" of problems—and makes it coterminous with prevention—thus dropping the public health field's distinction between primary and secondary prevention (case-finding and early treatment). Perhaps, she suggests, it is artificial to try to encompass so much of social work in a public health concept. In the remainder of her paper, however, she would seem to be doing just that, and doing it quite well. Let us recognize, she proposes, that much present-day social work is actually secondary and tertiary prevention, in the public health sense. However, we can and should build up primary prevention on several levels:

1. Promotion of well-being generally. Social work has a potential "watchdog" role here, though the whole of society is involved.

2. Strengthening of individuals in relation to specific life tasks as husbands, wives, and parents.

3. Provision of specific help to those under recognized haz-

---

[4] Harold L. Wilensky and Charles N. Lebeaux, *Industrial Society and Social Welfare* (New York: Russell Sage Foundation, 1958), Ch. 6. Also, Alfred J. Kahn, "The Function of Social Work in the Modern World" in Kahn, ed., *Issues in American Social Work* (New York: Columbia University Press, 1959), pp. 3-38.

ard: children separated from their parents, those whose income is cut off, children whose mothers must work, etc.

Wittman is enthusiastic about the potentials of "preventive social work;" he believes there is need for a social work analogy to the public health model of *study, control,* and *prevention*. He too holds that at present social work is largely devoted to secondary or tertiary prevention, in public health terms—to "the treatment end of the service spectrum." What is involved in going beyond this? He suggests, in effect agreeing with Rapaport, that social work prepare to work with the "socially healthy" at points of stress, crisis, and transition where breakdown may often be anticipated: at the "onset" of parenthood, entry in school, adolescence, marriage.

Wittman notes that the planning of prevention in social work is hampered by lack of relevant epidemiological and ecological data. Buell, who has probably done more to apply epidemiological methods to social work problems than any other scholar, emerges skeptical about primary prevention.[5] He questions an analogy between social work and public health on the ground that social problems are not transmitted "by specific agents through particular media of communication." In fact, he notes that the typical public health model does not apply to chronic disease, which he sees as analogous to the complex social problems with which he deals. On the other hand, he sees no validation of the claim that "programs generally promoting good health, good housing, good family life, good recreation and so on somehow would affect the onset of these physical and psychosocial disorders. . . . The good ends sought by these programs carry their own social justification; they should not try to ride in on the back of preventive claims that cannot be proven."

Buell has devoted himself energetically and creatively to what he calls a "therapeutic concept of prevention"—to secondary and tertiary prevention. He is helping to reorganize public welfare departments for a task-oriented approach to service and treatment and for accountability as to results.

---

[5] Bradley Buell, "Is Prevention Possible?" in *Community Organization 1959* (New York: Columbia University Press, 1959), pp. 3-18.

At a conference in 1961, social work educators recognized Buell's contribution to a philosophy and method of planned intervention but were also interested in the stress on epidemiology. They did not select a definition of prevention.[6]

Another current activity of the social work profession is also relevant. A year ago the NASW received a foundation grant to test social work's contribution to the control of social problems in the community. While the original plan was in the realm of secondary and tertiary prevention, the project "task force" developed a new tack. Under the leadership of Dean Nathan E. Cohen of the School of Applied Social Sciences of Western Reserve University the group developed a model for the analysis of major social problems from the perspective of social work values—and for comparison of the social work approach to these problems with other approaches. Currently a group of social workers is applying the model to such major social problems as poverty, neglect, delinquency, psychosis, deterioration of the inner city, the broken family, and so on. They are discovering that rigorous analysis of social facts and values leads to reconceptualization of social problems and defines avenues for action on the social system and in the community, as well as for improvements in social work's more traditional modes of intervention.[7]

Issues

The traditions and ideology of social workers would thus tend to support a role for them in "prevention," but the rigorous critics of our performance know that our claim as *practitioners* is strongest in relation to treatment and control—secondary and tertiary prevention. We range more broadly as members of professional associations and as citizens. On the other hand, there are those who define the social work profession in broader terms and who seek distinctive forms of social work practice in primary preven-

---

[6] Council on Social Work Education, *Concepts of Prevention and Control: Their Use in the Social Work Curriculum* (New York: Council on Social Work Education, 1961).

[7] National Association of Social Workers, "New Approaches to the Control of Social Problems at the Community Level," a project in process.

tion, while recognizing that relatively little has been done as yet.[8] It seems reasonable to ask, then, whether the public health model is a useful one in defining all the functions of social work and whether the prevention concept describes some of those functions adequately.

Alva Myrdal, Foote and Cottrell, and others have described the process whereby the modern world is moving slowly from charity to therapy to planning.[9] Polanyi has given the analysis an underpinning of economics.[10] In brief, and in our own terms, much of organized charity prior to the industrial revolution was oriented more to the salvation of the donor than to the specific welfare of the recipient. In the nineteenth century, with the industrial upsurge and creation of the "market" as a major influence in society, "poor law" became labor policy, because the common man always was or could become poor. In retrospect, we see that market values often dictated welfare policies. From the perspective of the objects of policy, poor law was repressive and punitive. The humanitarian charities of the nineteenth century corrected the greatest inequities of the system and sometimes freed those defined as "the worthy poor" from the stigma and cruelty of public help. But, to return again to the Wilensky and Lebeaux terms already quoted,[11] this was all "residual" provision: the assumption was that "normal" needs were met by primary institutions and by the institutions of the market place. With breakdown or inability to take advantage of or to function within the primary institutions, one might need social work services and

---

[8] The claim of community organization is evaluated by Herman D. Stein in "Discussion: The Function of Social Work," National Conference on Social Welfare, Community Organization 1961 (New York: Columbia University Press, 1961), pp. 23-38. Also see Alfred J. Kahn, "Current Conceptualizations of Social Work Practice: Their Significance for Social Work Education," Education for Social Work, Proceedings of Tenth Anniversary Annual Program Meeting (New York: Council on Social Work Education, 1962), pp. 28-44.

[9] Alva Myrdal, Nation and Family (London: Kegan Paul, Trench, Trubner and Co., 1945), pp. 151-53.

Nelson N. Foote and Leonard S. Cottrell, Identity and Interpersonal Competence (Chicago: University of Chicago Press, 1955), Ch. 4.

[10] Karl Polanyi, The Great Transformation (Boston: Beacon Press, paperback edition, 1957).

[11] Wilensky and Lebeaux, op. cit., see footnote No. 3.

social welfare provision. In this sense, all social work is therea-
peutic-restorative.

Indeed, the entire development of what is widely called the
Welfare State in the Western world has tended to follow such a
process. Gunnar Myrdal describes the Welfare State as having
"fairly explicit commitments to the broad goals of economic development, full employment, equality of opportunity for the
young, social security, and protected minimum standards as re-
gards not only income but nutrition, housing, health, and education for people of all regions and social groups." While the term
Welfare State is often confused, misunderstood, or attacked, the
interventions into the economy and social life listed by Myrdal
have occurred to some degree in all those western democracies
economically capable of supporting them. The process is under
way and is nowhere complete.

Because "individual acts of intervention" were not originally
part of a grand design, each being a response to perceived problems, there is need to labor constantly "with the tasks of simpli-
fication, co-ordination, rationalization, and achievement of efficiency." As one considers the many interventions "from the point
of view of how they combine to serve in the development of goals
of the entire national community" one is involved in planning.[12]
To Myrdal, then, returning to the vocabulary of the earlier paragraph, therapeutic-restorative-residual measures eventually become sufficiently important in scope and ramifications to require
planning. He does not make what would seem to be an additional
and quite useful distinction: as Welfare State programs become
more comprehensive and generate the coordination of policies in
relation to desirable ends (as determined by democratic political
processes), there is transition to what Wilensky and Lebeaux call
the institutional conception of social welfare. Or, in somewhat
different terms, values other than market values may begin to
dictate priorities and may indeed lead to plans and undertakings
which, recognizing human needs or a model of minimal social
provision as the point of departure, do not necessarily await

---

[12] Gunnar Myrdal, *Beyond the Welfare State* (New Haven: Yale University Press,
1960), pp. 23, 62, 63.

specific breakdown or pathology. Discussing health needs, a *New York Times* editorial of March 2, 1962, said:

> President Kennedy's message to Congress on the nation's health needs is a minimal program to cope with the opportunities and problems posed, respectively, by rapid advances in medical science and by the socio-economic evolution of America's population. . . .
>
> The market mechanism alone cannot be depended on to perform the tasks that are required. Effective government action on a broad scale is needed. . . .

For the fully developed "institutional" position takes the next step. Recognizing the "normal" hazards of urban industrialism and automation, it sees welfare services, from health to education to income maintenance, as fundamental, front-line components of the modern world, as "normal" as the computer and the rocket and not a cause for apology. Welfare services become available as a matter of right and do not await individual difficulty. Given information about social phenomena and social status (number of women in the labor market, decline of certain industries in a given part of the country, number of unattached senior citizens), it is possible to predict need on an actuarial basis. The question is not one of individual malfunction or inadequacy but one of status which defines requirements and needs. We move from therapy to planning, from treatment to social or developmental provision. Client, recipient, planner, and policy-maker become one as the issue becomes one not of individual inadequacy but of allocation of resources in the light of social priorities and objectives democratically determined. The institutional approach is not discontinuous with the residual, but it involves a distinctive stance.

In the Welfare State an institutional concept of social welfare is emerging. It remains part goal and part reality. There tends to be more coordination of independently devised interventions than there are long-term projections. Most programs and services today still are conceived in a residual context: to supplement, to fill in temporary gaps, to facilitate functioning within existing programs and institutions. Nonetheless, important segments of

American public opinion and of political and professional leadership are dedicated to somewhat more comprehensive planning—without rigidity and without sacrificing either diversity or individual initiative. They would not give up services of therapy-restoration-rehabilitation, but would provide more than these. It thus becomes possible to discuss the public health model, with particular reference to prevention, in the context of a social work profession closely aligned with this segment of opinion and endeavor.

Much of my own energy in the last several years has gone into an attempt to define the characteristics and components of an integrated system of services for delinquents and other children in trouble in urban areas. I have found public health concepts particularly useful in specifying crucial functions: case-finding, situation-finding, evaluation, service planning, referral, reporting. In general, it has been necessary to subdivide public health "steps" in order to provide for crucial social welfare functions.[13] At the prevention end of the continuum, the particular focus of this paper, I have found it necessary to distinguish between concern with broad social issues (public morality, economic trends, social stratification, international developments) which do affect deviance and delinquency, and concern with what may be called a second level of primary prevention: the interposition of positive factors (urban renewal, neighborhood self-help, "higher horizons" in education) between negative social determinants and those who are generally affected. To distinguish these two levels, I use the categories "ultimate" and "intermediate prevention." In effect then I too have found that the concept of primary prevention needs subspecification and refinement.

The public health literature has begun to take account of this distinction by differentiating "health promotion" and "specific protection" (both are "primary prevention") from early case-finding.[14] The concept of "perfective" medicine includes some of

---

[13] Alfred J. Kahn, *Planning Community Services for Children in Trouble* (publication by Columbia University Press pending). Also "Court and Community" in *Justice for the Child* (New York: The Free Press of Glencoe, Illinois, 1962). Also, *Protecting New York City's Children* (New York: Citizens' Committee for Children of New York, 1961).

[14] John J. Hanlon, *Principles of Public Health Administration* (St. Louis: C. V. Mosby Company, 1960), p. 25.

the broader notions and is suggested by Rogers as distinguishable from preventive medicine.[15] Along similar lines, question has been raised as to whether one should not see sickness and health as parts of two continua, not one: "sickness-absence of disease" and "health-absence of health."[16]

To return now to the question of conceptualization as it relates to the strategy for describing and implementing social work functions, it would seem desirable to visualize "provision" or "developmental provision" as going beyond that primary prevention which applies available knowledge to avoid development of specific pathology. This would be social work's equivalent of perfective medicine or health promotion, but I would argue against defining the concept within a prevention continuum at all. For ultimately, despite the work and the thinking of many fine people, several of whom are quoted above, prevention as a concept remains tied to the control and eradication of pathology, and it is useful that it be so tied. Its priorities are reduction or eradication of the specific causative agent(s), reduction of the host's exposure to the agent, changes in the host to make him resistive or immune, and early diagnosis and treatment to arrest progress of the disease and to ameliorate complications.[17] Oriented as it is to the "sickness-absence of disease" continuum, the prevention concept was and is adequate to a residual view of social welfare, not to an institutional view. To say this is not to minimize prevention in social work: we do not even know how to interpose positive influences between groups or individuals and many of the social hazards which are, predictably, undermining their futures. Nonetheless, it seems legitimate to provide within the totality of social work conceptualization for the functions appropriate to the institutional image of social welfare and not to distort it with inappropriate analogy. The public health doctor

15 Edward S. Rogers, *Human Ecology and Health* (New York: Macmillan Company, 1960), pp. 177-78.

16 Marie Jahoda, *Current Concepts of Positive Mental Health* (New York: Basic Books, 1958), pp. 74 ff. and p. 11.

17 William G. Hollister, quoted in John D. Porterfield, "The Place of Primary Prevention Services" in *Programs for Community Mental Health* (New York: Milbank Memorial Fund, 1957), pp. 186-87.

will probably also come to recognize that his "perfective medicine" is best promoted outside a medical context.

In summary, the public health model has much to offer in the planning and coordination of social work services. The prevention concept has considerable application to many social work concerns. Indeed, we have hardly begun to work well at that end of the continuum—defining prevention in its quite specific and more limited sense. However, all this said, social work should also make use of the "provision" concept and should avoid anchoring it to prevention or eradication of pathology. Our perspectives need to include "normal" front-line contributions to the shape and form of society today, justified by an "institutional" view of social welfare and not limited to helping those who fall by the wayside or who cannot function or adjust in their routine social relationships. The contributions we make to policy and provision in this sense should derive as much from a perspective of the social system and community as it does from our experience in meeting the needs of those who deviate.

Consequences of the Developmental Concept

Lest this appear a mere semantic quibble, let me illustrate why the distinction may be useful.

First, let us consider the field of vocational guidance, counseling, and retraining for adolescents who drop out before completing high school. For almost a decade now we have seen here a "therapeutic" (if I may use the term in contrast to "developmental") concept of planning. School dropouts and other unskilled youth were regarded as educational failures en route to delinquency. Counseling, guidance, work training, and work camps were proposed, all on a limited scale, and were advertised as delinquency preventives. Some small-scale creative work was done by "reaching out" employment services, and some unusual counselors found jobs for youths where others could not. However, job opportunities were limited. (After all, these youths lacked skills and were already marked as en route to delinquency!) The need was seen as residing in the individual to be served.

The above paragraph is written in the past tense. Actually,

it still describes the typical situation. However, a new theme has been sounded during this last year, namely, that demographic trends and the pattern of our labor market and educational structures create a labor reservoir of adolescents who are not being adequately absorbed by society. There is therefore need for large-scale training-retraining-guidance public works, and the need is in relation to a significantly large group. The individual concerned need not be defined as patient, client, or candidate for therapy. We can predict *a group* in need of these resources apart from the issue of the psychic health or attitudes of individual youths. There is need, in short, for social provision.

Of interest to me are two facts: (1) given this kind of definition, the *scale* of resource allocation under consideration jumps considerably; (2) the possible subjects of the program—as well as those who must support it—can begin to see these activities as part of what society does or should do for its youth (just as it offers college to others). The programs are thereby made more approachable.

Day care may provide another illustration. There are many exceptions throughout the country, particularly in the form of proprietary day care, but it may be said that, in general, day care is a small-scale activity, therapeutically rather than developmentally conceived. The mother who would use day care is processed through an intake service in which the plan is evaluated in relation to all factors affecting the family; financial eligibility is reviewed if the day care service is part of a public welfare program. Such processing and the introduction of evaluative criteria relative to the soundness of the plan assure that the program will remain small.

There is much current agitation to expand day care with federal support as part of the administration's new welfare program. The President's welfare message of February 1, 1962, pointed out that of the 22 million women now working about 3 million have children under 6 and another 4½ million have children between 6 and 17. In recommending revision of the child welfare provisions of the Social Security Act to provide for grants to localities to establish day care services, the President presented a simple rationale: "Adequate care for these children during their most formative years is essential to their proper growth and training."

Again this would seem to argue for developmental provision. The need, indeed the right, is defined by the status. A child does not have to have special or unique problems to qualify; he is eligible in the same sense that he is eligible for admission to elementary school: on the basis of age, health, local residence, inoculation. One should not have to prove that day care is "good" for one or "necessary." Day care is a public "utility" in an advanced industrial society.

Although there will be differences of opinion about specific illustrations, illustrations can be found. Family life education is another area, homemaker services a less clear one. Urban renewal and children's allowances might be discussed. Certainly, however, the expansion of our concepts of social welfare will involve increasingly more provisions and increasingly less individualized, therapeutically-premised intake as the portal of entry to services.

I have suggested elsewhere[18] that these matters are in the province of social welfare administration, social policy, and community organization planning. Social work is uniquely situated to define emerging need and to participate in the social invention whereby need is validated and implemented—and redefined as right. As planners, social workers tend to hold a characteristic concept of the social human being which provides a perspective of broad implications. We need vehicles to translate all this into programs, services, and goals. Social work's contribution to content and implementation of developmental provision should eventually be defined in ways characteristic of the profession.

Community organization-planning in social work and social policy analysis will require considerable reconceptualization to carry teaching in this realm, but are probably the most promising vehicles. There are implications for social work recruitment, the core curriculum, and the refinement of practice and research. All

---

18 Alfred J. Kahn, "The Function of Social Work in the Modern World." *Issues in American Social Work,* ed. Alfred J. Kahn (New York: Columbia University Press, 1959); and "Current Conceptualizations of Social Work Practice," *Education for Social Work, Proceedings of Tenth Anniversary Annual Program Meeting, St. Louis, Missouri, January 17-20, 1962* (New York: Council on Social Work Education, 1952).

these matters can and should be elaborated. For present purposes
we may conclude with the following:

1. Much of the public health model applies to social work
   services.
2. Social work has done too little by way of prevention in
   recent decades.
3. Much should be done to strengthen specific prevention.
4. Our image of social welfare and social work demands that
   we go beyond this.
5. The concept of "provision" or "developmental provision,"
   defined as independent of prevention, may point to a
   broader role for social work, one limited neither by the
   continuum of pathology nor by residual conceptions of
   the role of the profession.

Concepts do not determine the goals of a profession but a
profession's direction requires conceptualization, which in turn is
potent in shaping the self-image. These definitions would seem
to be on contemporary wave lengths as social work looks ahead.

Who Is the Patient in Public Health?[*]

by ROSCOE P. KANDLE, M.D.

Framework of Public Health

Health is feeling well in body, mind, and spirit.

Health is satisfactory adaptation to the environment in order to function well and happily. Man is radically changing his environment; his environment is changing man. This interchange is constant, relentless, inescapable. It is dramatized in major public health problems. Almost the only deprivations seen today are social deprivations. There are great and urgent problems of excesses: too much food, too much and wrong kind of fats, too many automobiles, too much speed, too many chemicals, too much pollution of air, land, and water.

Health is a norm, and a changing condition eternally to be striven for. When a change occurs below normal, the process may become irreversible. The obvious end point is death. But what is the other end of the spectrum? Has any person or any community yet achieved the optimum? Is it infinity?

These concepts are the framework of public health, which is concerned with the whole man and the whole community of man. In every health issue, starting with an individual, there are always four aspects: the physical body, the person, the physical environment, and the social environment.

Problem of Diagnosis

Medicine, particularly social medicine in its best and broad connotation—the practice of medicine as a social science—has

---

[*] Paper delivered March 8, 1962.

barely begun to acquire the vocabulary and skills to make diagnoses and recommend therapies in this context. While in some ways community or public health diagnoses have developed a little further, they are obviously crude.

Social workers see this problem of diagnosis and therapy in their efforts to bring the social aspects of a diagnosis into the consciousness and appreciation of physicians and other members of the health team. Sometimes we physicians feel frustrations because "treatment" in social work can be empirical and often appears to us to lack a basis in diagnosis and logic from our way of practicing. One of the most urgent problems is to achieve functional diagnoses in our efforts to provide restorative services. In the simplest terms, after a stroke a patient may be unable to communicate because of inability to speak and write. The therapies for these two conditions differ vastly; in speech paralysis, of course, speech training is required. Even in so crude an instance it is necessary to think this way, to consider speech training. But when one moves to a diagnosis of the social and environmental factors which control motivation, return to home or job, or the value systems of the chronically ill, their families, and society, it can easily be appreciated that the prescription of a prosthesis, of home care, of progressive care, etc., needs better diagnostic tools than expediency of the institution, exigencies of money, or decisions by well-intentioned, omniscient who know "what is best." What in fact are the communications systems among the several practitioners who must contribute to this diagnosis?

On a much more sophisticated scale the splendid pioneering work of Bradley Buell[1] is, in my opinion, outstanding. Here is one of the earliest and best applications of epidemiology to social welfare. Here the emphasis is on prevention and priority-setting. Here is a classification, identification, or community diagnostic system—whatever words you prefer. You may recall that Buell's work classified social problems under four headings: dependency, ill health, maladjustment, and recreational need. He developed a philosophy and a machinery by which to identify and screen the

---

[1] Bradley Buell and Associates, *Community Planning for Human Services* (New York: Columbia University Press, 1952).

multiproblem families—that 6 per cent on which St. Paul had to spend 50 per cent of its social welfare dollars and effort. The recently refined family classification system and the improved tools for applying this epidemiological concept to community planning and to comprehensive preventive welfare and health programing are well worth your attention.

The Body Politic as Patient

The body politic is often the patient in public health. This body politic has all the complex attributes of the individual plus those of the interaction of people per se plus the totality of group action plus the great cultural, economic, and social forces of the community. The community has a physiology and often a pathology. In keeping with the concepts expressed earlier, we in public health are now more interested in functional diagnoses than in merely descriptive clinical diagnoses of cytology or abnormal anatomy.

Our goal too is functional: the prevention of disability. With this as a common goal all health and social professions come together. It unifies all our basic activities. It brings social work and medicine inseparably side by side.

Public health follows two pathways deliberately and properly; the nicety of the balance is part of the skill of public health administration. We are at the same time disease-centered and generic service-centered. Traditionally we have been concerned with tuberculosis and polio and more recently with diabetes, stroke, and galucoma, each with its particular epidemiology, pathology, and more or less specific therapy. At the same time we have been concerned with generic services—services to the whole community, or substantial segments of it, which materially and often dramatically help to prevent disability. We see that the community has a pure water supply, a public health organization, public health nursing, casework services, good hospitals, adequate high-quality medical care, rehabilitation services, and homemaker services. Each of our programs has its zealots; to keep them working together smoothly is a first-class administrative challenge.

Value in Stating Objectives

One of the procedures useful to us is the development of program plans and of short- and long-term objectives. The programs can be either disease-centered or service-centered—a tuberculosis program, a homemaker program, a potable water program, a nursing program, a social work program. In considerable measure this process has been refined underpressure from the federal government as a valuable tool of the Public Health Service and Children's Bureau in administering grants-in-aid. The New Jersey State Department of Health operates nearly 25 programs. The discipline of writing the plans in clear, succinct language is valuable. Furthermore, each written plan is subjected to the scrutiny of all program directors, who thus have an opportunity to comment, criticize, and make suggestions before any plan goes into operation. Admittedly, this is a mountain of paperwork but worth the effort. The process of deciding on specific objectives, particularly short-term objectives, committing them to paper, and working toward them is helpful at every stage of diagnosis, planning, operation, administration, and evaluation.

A complex issue, of major importance particularly in New Jersey and this section of the country, is the identification of the relevant community. We think it varies widely with function. We are thus deeply involved in determining the actual and then the best service areas. Obviously, a hospital-centered rehabilitation or home care program will relate primarily to the service area of the hospital, a unique aea influenced by roads, by where doctors live, by admissions policies of the institution, etc. Retail restaurant control, private sewage disposal, rabies control may relate to a municipal service area since they are functions of law and government, though the logic may not be sound. In New Jersey we think the state as a whole is the best service area for radiation protection and control. This is a matter of current research with Rutgers and a matter of urgent and active study, dispute, planning, and operation at all levels in New Jersey and elsewhere. This issue deserves a high priority in your considerations.

This question of service area has a large cultural component, especially in New Jersey. Our state's systemless system of public

health is characterized by real ingenuity, improvisation, and concentration on getting a particular job done, rather than on administrative stereotypes. It is also characterized by the quality and
quantity of its voluntary leaders and their dedicated service. It is
further characterized by 53 cities, 257 boroughs, 233 townships,
20 towns, four villages, two camp meeting associations, and Pali-
sades International Park—a total of 570 boards of health. Add 21
counties, 548 school districts, and 81 special districts and the governmental aspects of public health begin to come into perspective.
The equally important hospitals, state, county, and local voluntary
health agencies characterize another aspect. A list of our allies—
in mental health, vocational rehabilitation, disability insurance,
unemployment compensation, health and hospitalization insurance, public assistance, child welfare, social casework, community
planning, the health professions, the religious bodies, and many,
many more—vividly illustrates the complexities of our chosen field
and its interrelatedness to our social and physical environment.

Let me illustrate this issue of service area. There is a city at a
point where three New Jersey counties meet. It is an important
medical trade area for a substantial population in about twenty
municipalities in the three counties. You can easily imagine how
complicated this can be in terms of government and in terms of
voluntary health agencies organized and collecting funds often on
a county basis. Fortunately, there is a visiting nurse service whose
organization and service areas are based on the cultural and economic realities; hence, it is proper and wise in many instances
for the Department of Health to support and work through this
agency.

Broad Base of Responsibility

As we move into the control of chronic illness and more and
more deeply into the prevention of disability, as we widen our
concept of the spectrum of health and morbidity, the interplay
of agencies, professions and people must become more effective
and efficient. The Declaration of Policy of the New Jersey Prevention of Chronic Illness Act of 1952 states it well:

26:1A-93. Declaration of public policy.
The growing problem of prevention, detection, and care of

chronic illness, which is of such character as not to be exclusively medical, educational, or welfare, has now reached such proportions in this state as to require the participation of the state and of the agencies administering public health, education, and welfare within the state and it is hereby declared to be the public policy of this state that the responsibility therefore must be shared by the state and the counties and the several municipalities and health districts and the voluntary agencies and institutions within the state and the public at large.

A direct result of this has been the policy of the chronic illness control program in the New Jersey State Department of Health of making grants directly to hospitals to help them develop rehabilitation and medical social work services, work classification centers, and diabetes- and other disease-detection programs.

Function of Local Health Administration

Program drives and administration are reasonably well understood by most of the health professions; they have many similarities, whether in ophthalmology, casework or outpatient service administration. Not so well understood is the public health concept of local health administration. This is a coordinating, expediting, balancing, facilitating unit which enriches programs by adding local diagnoses and local knowledge and using these tools to adapt programs to communities and service areas. In New Jersey we have four district offices, arms of the State Department of Health. Each is staffed by a small team representing the basic disciplines of casework, engineering, nursing, nutrition, medicine, veterinary medicine, etc. Each serves several counties. The district teams are like vigilant antennae: they receive messages, bring knowledge of details and changes in the environment, give warning and advice. They maintain rapport with their professional counterparts in all sectors—municipal officials, health organizations, hospitals, and other health facilities. They are clearly the negotiators of projects and activities. With this kind of local evaluative data, we can make sound decisions within the framework of centrally developed programs and priorities of money, staff, and many other factors.

A pertinent illustration of how this system works was the attempt by our central program staff, over a year or more, to develop rehabilitation services in a suburban county. At first we failed to use our own machinery, the district team, and dealt more or less directly with the leading large hospital. When the project was discussed at a meeting of the district and central staffs, the district people gave us information on aspects of the power structure that we had not recognized and also pointed out some crucial changes which had taken place. We made short study of the agencies and people involved. A strategy was agreed upon and a tactical plan of visits, calls, etc., by assigned district and program staff was begun. There is now a growing rehabilitation service, a tie between the hospital and a nursing home, a dental restorative demonstration among elderly people, and a good basis for comprehensive home care services.

An old, but valuable and widely used technique of public health, is the survey. The range in types of surveys is very wide, from small localized diagnostic or data-gathering actions to comprehensive community-wide formal surveys or state-wide surveys, usually relevant to particular problems or groups of people. For example, with the help of the State Department of Health, the School of Social Work of Rutgers recently made a survey of the quality and quantity of field training opportunities for social workers in a health facility; I am glad to report parenthetically that the nucleus is the product of grants-in-aid to hospitals by the State Department of Health, which has been responsible for a considerable number of the qualified medical social workers in general hospitals here. Currently under way are interdepartmental surveys of tuberculosis control and alcoholism services.

Raising Standards

Public health in New Jersey has been helped by the promulgation of Recognized Public Health Activities and Minimum Standards of Performance For Local Health Departments. Action by the Public Health Council made these law. Each municipality is responsible for developing a plan for services which at least meet these minima, and for evaluating their effectiveness. As a result, there have been literally several hundred local self-help surveys to determine how far our communities measured up to these criteria. You can appreciate the potency of this activity when multiplied by hundreds of boards of health, each with six to ten members, and their relevant staff in as many communities. This is the basic technique of developing a set of standards and then applying them broadly. The standards themselves came out of almost nine years of patient, extensive committee work.

Role of the Council

This review would be incomplete if we did not acknowledge the function and good work of dynamic councils of social agencies. Here is the machinery for making the community diagnoses and writing the prescriptions; for developing the programs; identifying the goals, objectives, and priorities; continuously surveying facilities; and analyzing critical issues. Here is the place where the professional and the nonprofessional meet to solve specific problems.

It is easy to illustrate the type of work a council can do. One small but vital action in New York City was the development and adoption of a standard interagency referral form; this didn't do the whole job, of course, but it was the thing most needed at that time. This council also developed a standard method of determining family budgets on the basis of need. In New Jersey the State Department of Health recently helped the Council of Social Agencies analyze and then change the role of a communicable disease hospital within the framework of the community's total needs. In Omaha a drive for a children's hospital led to the development of a comprehensive sysem of rehabilitation services. The extensive activities in Kansas City, Missouri, in this field are, I hope, known to you.

In short, a Council of Social Agencies is most effective in identifying areas of remediable need, in planning how to get these needs taken care of, and in facilitating communication and cooperative action.

We are the Tools

Community organization is hard work. There are no easy ways, no pat formulae, to my knowledge. Where applicable, the principles of epidemiology can be very effective. Essentially they include case-finding, diagnosis, planning of treatment, rehabilitation, and, first and last, prevention.

In my opinion, Community Research Associates under Si Buell's gifted leadership have contributed substantially by applying these techniques to the social services, particularly to public assistance and child programs. Many efforts are now being made to use these methods in the broad program fields of corrections and delinquency.

Greatly over-simplified, the basic processes seem to be: get the fact, get them understood, and get them applied.

Since our tools are we contrary human beings, it isn't easy.

Community Planning for Health—The Social Welfare Experience*

by ROBERT MORRIS, D.S.W.

A Field in Flux

We are on the threshold of a major shift in understanding about social work's aims, processes, and techniques in community organization or planning for health and welfare. Our terminology and methods have become subject to critical analysis and evaluation, and renewed attention is paid to the dynamics of community and organization behavior through which group decisions are made about common problems.

Social work, beginning with a pragmatic attack on specific social problems during the nineteenth century, very early developed a theoretical framework which emphasized the relationship between social work and the total community of which it is a part. It has stressed the individual in his family, which lives in and is affected by a community, which in turn is part of the nation. Each element should be understood but so should the reciprocal relationship of the parts. In all candor, precise understanding of this unity has lagged, but the principle is a useful one.

This view of the world, this search for comprehensiveness and unity, has been shared by many other professions. As they have done, social work has developed its specialized means of attack upon selected social problems, the basic elements of which can be summarized:

1. A liberal belief in the capacity and right of ordinary citi-

---

* Paper delivered March 8, 1962.

zens to assess their needs and to choose wisely the steps
to take in meeting them.

2. Recognition that any community problem touches on the
   interests and lives of many divergent groups in society,
   and that decisions or solutions must allow for these differences rather than be imposed.

3. A belief that there are sufficient dollar and personnel resources in our expanding society to fill all needs.

4. Recognition that fact-finding is an essential tool which
   precedes action.

5. Confidence in the representative committee and the conference as the key method for reconciling group differences in order to solve community problems.

6. Use of a representative federation[1] of community groups
   as the central instrument for voluntary planning and coordination.

7. Use of professional worker as a generalist in helping citizen leaders and groups work together.

A Nation in Flux

Several conditions have developed which alter this rather
logical approach. Our world is undergoing so rapid and so radical
a technological revolution that technical skill and specialization
have challenged any simple view of the roles of the professional
worker and the ordinary citizen in policy-making. We live in an
age created by multiple specializations. Each profession is in turn
subdivided into scores of subspecialties. In social work, community organization has been committed to the generalist approach;
now, in an era of specialists, we must learn to be *effective* generalists. Perhaps our hope lies in the new generation of hybrids who
combine two or more specialties in one person: biochemists, geo-
physicists, social physicians, social-psychiatrists, public health
social workers. It has been said that no man today survives in a
world for which he was educated. The education of his youth is

---

[1] Defined as a federation in which individuals act simultaneously as community
leaders and as representatives of the groups or organizations which select them.

often outdated by the time he reaches maturity. This may be as true for us as for the space scientists.

In addition, we are experiencing a massive expansion of population, which means massive explosion of human need. The increase in population is sufficient to populate each month, every month, year after year, a new city the size of Chicago. This brings in its wake a demand for massive and continuous expansion of facilities and services for which our traditional ways of thinking have not prepared us.

These technological and population changes have placed very special strains upon community organization or social planning. The needs we confront greatly exceed the resources now mobilized or at our disopsal. Over the long run it is quite likely that we shall be able to close the gap between needs and resources. In the short run, however, we lack sufficient dollars or personnel for all the tasks we see as essential. There results a vigorous and strenuous competition for funds, staff, and community support. This competition takes place not only among various social welfare services but between them and the health agencies, and in a large context between health and welfare services on the one hand and the many other interests of our complex society. As a result, community after community, and our nation, has had to consider new ways for setting priorities in tackling proliferating problems.

Compelling Need for Knowledge

This situation is accompanied by a new realization of limitations as well as potentialities imbedded in man's social institutions. We need to study community growth and behavior as deeply as we now study individual or human growth and behavior. Communities and organizations are living systems or organisms which obey laws we understand imperfectly. We can do things which make the systems react; and they usually act without much respect for what we do. Our present knowledge about the social organizations we have created indicates that they change slowly, far more slowly than our population and technology change.

Moreover, social organizations behave in subtle and complex

ways. Any organization must simultaneously meet pressures from two directions: (1) internally it must satisfy the associational needs of its members, find ways of pleasing them in their internal affairs; (2) it must also be capable of adapting to pressures from the external world, pressures for action, production, etc. Once an organization strikes a balance between these two, its tendency is to keep that balance, to maintain the *status quo,* not to change, or to change as little as necessary to maintain the balance.

With this context of change and new knowledge I should like to discuss briefly the subject of community organization as viewed in social welfare. These views combine generally accepted concepts and a personal interpretation of trends—a limitation to this presentation which is perhaps inevitable in the situation.

Community Organization Defined

To oversimplify, community organization is commonly defined as that social work activity concerned with achieving an improved—or a continuously improving—balance between human needs and social resources to meet those needs. In the practical sense, this may at various times call for better coordination among resources, alteration in the character of some services, the creation of new facilities, or the mobilization of additional resources in the form of funds and personnel to achieve any of the foregoing. The process undoubtedly varies according to which purpose is paramount at any one time.

Within this generalized definition two substrains can be identified. For some the means for bringing about the desired balance is more important than any specific end result. This has led one group of social workers to concentrate upon the *processes* by which needs and resources are brought into balance. For them the fundamental aim is a strengthening of ties among groups which make up the community, an increase in community cohesiveness and solidarity. The most practical expressions of this approach have been found in settlement houses, in attempts to mobilize citizens into self-functioning and self-realizing organizations, and in the early councils of social agencies. It relies upon the potential of all citizens to evaluate facts, create satisfactory forms for collective action, and select a proper course of action.

This strong survival of the nineteenth-century liberal view of man and his society has been extensively elaborated in the professional literature.

For another group of social workers the selection and definition of practical and specific *goals* and the practical mobilization of support to achieve them become primary objectives. They tend to view the community as a community of organizations rather than as a community of individuals, and thus draw upon the concepts of political science. This emphasis upon goals and plans for reaching them distinguishes social planning. This group of social workers seeks to modify the environment. As social workers, they value the individual; they also value the logic of facts and studies, professional interpretation of these facts, and political strategy as bases for a course of action. Their plans for action on behalf of the community thus include facts, interpretation, and various strategies for assuring citizen support. This approach, little elaborated in theoretical or professional terms, is widely found in practice.

Congruence and Contradiction

In sum, all of us credit a certain formal and logical process which consists of these elements: the identification of need, felt by the community, for improvement or change; the study of facts; the evaluation of these facts to develop a plan of action; action to ensure support and adoption of this plan. We differ in our emphases and thus in our actions, depending upon the intensity of our commitment to the process or to the practical end result. These differences now require analysis if we are to deal with certain dilemmas which have long plagued us:

1. The tempo of events frequently forces us to act in a situation fraught with uncertainty. Available data do not answer all our questions, and further study may not replace reliance upon judgment and choice. Plans must often be prepared on the basis of limited evidence.

2. Planning requires that we anticipate or predict the future, at least in part or imperfectly; the past, while prologue to the present, does not forecast the future.

3. The complexity of social change requires specialized technical and professional knowledge; but our history makes us wary of our own expertness, and this in turn blurs our relationship with citizens. We are reluctant to propose sharply formulated solutions which anticipate the future.

4. Our social organizations change very slowly. The more groups we involve in planning the changes we seek, the more differences we must bridge, the more we must dilute or adjust our plans, and the more change is retarded. We have not separated participation in identifying needs from participation in arriving at solutions. Is everyone equally involved in both?

It is no longer sufficient simply to mobilize citizens. It is necessary to mobilize them in relation to rather clear-cut plans which require specialized competence for effective implementation. Nor is it sufficient simply to develop carefully thought-out and documented plans, for these are frequently filed and ignored.

These dilemmas and contradictions can be resolved only after deeper attention to the character of the community and to the conditions and tools for community and organizational change or growth, especially the functions and uses of power, leadership, and research. These do not constitute a complete analysis but are, I believe, necessary elements now being elaborated, so that in time a more systematic body of theory can emerge.

The Character of the Community

The community in which we function—a town, a region, or a state—is neither a tightly structured phenomenon nor an amorphous assembly of individuals. Instead, it is a subtle blend of individuals and of institutions created over many hundreds of years to meet social needs. These social institutions, including social agencies, were seldom rationally planned in the sense that we mean today, but they have served in a rough-and-ready fashion to meet human needs.

This community, the loose entity we all refer to so familiarly, consists of a complex of subgroups with memberships which frequently overlap. Each subgroup—which may have a religious, economic, political, social welfare, or other function—was developed to meet some need of its members. These subgroups are the building blocks of the community in our western, industrialized, urban world of formal, corporate, and informal organizations. They are not static; new ones constantly emerge and old ones change. Note, if you will, the origins of the 56 national health agencies.

These subgroups created the health and welfare agencies with which we deal and which employ us day by day. Their requirements determine the policies of our health and welfare agencies as much as does the logic of our professional practice. Social planning must take those requirements into account: the need for the group (and its institutions) to survive; its desire for prestige and status; the importance of its ideology—political, religious, or professional. These group needs are frequently given the invidious term of "special interest" but satisfying them is the very object of group life. A subtle and complex blend of altruism and self-interest governs the behavior of health and welfare organizations, and both elements need to be understood.

One consequence is that social planning cannot be approached solely through the interests or activities of individuals without regard to their group affiliations and associations. Lay and professional welfare leaders are usually leaders of subgroups and agencies. The need to maintain these latter positions of leadership is as strong as any interest in that more vague entity, the general community. A few leaders emerge who identify the interests of many groups and thus the interests of a wider human community, but the proportion is small. Their efforts can be seen in the work of our health and welfare councils, some of our governmental organizations, the Congress of the United States, and the United Nations. These gropings for a wider unity cannot, however, ignore the more parochial behavior of organizations and leadership efforts.

In this view, informal associations are as significant as formal ones. The relationships among various organizations and their leaders are too intricate and complex to be contained within the formal kinds of exchange that we usually provide for in our professional operations. Thus far, our efforts in social welfare have concentrated upon bringing together individuals and organization representatives through a complex mechanism of committees, conferences, planning organizations, etc., in the belief that the key elements of planning can be recognized in this formal arena.

This formal area is important, but it is only the exposed portion of the iceberg of group and community association. We therefore need to give much more attention to the informal associations among policy-makers. Many key planning agreements are achieved less in the formal planning of the conference room than in the exchange of views among policy-makers as they meet informally at dinner, lunch, cocktails, parties, or each other's offices. Unfortunately we do not know how seriously the lack of an informal medium hampers community planning.

With a few exceptions, we know that our voluntary planning organizations are heavily influenced by certain social and economic interests which may have a natural pattern of informal contact with each other. On the other hand, our governmental organizations are likely to represent quite different social and economic strata. Is there sufficient informal cross-over between these two groupings? Does the existence of two systems and leadership groupings account for our difficulty in effectively welding public and voluntary organizations into one planning mechanism? Can our professional techniques bridge the two groups?

Elements and Tools of Community Change

Community planning either anticipates or initiates change in our social organizations. Change, of course, occurs without being centrally directed or planned, and understanding of this natural organic process in society is valuable. There is justification for awaiting the natural change, and then responding to it. A profession or agency dedicated to planning exists, however, because it recognizes the potentiality for initiating or bringing about change according to human design.

We have examined the formal bases for action; less is known about the many levels at which change can occur. There are plans to bring individuals into a new neighborhood civic association; to expand the services and facilities of one hospital; to develop a regional medical center; to coordinate all health and welfare agencies for the chronically ill; to renew and redevelop the metropolis; to extend security coverage to meet health needs of the aged. In each of these plans, the persons involved, the forces affected, the mechanisms to be activated, and the tasks are different. Until we analyze the distinctive requirements of each level, our concepts remain general and of minimal use.

Certain preconditions must also exist for planned change to be successful. We glimpse some of them—a crisis in the affairs of agencies or communities, a nucleus of dedicated individuals, a mechanism for convincing persons—but our capability in assessing them is most limited.

Once we know these preconditions exist, we must take into account the voluntary nature of our health and welfare organizations and agencies. (Even in governmental units, decisions usually depend on free agreement.) Some degree of consensus must be achieved among independent actors on the scene. Although this subject has beguiled us, we still lack a clear formulation of what is required to bring about consensus.

Agreement by some participants may be sufficient to achieve a goal that would be unattainable if we widened the area of consent. Is this democratic or not? Are we satisfied with consensus when a group of organizations agrees out of political realism to support a course of action without necessarily believing in the action?

To act upon these other levels of consensus requires a belief in the negotiating process that is more characteristic of our political mechanisms than of our social work and sociological concepts. Political science has much to tell us about the processes by which groups accommodate themselves to each other's requirements in order to maintain a viable political system. In practice, leaders of organizations and of social and health agencies engage in this process of accommodation in negotiation to reach a practical consensus for action. In a theoretical sense, however, this has received very little attention, and we are only on the threshold of reviewing the insights of political science for this purpose.

The Tools of Change

If these are some of the conditions with which we must deal

—the conservatism of organizations, the need for informal associations, and the less-than-pure levels of consensus—have we any tools with which to plan? Let me select a few: power and influence, goal-setting, leadership, and community studies.

Social work has usually viewed *power* as the villain behind the scenes in democratic activity, a monolithic influence at once to be sought after and avoided. In one interpretation there exists a clear but remote power structure which can somehow be mobilized to support and drive through the logical plan of any professional group if only this power group can be sufficiently impressed with the logic of professional planning. Of late this view has been replaced by a more realistic recognition that there are multiple power structures or power centers in any community, that our pluralistic society contains pluralistic interests with self-selected leadership and variable control over influence and resources. These influences are only sometimes represented on our policy-making boards. Health and welfare causes appeal to only some of them; many influential elements remain quite aloof or passive. Nothing indicates that all must or necessarily should be deeply or intimately involved in our daily affairs.

It has become necessary for us to view power not as an absolute but as a series of influences which are frequently passive or indifferent to our affairs but which can sometimes be drawn upon with a proper exercise of skill. We have much yet to learn about how this power can be mobilized and about its limitations for our purposes, and its disadvantages. There are many in the social welfare field who successfully mobilize power, but little has been systematically written or theoretically developed in relation to it.

It is timely to study the practical experience of these successful practitioners and to supplement it with insights from other disciplines, especially political science. There is a vocabulary which can be drawn upon or added to our own: the making of *coalitions* among groups to achieve specified ends; *negotiations* to balance ideal and practical ends; the operation of *influence* (and how to mobilize or use it ethically rather than venally).

This new language also requires that we re-examine our usual concepts of *leadership*. There is no single measure of a leader, except that he influence others by virtue of wealth, control of employment, social position, political skill, intellectual acumen, or dedication to ethical concepts.

Although we have not sufficiently defined either the aims of social planning or the leadership required for each, we recognize that different aims call upon varying leadership skills. To coordinate the efforts of many participants requires a bridging skill to bring self-interests and common interests into some form of alignment for action. Other leadership talents are required to obtain large sums of money for a new program or to negotiate new legislative frontiers.

We have a healthy respect for the capacities of citizen leaders of all kinds. We have some skill in identifying latent leadership ability and helping it find expression. We have some skill in helping leading personalities understand the broader implications of community welfare problems so that their narrow group interests become slowly blended into a kind of community statesmanship. Unfortunately, our concepts about these processes are quite pragmatic and not reduced to teachable form. We need to study this phenomenon, to understand it in all its manifestations, rather than rely upon the continuous relearning by each of us.

Incentives, especially financial, are important aids in planning. The vast growth of federal appropriations for health has aroused some unwarranted concern about centralized dictation. We have evidence that the offer or denial of funds seldom forces any organization to do anything it does not want to do. Federal and other funds help groups try new patterns and approaches.

Goal-setting is another practical tool. Any plan requires a goal to be achieved; a plan is not something that just happens. We may have overstressed the rights of self-determination until the values of clear-cut goals have been obscured. As a profession we have learned that goals cannot be imposed. We must now apply an equally valid principle—that the exercise of professional leadership also requires us to select our goals for action. Here our strengths have been at two extremes. We excel in fixing our sights on the broadest social goal—a healthy society, for example—and on the narrowest—such as increased employment of caseworkers in public health departments. We are weak in filling in the spectrum of intermediate goals as a series of steps which guide us and our communities to clear-cut ends. In this arena our democratic ideals may lead us to abdicate much to the initiative of others. Our concern with helping others make up their minds does not excuse us from the obligation of making up our own.

In this era *priorities* are as important as goals. In time, our lack of good criteria can be overcome. Until then we can accept the responsibility of deciding what order of priority we give to all the things we would like to do. Are co-operation and co-ordination enough? When and how shall we wholly reorganize the pattern of agencies? When should the programs of individual agencies be altered and how far? When are new resources essential, and just what new services, buildings, staffs, and budgets are needed?

A few words are unavoidable about *the community study*. The everchanging character of community affairs and of man in his community requires the effective blending of several modes of study, including specialized research, regularized assembly of factual data, and professional observation. The most formal methods of study and analysis supplement but do not replace the observations of the skilled observer in the course of daily operations and practice. Each amplifies and corrects the other.

We have a network of staff observers in our health and welfare agencies. What is usually lacking is a satisfactory community-wide system for regularly gathering and assessing their observations about our services and needs, new and old. Can we develop some systematic way of bringing together these observations as we bring together vital statistics and service reports? Observations are especially useful in understanding the social disorders which lack sharp definition: juvenile delinquency, functional disability, alcoholism, and chronic disease.

Mechanisms for Planning

Social welfare in its liberal and democratic tradition has shown that much can be achieved by exposing individuals and organizations to the influence of their peers, by bringing leaders of organizations into regular contact with each other. This has slowly and subtly led to a system of welfare agencies and services bound together by a welfare council or an interdepartmental committee. The requirements of the whole system have slowly begun to influence the activities of individual members. This is sometimes done formally by developing common standards and criteria. However it is done, the "system" is now an asset for influencing its members.

We now ask ourselves: can this cumbersome system—these slow, integrating processes—be used to achieve specific goals, to realize comprehensive plans? Welfare councils and official agencies (such as health departments) seek to perform in this manner. I suspect their aims and methods are moving closing together. Each is now trying to reconcile two factors: the desire to plan, to take rationally calculated action to achieve a goal, and the knowledge that much action is not rationally calculated. Each stream of experience can freshen the other in the interests of a healthier community.

As we move along, we shall need to evaluate our experience more critically than ever before. It's a harsh fact that our present approaches give us no yardstick by which to measure our planning actions and find out which really work and which fall short. The period ahead should stimulate us to look to our results as well as to our high aims. To do this well, we need to use one another's experience fully and systematically.

To accomplish all this, welfare has a network of public welfare agencies, each heavily invested in health care; some 2,000 community councils and chests; over 50 national health agencies; and thousands of social workers employed in health agencies. Can this complex be moved by design to serve the public health, or must it serve by the workings of chance?

The Role of Social Work in Meeting the Challenge to Public Health*

by DAVID E. PRICE, M.D.

It is indeed an honor to have the last word at a conference that has been actively planned for a year and a half, and envisioned for an even longer time by many foresighted individuals sensitive to the common needs of public health and social work.

I think it is appropriate, in concluding this seminar, to place the ideas and courses of action we have discussed in a perspective that we sometimes lose sight of in dealing with our everyday problems—the perspective of the long-range, over-all significance of what we are trying to accomplish through our public health programs.

President Kennedy, in his recent message to Congress on national health needs, stated that the nation's strength resides in its people, their health, and their vitality.

We all share a common concern for keeping America strong and healthy, but we sometimes tend to view the concern more in terms of our own activities and professions than from the standpoint that what we are doing has tremendous national and international significance.

The Crux of Our Problem

Our ability to bring the gift of health to all our citizens has tremendous implications, not only for our own people in our own country in our own time, but for other people in other countries in this and future generations. The United States has become the

---

* Paper delivered March 9, 1962.

mecca of medical discovery and advancement. We must continue
to develop our knowledge of medicine and science, and to refine
our techniques of organizing and bringing health services to our
citizens.

Our progress in caring for our own transcends national
boundaries, for our activities and values are under careful scrutiny by many of the young emerging nations of the world, who
are constantly told that our capitalistic system of freedom and
individuality contains the seeds of its own destruction. Our health
programs are a vital component in making our system work. Their
success is a major source of national strength.

This is the crux of the problem that we, as members of professions sharing common goals, face. Our success in attaining
these goals will be complicated, rather than eased, by a number
of major forces operating in our society today. These forces call
for more and better public health services, and at the same time
cause impediments to the provision of those services.

Trends and Issues

First, we are faced with population increases which demand
a growth of all kinds of health services and well-trained professional manpower.

Secondly, economic forces at work—the decline of agriculture, increasing industrialization and automation, the movement
of our population into the cities—are giving rise to problems
rarely dreamed of a few years ago when public health's primary
concern was the control of transmissible diseases through protection of milk and water supplies and provision of adequate waste
disposal. Today we must worry about new environmental hazards
of water and air pollution; accidents caused by the machines we
have invented; radiation hazards; and poverty, crime and other
social problems predominant in large cities.

Finally, what I like to call "changes in the state of the art"
have spawned another set of problems for us. While advances in
health research have eliminated many of the diseases that used
to decimate our population, now our citizens are growing older
and we must contend with such things as chronic diseases and
problems of the aging. The growing demands for health services

pose problems of how best to organize those services to the benefit of all who need them.

These trends have inevitably broadened the concept of health to include physical, mental, and social well-being. Public health problems must now be defined in terms of their social as well as their physical components. That their solution will not come easily is something that you realize as well as I. Even by working together, our job will not be made simple. Working separately, it will be impossible.

I have no doubt that we can pool our efforts in this time of necessity, when "public health" problems are no longer separate from "social" problems. Just as a medical problem like venereal disease has an important social component, so has a social problem like poverty or poor housing a high public health component. I should like to illustrate some ways that social workers can make important contributions toward preventing and solving health problems.

The Social Worker and the Disabled

Only half of one million chronically ill persons in the United States are receiving any kind of services following hospitalization. What happens to a person who finds himself suddenly, or even gradually, chronically disabled? Suppose he has a heart disease. In many cases, even though these patients are given the best possible care in the hospital, they regress upon returning home—notwithstanding home care by physician and visiting nurse—because they are not aided by social workers who can help them develop a new orientation to their altered state of health.

Social workers, moreover, have a potential that goes far beyond helping patients through crises, for they are indispensable in joining with members of the health professions to make our citizens aware of medical advances and are able and willing to cooperate in health practices.

Our progress with immunization procedures illustrates this point. The President has recently called for grants of $35,000,000 for the immunization of all children under five years of age against polio, diphtheria, whooping cough, and tetanus. If this program goes into effect the federal government will pay for the vaccine and will assist state and local governments in financing operational costs. Yet the ultimate success of this program will depend on whether or not individual citizens cooperate. Parents cannot be forced to immunize their children, and the sad fact is that many thousands of people still needlessly suffer from infectious diseases for which preventive measures are available. Social workers can make an invaluable contribution simply by increasing public appreciation of the importance of immunization.

The potential role of social workers in dealing with tuberculosis is illustrated by a project undertaken some time ago in North Carolina. Here social workers were employed to help convince tuberculous patients that they should remain in the hospital until the doctor recommended their release. Part of the persuasion involved making the patient aware of the importance of his remaining institutionalized for his own benefit as well as for the benefit of his family and community. A very important part of it involved setting the patient's mind at ease by seeing that family needs were met.

Nutritional disease, venereal disease, and diseases of the old and the very young all have a high social component. New environmental health hazards posed by the introduction each year of 400 to 500 new chemical compounds and physical and biological elements into our environment depend for successful control on the extent of public cooperation and, in turn, on the success of the health professions in enlisting cooperation.

Social Work's Role in the Public Health Service

Our working together is not a one-way street. The public health profession has the responsibility of making its members aware of the social elements involved in the public health problems with which they deal. Poverty, unemployment, poor housing, juvenile delinquency, crime, desertion, and neglect have an important impact on public health, just as the medical problems of tuberculosis and venereal disease have important social implications.

The Public Health Service brought social work services into its programs many years ago when the first social worker was employed in the U.S. Marine Hospital at Ellis Island in 1921.

Since that time there has been a gradual growth of social work staff until today their activities range from providing direct casework services, consultation, and training to participating in research projects.

There are over 30 social workers assigned as consultants to the tuberculosis, heart, and chronic disease control programs. In the Indian health program, social workers provide services to Indians while operating as part of the Public Health Service field health centers. They devote more than half their time to consultation on medical social problems and to coordination of plans with other members of the field health teams. The rest of their time is spent in direct involvement with the most difficult and complex social problems presented by the patients at field health centers.

At the National Institutes of Health Clinical Center, a 500-bed combination hospital and research facility, over 30 social workers give direct social services to research patients and function as consultants to various clinical investigators studying the social and emotional factors affecting the patients at the center, many of whom have chronic diseases and, as a result, serious social dysfunctioning. The job of the social workers at the Clinical Center is complicated by the fact that these patients come from widespread geographical areas, with the result that casework planning and help must frequently span great distances.

Besides providing social services to patients at the Clinical Center, the social workers are an important part of the research program. The majority are involved in mental health research, helping to screen patients who participate in projects, working with psychiatrists in conducting interviews, and helping to select individuals for biosocial groupings. They have participated in studies of resistance to vocational rehabilitation, emotional problems of children facing heart surgery, and stress in hospitalized patients. They are presently participating in studies of normal patterns in marriage and their effect upon child development, stress exhibited by parents who have leukemia, and the epidemiology of reading disability.

I feel that these illustrations serve as proof that social workers can participate in public health programs—but they represent only the beginnings of what should become the rule rather than the exception.

Four Opportunities for Action

We decided to meet because we all know that social workers can participate much more deeply in the public health movement. During the meeting we have considered how they could participate. Now as the seminar concludes, I would again like to touch upon four major areas which have been discussed in considerable detail and which represent our greatest need for action.

Prevention

First, social workers can help improve health services by educating to health problems and needs the many individuals and families with whom they come in contact and by enlisting their cooperation. Because social workers are usually first on the scene, they have a unique position from which to detect potential health as well as social problems. By bringing the proper resources to bear on these problems, they can do much to make preventive public health function effectively.

Community Plannning

Secondly, as a past leader in public health, Dr. Charles-Edward A. Winslow has pointed out that the key point in the definition of public health is *the use of organized community efforts* to prevent disease, prolong life, and promote physical and mental health. The use of organized community effort means not only the effective organization of resources, but also an understanding of the community itself. Social workers can contribute much toward our understanding of the stresses, pressures, prejudices, and resistances of community groups. Therefore, it is important that they serve in health departments and make their specialized knowledge available to other health specialties, community leaders, legislators, and public policymakers.

Research

Third, social workers can participate in our progams of research and epidemiology by contributing their knowledge of social factors and social work methods and by working directly in research and epidemiological studies. By viewing those to whom they provide social work services as members of groups of patients whose problems are similar, social workers can analyze common factors and help detect problems which occur with the greatest frequency.

In public health research we are concerned with evaluation of experimental results which will lead to the establishment of new methods. Social workers are directly in touch with the end results of both illness and therapy—notably the social and psychological effects. Can social workers do more to help feed back to the health field the relevant knowledge needed for assessment of the impact of environment and the results of treatment? I believe that social workers, with their experience in casework, can help determine in depth the impact of acute and chronic illness; can provide useful information on the social aspects of typical institutions such as schools, hospitals, and health departments; and can assist greatly in the "tracing function"—the follow-up phase of a research project.

Professional Education

Finally, because improved preventive health measures, better community programs, and research studies are not possible unless there are persons properly trained to execute them, there must be an expansion of public health content in social work education. That you are well aware of this need is evident in the very fact that this seminar has taken place. It is the first in our history to be concerned with this issue. I believe it strikes at the very root of the problem—the bonding of two areas during a period when individual skills and ideas are being formed.

What I am proposing is a "liberal health education" for social workers. While every social worker must know his own profession, he can no longer emphasize casework to the exclusion of the the broad public health issues surrounding social work. A social worker must become less the specialist and more the generalist, aware of the theories and techniques of public health, aware of the total health needs of the individual, and aware of his responsibility to contribute his knowledge and experience.

To meet this responsibility, social workers must have a better understanding of public health problems, of community dynamics, and of social issues and trends as they affect health programs. They must develop more refined skills in research and experimental design, statistics, epidemiological methods, and over-all administration.

It now remains for you, the leaders in social work education, to assess existing educational resources and determine the best way to integrate public health content into classroom and field activities. In many of our social work schools, it will be a question of whether these things are being done. In others it will be a question of whether they are being done enough. In still others it will be a question of whether they are being done well.

You must ask yourselves these questions, and find answers to them, because they get at the heart of our most pressing health need—that of forming a united front against our health problems.

PANEL PRESENTATION

Post-Master's Preparation for Practice in a Particular Field

GRACE WHITE

The purpose of this session is to engage practitioners and educators in discussion of a subject that has had only fragmented and sporadic attention by the profession. All would agree that preparation for competent professional practice cannot be gained in two years of graduate study and that continuing education of each practitioner is essential. All of us recognize that the master's program does not aim to prepare for practice in a particular field. Furthermore, we are keenly aware of the urgent need for competent practice of social work in whichever field the graduate enters. The question before us, then, is what means are currently used to help practitioners in their continuing preparation for practice, and what more is indicated.

Our group sessions devoted to the curriculum are focused on the master's program. It seems appropriate that we include in this seminar some consideration of post-master's learning opportunities. We recognize that the learning experiences provided for all practitioners should increase their comprehension of the basic concepts, principles, and methods of social work as the learning of the specifics of a field proceeds.

Mrs. Esther C. Spencer will present some competencies needed for practice in public health that she identified by analyzing the functions of social workers in the California State Department of Public Health.

ESTHER C. SPENCER

The analysis referred to has not yet been systematized. It derives from our experiences these last ten years in recruitment and deployment of social workers in state and county health departments. I will not presume to suggest where or at what level competencies should be taught—in the master's program, in an advanced program, in in-service education. Rather will I offer some general observations, none of them scientifically derived.

These break down into three categories having to do with the knowledge, methods, and attitudes that I think make up the public health social worker's sense of professional self—a somewhat different self than I perceive the typical product of a graduate school of social work to be. Although this may sound like a value judgment, it is not meant to be!

As to knowledge, I do not have to go into much detail at this point in the seminar. The public health social worker must know such subjects as epidemiology and biostatistics—the arithmetic of public health—and be familiar with life tables, what they mean, how they may be interpreted in planning programs. In some dimensions this material differs from that taught in the graduate schools, and in others simply elaborates basic knowledge. Certainly there are aspects of epidemiology representative of the latter.

As to methods, consultation as an essential feature of problem-solving is not taught to any practical extent in the master's program. (Speaking of consultation, you know George James' definition of a consultant: a social worker who is perfectly willing to do God's work so long as it is in an advisory capacity).

Perhaps these illustrations will convey what I am trying to say. When we talk about and try to hire people with "research sophistication" we look for those equipped to do research *who can stimulate others to do it;* who are sufficiently knowledgeable to add social factors to other people's research; who can evaluate the research designs of others in critiques that state whether the social component is properly expressed, or should be more fully expressed, or should be expanded; who can assist in constructing questionnaires that reflect social work values, experience, and knowledge; who can help to orient and instruct field investigators who are not skilled interviewers in the social work sense; who can conduct field investigations that apply the skilled interviewing techniques required in certain types of research; certainly who can use research findings in programing and can interpret research data. We look for people with enough knowledge, understanding, insight, skill, and awareness to marry research to social work in public health and produce a variety of offspring.

This requires certain attitudes and certain skills in diagnosis that are present in all good social workers, but more conspicuously present in the people I want. Their diagnostic capabilities must be such that they can handle the whole range of ideas about the ecological forces with which public health deals. They must do more than translate from theory regarding the dynamics of human development or the individual's place in society, or from the aggregate of the individuals a particular program is intended to serve. They must be able to establish the sequence of priorities, the spectrum of disciplines to be involved, and the level of intervention. Somehow or other these dynamics and program necessities in public health social work must be synthesized in an appropriate course of action.

Turning now to the sense of professional self, the distinction made here may be somewhat artificial, but we have come to rely on it. We speak so much of the use of self in social work. This needs translation in the public health setting, because there mostly we are placing our skills, knowledge, awarenesses, and even our technological know-how at the use of other people. The commitment we must hold is that others can do what we are trying to help them do—management of cases, for example; that others in public health are just as concerned as we with social factors, with socio-epidemiologic values; that they have a right to these concerns, often well expressed in programs. The public health social worker cannot afford the luxury of feeling that only he can successfully contribute to case management—that others cannot and should not. The belief that others can do this, are doing it, and need to do it represents a background for use of the professional self that has to be learned. At least this appears to be so from our experience with people who come to us for employment. Moreover, it takes quite a long time for the average social worker (we have very good ones) to give up the idea that he is the only one who can intervene in complex social situations.

This brings up another point along the same axis, namely, that we are interested in individuals who are more concerned with *appropriate* functions than with *traditional* functions. This is exceedingly important in public health, where social workers have many opportunities to improvise as they apply social work knowledge and understanding to the variety, scope, and complexity of situations that confront public health. Two factors operate here. The first is logistics. The ratio of social workers to other professional personnel in public health is extremely small, the number of social problems extremely great. Whenever social workers hear someone refer to a social problem—for example, that "senility is a social diagnosis" is acknowledged by just about everybody in public health (and there are many other examples) —they immediately feel that here is an opportunity for social work. Most other professionals in public health believe social workers like to build empires and expect to play a direct, active role in solving any "social" problem. This is seldom true. Social workers very often work in the background, critically looking at programs to see, for example, whether they embody appropriate ego supports, whether they fully recognize the social component. The other factor is time. The tempo in public health is very different from that in other fields. This helps to determine the spots at which social workers are directly or indirectly concerned. But few social workers can stand this. In setting priorities, you might decide to emphasize a particular problem (perhaps a relatively minor one, in the social work lexicon) for a year, because you had a hypothesis and a methodology and a faith that you could add to a larger body of knowledge that might be useful in four or five years. This is too devastating for many social workers, particularly for those inflexibly committed to a one-to-one relationship that will produce some change in a much shorter period of time.

GRACE WHITE

Mrs. Spencer has given us quite a bit to think about as to what is needed in learning for satisfactory practice in a particular field. The four remaining speakers will describe various learning opportunities that are available. One way to continue learning is to "get on the job," but we know that some employment opportunities offer better possibilities for on-the-job learning than do others. Marie McNabola will present an agency-based training program tailored for specific purposes.

MARIE McNABOLA

What constitutes preparation for practice in a particular field? Pending definition of adequate preparation by the profession, or by any field, a variety of approaches to better preparation have been made. We are all familiar with the attempts to influence schools of social work to include specialized learning experiences in the master's program and the development of "third year programs" in a number of schools. The advanced third-year programs in universities have now become merged with the doctoral programs and, with a few exceptions, are not designed for specialized preparation. Two types of training programs have developed in agencies: a training program for "social work fellows" which combines selected experiences in the agency and study in a university, and the structuring of programs to reach specific goals in staff development. An internship for the beginning practitioner has been discussed for many years, and the recent NASW certification plan has refocused attention on desirability of formalizing the beginner's experiences in practice.

The post-master's training programs are designed to meet manpower shortages in critical areas, to provide training for a field in other than the basic tenets, and to enable educators and practitioners to conceptualize the trends of emerging fields of practice. Some of these programs are connected with a university center; others are not. They have developed in the following areas: public health, vocational rehabilitation, community mental health consultation and services, clinical practice with children, and research for community chests and councils. This seems to be a healthy, creative pattern which will provide additional training opportunities for practitioners and will force further clarification of concepts of practice which may apply to more than one field.

In this presentation I will discuss an experimental training program in community mental health, designed for the experienced practitioner and developed at the Massachusetts General Hospital in Boston. Under the direction of Dr. Erich Lindemann, in cooperation with the Harvard School of Public Health and selected community agencies, the program for social workers is combined with similar programs for psychiatrists and psychologists. The training is individually designed to meet the needs of each fellow and to satisfy his special interests. A series of seminars are conducted by the training staff. The core experiences include mental health consultation, work with groups, and clinical experiences focused on short-term treatment. Selected courses at the Harvard School of Public Health and Brandeis University are offered, for individual election. Wherever possible, each fellow is related to an ongoing research program. This experimental program was initiated to evaluate the feasibility of providing specialized training in community mental health and to experiment with various patterns of training.

A few points may have general relevance: selection of practitioner-trainees; advantages and stresses of specialized programs; and effects on the agencies and on community resources.

Selection of Trainees

Since the program was designed to help the trainee add to and integrate knowledge of clinical and community mental health for use in a different pattern of practice, fellows were selected from those in clinical practice who wished to move into community mental health programs as well as those already engaged in local and state community health programs. Several factors should receive special note. An essential feature of the training experience was that it engaged each fellow in refining his knowledge and his practice. This required an active, conscious distilling of previous experience in the process of acquiring new or different skills.

Many aspects of practice in community mental health, as in other special fields, are in the process of development. Those whose commitment to mental health was clear and of some duration made the most effective use of the training. They had a pre-determined investment in the resolution of problems arising in practice. They were able to tolerate lack of clarity in the field and to experiment with their new skills in order to further their knowledge. The difficulties were similar to those of many programs. Some social workers are attracted to special programs because they seem to be the latest bandwagons; others are not clear about the kind of career they want, or have a special interest and think a new tack will help them. The least effective were those who expected a training program to *give* them competence in practice. Experience has indicated that they lacked a sound understanding of professional principles.

Advantages and Stresses in Special Training

Obviously, such programs provide trainees with opportunities for concentrated review of an area of practice and for experiences specifically designed to help them integrate new and established methods of practice. The practitioner is given a special role, that of colleague-learner. Practice in community mental health requires some understanding of institutional stresses, and sensitivity to the checks and balances in social systems. Trainees critically observe the interaction of their peers and superiors as well as of individuals in the community. In the training process the analysis of these observations is probably less veiled by social determinants than it would be in regular staff relationships.

The training center usually provides a range of programs in the same area of practice so that fellows are able to obtain experience in situations at various levels of development. Certain stresses are inherent in a setup which involves a number of institutions and communities. Trainees must respond to direction from a variety of people, and the staff must play several roles. This is especially true for the staff member who is both preceptor and practitioner. The experience of collaboration is useful to the fellow and advances the learning process, but creates problems for the staff worker who must analyze his own performance in evaluating the program.

Effects on Agency and Community

For an agency perhaps the most crucial aspect of a training program is in scheduling enough time for communication among members of the staff. The benefits to the community lie in increased consultation and clinical services. Consultation services are offered primarily to established programs and institutions— hospitals, public schools, and community agencies. By its nature mental health consultation is a form of privileged communication focusing on the problems of an institution and the concerns of an individual. The introduction of a training fellow who serves as consultant for a limited period requires certain balances to offset the impact of change for the individual or institutional consultee. This can be achieved if one is able to place the fellows in a number of institutions as well as in different communities. The critical feature here is the continuity of staff services and consistent communication at the administrative level. I point out these simple and well-known principles of planning because in operation they become a three-dimensional chess game! They are also important because feedback from the institution is esential in evaluating the fellow as a consultant and in distinguishing between the personal and institutional reactions of consultees.

Post-master's programs provide one means of preparing practitioners for leadership and training responsibilities in special areas of practice. They enable practitioners to adapt their professional experience to new areas in a more orderly and disciplined manner than is possible on the job through general staff development programs. Perhaps the most important contribution of these programs is that they expose experienced workers to an intensive review of the questions confronting a particular area of practice and to experimental methods, techniques, and patterns of service.

GRACE WHITE

Miss McNabola's presentation stimulates thought about the problems involved but also the advantages that might be gained were social work to consider an agency-based residency program or some other tailor-made training program for social workers who have completed the two-year curriculum and have had a year or two of practice. At present only a handful have learning opportunities of this nature.

Institutes are a learning device frequently utilized in social work. Many types and qualities of institutes are given under a variety of auspices. Some have good educational components and meet good educational standards. Eileen Lester will discuss an institute program that has developed into a significant educational resource.

EILEEN LESTER

The Regional Institute Program is an exciting one and is doing much to update our practice in the fields of health, medical care, and rehabilitation. Ten years ago the idea was only a gleam in Eleanor Cockerill's eyes. She allowed no obstacle—and there were many—to prevent the "gleam" from becoming a reality. As a result, the Medical Social Work Section of the National Association of Social Workers sponsors a continuous regional program providing advanced training for social workers in health, medical care, and rehabilitation settings. The criteria for attendance at an institute are completion of the master's program in a school of social work and current employment in one of the three fields.

Ten years ago, when many of us were members of the American Association of Medical Social Workers, a continuing educational program for our membership was one of the goals of the Committee on Education. A subcommittee, appointed in 1953 to explore this idea, made two surveys, the first to determine the professional interests and needs of practitioners in health, medical care, and rehabilitation programs; the second to determine the nature, extent, and availability of educational resources to meet these needs and interests. The findings led the subcommittee to recommend a long-range educational program designed to increase professional competencies in the constantly changing programs. The generous support of the U.S. Office of Vocational Rehabilitation and the National Foundation (at that time the National Foundation for Infantile Paralysis) enabled us to launch and carry on this program.

In 1955 a two-phase training program for institute leaders

was conducted. The first phase emphasized the newer professional knowledge needed by our practitioners; the second phase, six months later, concentrated on methods of planning and conducting an institute. The following year two pilot institutes were given, one in the South and one in the Great Lakes region. The pilot institutes helped the national committee identify the problems involved in the development of a nationwide program of regional institues, each tailored to meet the needs of a particular group of social workers. Further, two different educational designs were developed and tested in the pilot institutes. The national committee then developed principles and guidelines for the program and employed a consultant to help committees organize regions and plan for regional institutes.

The regions in which the pilot institutes were held were the first to organize. The Southern region held its first institute in 1957 and the Great Lakes region in 1958. Each was planned and conducted by a committee made up of representatives from each state in the region. These two regions were active through all the developmental stages of the project and were willing to test new ideas as the thinking of the national committee changed. Without their continued interest and support the program would not have been possible.

The Pacific Southwest region and the Pacific Northwest region were organized in 1959. Each organized region has held an institute every year with an average attendance of about 75 persons. The Mid-continent region is now organized and will hold its first institute this spring [1962]. The regional institute program now covers 37 of the 50 states. We hope the remaining 13 states along the Eastern seaboard will be organized before the end of 1962.

As we proceeded, we had to revise our original conception of the duties and responsibilities of the institute leaders to achieve our goal of progressively advancing the competence of professionally educated social work practitioners. The revised plan provided for employment of an educational director by each region to carry the following responsibilities: (1) to develop the educational design, (2) to select the faculty, (3) to conduct the actual institute, and (4) to participate in evaluating the institute. To prepare a pool of educational directors to assume appropriate roles in the regional institute program, the national committee has given two invitational seminars—in 1960 in San Francisco and last November in Washington. We now have a small pool of potential educational directors who are well oriented to the philosophy and goals of this program. Despite heavy job responsibilities, each has agreed to accept, if possible, the responsibility of serving as an educational director, if invited by a region.

The success of a regional institute depends on two closely related components, good administrative planning and a sound, well-implemented educational design. The outstanding characteristics of the over-all program are these: (1) toward the goal of improving practice, the entire program was built on and constantly reflects practitioners' needs and interests; (2) it is a national program carried out by regional planning committees of practitioners who select the subjects for the institutes; choose the educational directors; approve the educational designs developed in consultation with the committees; and carry out systematic administrative plans which are not completed until reports are sent to the national committee, and the regional committees' responsibilities have been transferred to the next regional planning committees. One reason the program has grown constantly has been the competent staff assistance to the national committee in implementing the various stages of the program plan.

Another contribution of the program has been a series of monographs containing some of the outstanding papers presented at the various institutes. As funds become available we hope to publish more of these and thus make this material available to a much larger audience.

Other interesting institutes also offer refreshing experiences to practitioners to keep them up-to-date on new knowledge constantly becoming available in medical care, rehabilitation, and public health. The New York State Health Department, for example, has conducted three institutes in connection with schools of social work in Syracuse and Buffalo, and at Adelphi College on Long Island. These have enabled social workers in health, medical care, and rehabilitation, in family and children's agencies, and in services for the aging to keep up with new knowledge and program planning in the health field. Most of the agencies sending representatives to the institutes have provided field instruction for students in schools of social work. The summer institutes planned and coordinated by Dr. Alfred Katz at the University of California at Los Angeles are another type of program which offers new knowledge immediately applicable to a public health social worker's practice.

GRACE WHITE

Doubtlessly you are familiar with the regional institute programs of the Family Service Association of America and the Child Welfare League, and with the extensive institute programs offered each summer by schools of social work. Workshops and institutes can be excellent educational devices, but many do not meet the test of a true educational experience for the participants. Perhaps more attention is warranted to the safeguards needed to make an institute a substantial learning experience.

One way to prepare for practice in public health is to study in a school of public health. We regret that Elizabeth Rice cannot be with us at this seminar because the ice in Boston was too slippery and she is in a cast. Many of us think of Miss Rice as the dean of social work educators in schools of public health. She has been in the Harvard School of Public Health since 1948 and has kept abreast of all developments in schools of public health around the country since then. Social workers can now study in all schools of public health. We had hoped that Miss Rice could tell us about the various programs which are available, particularly the one at Harvard. She has sent a few copies of a report of a workshop of full-time faculty members from seven schools of public health. This workshop, in 1961, was on the social worker's total contribution to the school, including class teaching, field work or demonstration, research, and administrative responsibilities. The report contains information of particular interest to educators. Miss Rice has generously offered a copy to any who request it.

Although the programs for social work students in these schools vary widely, we can describe only one this evening. Sophia Bloom will discuss the combined program for social workers at the University of Pittsburgh.

SOPHIA BLOOM

In Pittsburgh we have a joint program between the Graduate School of Social Work and the Graduate School of Public Health to prepare social workers for the field of public health. We offer a curriculum for advanced social work students, composed of courses in both schools, with the objective of teaching the principles, knowledge, and methods of public health, and of deepening pertinent social work knowledge and understanding of principles.

Students are enrolled in the School of Public Health and at the end of the year receive the Master of Public Health degree. The committees on admissions of both schools determine eligibility, but final action rests with the School of Public Health, which actually admits the students. Approximately two-thirds of their work is taken in the School of Public Health, the remainder in the School of Social Work. (This varies somewhat; insofar as possible we try to meet individual interests.) The School of Public Health credits the social work courses toward the Master of Public Health degree. If the students want to go on for the doctorate in the School of Social Work they must be admitted to that school and must pass the qualifying examination. Once they are admitted they are credited by the School of Social Work with some courses taken in the School of Public Health.

We are preparing social workers for work in public health. One responsibility of the public health social worker is to give consultative service to professional people, other social workers, disciplines in the health department, other social and health agencies, various caretaker persons and groups in the community, and to laymen trying to develop programs concerned with health. Direct service is given sometimes to meet emergencies, by filling a gap, and sometimes for the purpose of demonstration of services. Public health social workers participate increasingly in community organization, which has always been an integral part of the public health social work job. They also participate in program planning and policy-making in health departments and cooperate with other planning bodies in health and social agencies. Social workers are specifically concerned with incorporating certain social work values and knowledge, and sometimes methods, into the over-all program planning and policy formulation of health departments. They participate in educational activities within and outside the health structure; they cooperate with and, hopefully, initiate research, although there is not as much research as we would like to see. Obviously, public health social workers have to be very nimble. They move very rapidly at times from one to another of these activities, programs, and services.

To prepare advanced students for social work practice in public health the following course of instruction has been designed. Social work students in the School of Public Health, like all other students, must take the core courses required of all degree candidates and considered essential to anyone in public health. They include courses in administration in public health practice, ecology (which we call man and his environments), biostatistics, and epidemiology.

We also have electives; they are indeed electives, but we admit we push them a little in certain directions. For example, we think it is important for social workers in public health to have some knowledge of the organization and distribution of medical services in this country. Aside from the fact that they need this to work in the field, medical care is one of the major social issues today. We also hope they will take courses in public health nursing, not only to learn about public health nursing and how nurses see their function in the field of public health, but to have some very real experiences in the interdisciplinary give-and-take which is charcteristic of the entire public health field. In the last two years students have shown a very strong interest in some of the social science courses in the School of Public Health. Some of these students majored in the social sciences in college or have taken social science courses in schools of social work, but they want these additional courses because they apply social science to public health.

We have conferences, or an informal seminar, throughout the year to get at some of the principles and issues in the administration of social work and public health. We also try to identify the public health principles they are learning. I must admit we have not proceeded very far with this because of the time lag in acquiring new material and integrating it with the knowledge the students already have. Often, it is not until later that they can tell us what they have learned and incorporated.

The School of Public Health also requires a small research project of all students to enable them to apply the principles of public health, research, epidemiology, and biostatistics to a problem; the problem chosen by social work students usually involves both health and social work. Some very interesting small studies have come from this attempt to apply public health methods to a social work problem.

To date, the courses taken in the Graduate School of Social Work have mainly been advanced courses in the behavioral sciences, community organization, research, and the principles of consultation, although we try to tailor the selection of social work courses to the student's interests. In addition to class work, we require two months of field work at the end of the academic year. The main purpose of this is to provide the students with an opportunity to observe and analyze public health and social work theory and principles, as they are applied in health departments in relation to policies and programs, interdisciplinary functioning, and relationships with other health and welfare agencies. The second purpose is to provide them with an opportunity, although limited, to function as a public health social worker under the supervision of a social worker. Their learning experiences are selected to enable them to carry social work responsibilities in a health department, to work with other disciplines, to observe the similarities and differences in values and methods of social work and public health, and to help them identify social work's concerns and contributions in public health.

Any school of social work embarking on this kind of program

will need to face the fact that some fine and fancy plans can be blown sky-high by mechanical difficulties in trying to integrate the class schedule of two schools which operate on different terms and semesters. When we look at the class schedules and ask the students what they want and try to think about what they may have, our problems begin. We have succeeded as well as we have only because of the great flexibility of the faculty of the School of Social Work, who have quite cheerfully pushed themselves and their classes around. Much of what we have been able to do in combining the curricula has resulted from this flexibility.

During the academic year and period of field work I have fairly frequent conferences with the students to try to identify, to the extent they are able, the principles underlying public health practice and public health social work practice and to relate them to the content of the academic year. We ask them to write an analysis or report of their experience at the end. These reports vary, but there is one comment they all make—that a health department is nothing like the books.

GRACE WHITE

Among the seminar participants are social work educators from three other schools of public health—William Hall, University of Minnesota; Alfred Katz, University of California, Los Angeles; and Elizabeth Watkins, University of Michigan. The discussion period (see pp. 199 ff.) may offer an opportunity to hear how their educational programs differ from that described by Miss Bloom.

We now come to the fifth member of the panel, Katherine Kendall. One way to get post-master's education for social work is to study in a school of social work that offers an advanced program. Dr. Kendall will tell us the nature and trend of these advanced programs in social work education.

KATHERINE A. KENDALL

Sixteen schools of social work in the United States and Canada offer doctoral programs. Eleven of these also offer third-year programs of one type or another, and two others—one in the United States and one in Canada—limit their post-master's offerings to a third-year program.

The first person to receive a doctorate in social work was graduated from Bryn Mawr College in 1920. Since then, there have been 276 graduates of doctoral programs in social work. This small number does not represent the considerable number of persons with doctoral degrees in a variety of fields who are or have been active in social work education or practice. A total of 164 students were enrolled in doctoral programs in November 1961. There appears to be a steadily growing interest in post-master's education and each year the number of applications increases.

Doctoral education in social work cannot easily be described in general terms. The programs have a much more individualized flavor than do master's programs; this is highly desirable since advanced education builds upon basic preparation for the profession and should take a variety of forms. The emphasis varies with the school. The School of Social Work at the University of Pittsburgh, as we learned, offers a joint program with the School of Public Health, in addition to its regular doctoral program. The School of Social Work at the University of Michigan has a joint program with several social science disciplines. Some schools have special programs for career teachers.

Nevertheless, there is also a measure of similarity in the programs because all share certain objectives for advanced education in social work. In general, they tend to emphasize scholarship and research and to focus on broad professional perspective and competence, interdisciplinary study, social policy, the development of theory, community planning, and administration. Teaching, research, and administration are most often mentioned as the professional activities for which these programs prepare students. Most offer courses related to the history, philosophy, structure, administration, and planning of social services. Some offer seminars or courses intended to increase skill or to deepen understanding of the theoretical base of social work practice. Courses and seminars on various aspects of the social sciences are also offered in a number of schools. Doctoral students frequently take courses in the social and behavioral sciences in other departments of the university, and follow programs or take courses in other professional schools. Content on social work education and learning theory would appear in a number of these programs. And all, of course, since this is doctoral study, prepare students for research. A dissertation that is expected to make a contribution to knowledge is also required.

Of the 164 students currently enrolled, 57 are in field instruction. The statistics do not indicate how many of the field placements are in doctoral programs; I would guess not too many. Field instruction is characteristic of the third-year program, but students placed for field instruction in research might be in doctoral programs as a research practicum is sometimes used as a learning experience for doctoral students.

Third-year programs may be an entity in themselves or, in some schools, may be taken as the first year of a doctoral program. The third-year programs, which almost always include field instruction, were inspired to a considerable extent by the National Institute of Mental Health, which made funds available in 1946 for advanced training in psychiatric social work. The University of Pennsylvania, however, had initiated a third-year program before that time. These programs generally aim at extending and deepening knowledge and skill in an area of professional practice. This is the major difference between the third-year and doctoral programs. The types of activities for which third-year programs prepare include supervision, teaching, advanced practice, and administration. Community welfare research has recently appeared as a new area for third-year study. The statistical tables reveal that a majority of the students are in casework field placements. The most frequently used fields of practice in 1961 emerged as psychiatric and medical, which includes public health.

Who are the students who enroll in doctoral programs and in advanced programs generally, and what are the requirements for admission? In respect to requirements, there is considerable uniformity. Most schools require a master's degree in social work and at least three years of successful experience. Some, however, are beginning to question the experience requirement and to suggest that it might be desirable to encourage promising students in master's degree programs to enroll for doctoral work.

Certain recent developments in advanced education may be particularly relevant to our concerns at this seminar. We have noted the considerable increase in the number interested in post-master's education. There has likewise been a steady increase in the number of schools offering post-master's education. This increase reflects, in part, the greater interest in research in social work. Certainly, the doctoral programs are producing many of the teachers and research people whom we so urgently need. The increase in doctoral programs is heartening in some respects, but, in other respects, it gives us pause. Doctoral education of high quality requires excellent resources in the school of social work and in the university in faculty, in educational resources, in library holdings, in finances, etc. Funds are needed for scholarships and research as well as for additional faculty with high qualifications. It would be unfortunate to have a sudden flourishing all over the country of advanced education unless sufficient resources are available.

In doctoral programs we see a good deal of interdisciplinary research. Three third-year programs in community welfare research have some relevance to our special interest at this seminar in community planning; they have been initiated by schools of social work at Bryn Mawr, the University of Pittsburgh, and the University of California at Berkeley. It is too early to evaluate them as yet as they have been in operation for little more than one year, but this development might well strengthen social work's contribution to research and community planning.

Finally, it gives me pleasure to announce that the Council on Social Work Education has received a grant from the National Institute of Mental Health for a five-year project in advanced education for social work. The project focuses on preparation for research and on the use of the social sciences and social scientists in post-master's programs, but the work that is now being done by an advisory committee touches on every aspect of advanced education. The committee, made up of representatives of all schools with post-master's programs, got under way in the fall of 1961 to map out an ambitious program of study and has already produced a wealth of information on current programs. In due course, the materials prepared by the Committee on Advanced Education in Social Work will be available.

From the work already under way, we know that post-master's programs in social work education are by no means free of problems. We know, too, that they represent a tremendous hope for the future and that the profession has every right to take pride in this new development.

GRACE WHITE

Our panelists have shown that schools, agencies, and the professional membership association are giving thought to post-master's educational opportunities. The emphasis on preparation for practice in the field of health is appropriate to this seminar, but all fields of social work practice face the same need for adequate and continuing preparation for competent practice in the field.

Three questions are posed for consideration by this audience as we turn to a general discussion period. Although many practitioners gain competence through experience, should social work give further thought to structuring ways to assure that increased competence does not depend wholly on the diligence and motivation of the individual? Have we been imaginative in devising programs, exploiting existing resources, and finding new resources for the continued education of graduates of schools of social work? In view of our intent—yea, our commitment to competent professional practice—does social work have enough formalized opportunities for continuing education, and is what we have all "good enough" to assure the attainment of widespread, competent practice, which is indeed professional practice?

SUMMARY OF DISCUSSIONS

PART I

Public Health and Social Work
Their Common Concerns and Vital Differences

PART II

Implications for the Social Work Curriculum

Public Health and Social Work
Their Common Concerns and Vital Differences

The aims of the first two group sessions were to clarify the basic concepts of public health and to find the common ground of public health and social work. The groups gave attention to similarities in goals and concepts, noted contrasts in methods, and by the end of the second session recognized many reciprocal concerns regarding social functioning, including health.

This summary shows the trends of the discussions in the five groups and includes excerpts from individual reports. The members of the groups did not always agree or reach conclusions. In discussing points of contrast, they expressed themselves as individuals rather than as representatives of a practice, either public health or social work. The recorders' reports reveal that the participants made considerable effort to get at pertinent underlying factors.

Clarification of Terms and Concepts

Public Health—Used as a noun, the word "public" refers in some situations to the people as a whole; in others, to a specific part of the community at large, such as the recipients of a service or the object of concern. Used as an adjective, as in public health, "public" again refers in some cases to the community, or to the object of concern of a tax-supported agency, or to a focus of activity. Used as an industrial term, "public health" parallels the term "social welfare." As an occupation, public health carries the leadership role of providing professional services in the field of health as social work carries the leadership role in the field of social welfare. "Public health" is most often used to designate the tax-supported bodies—federal, state, and local—which are legally responsible for the health of the people, but the term is frequently applied more broadly to any organized community effort toward health, whether under voluntary or public auspices or joint auspices.

Health—Health is conceived as a state of physical, mental, and social well-being. The public health concept of health is not merely the absence of disease or disability but rather a state in which the individual functions adequately with a sense of comfort. "Absolute health" is probably never achieved; hence, the concept of "functional health" is more meaningful. The concept of "adequacy" raised the question of what standards are to be used in evaluating the functioning of any individual in the multiple roles expected, even demanded, by society today. Public health has found the concept of adequate performance according to a person's roles and potentialities a useful yardstick in judging the state of his health.

Social functioning and social dysfunctioning—These concepts are to social work as "health" and "morbidity" are to public health: the primary focus of responsibility and indices. Participants agreed that social dysfunctioning or social disability is difficult to diagnose and measure.

Better methods have been devised for evaluating physical and mental diseases and disabilities that have yet been devised for social malfunctioning. Cultural factors and social pressures necessitate value judgments in measuring social functioning; elements of authority are involved; factors in prediction are not clear. One group questioned, inconclusively, whether social workers want to try to measure social disability since value judgments, authority, and prediction are involved. It was recognized that measurement of social disability is implied in the public health concept of health, which includes social well-being and adequate functioning. Public health has developed better devices than has social work for evaluating the success or failure of specific programs, but question was raised whether evaluating chronic disease programs will not pose difficulties similar to those now facing social work.

Environment—The public health concept of environment

stems from the basic idea that people adapt to a given environment in certain ways. Contrary to a general misconception, public health workers are interested in social as well as physical environment. True, their early achievements—in mosquito control, for example, and water purification—and their continuing struggle against such problems as air pollution stress their concern with deleterious physical factors in the environment. But the modern public health worker subscribes to the view that environment, physical and social, is indivisible. When he sees people reacting and adapting in various ways to a given environment, he makes a point of studying specific physical and social aspects of that environment to find out what is responsible for the variations.

The pioneers in social work, like the pioneers in public health, directed considerable effort against dangers in the physical environment. Lessened attention was observable in the forties and fifties. All recognized that social work practice today is primarily concerned with psycho-social aspects and that much of the achievement of social work is in effecting changes in the social environment of individuals. Examples were given of social work's present concern with physical conditions, notably housing, expressed by support of legislation for urban renewal. Public health manifests ever-increasing interest in social factors, notably in programs for the chronically ill. Overlapping concerns and responsibilities are shared with sociologists and anthropologists for expanding the body of knowledge about forces in the environment which affect physical and social well-being.

Summarizing, the participants emphasized that both public health and social work are concerned with environment; both undertake research as a means to an end, as a sound guide to action; and both take dynamic steps—by designing and administering a variety of programs—to improve the environment in ways that benefit people.

Community and "Population at risk"—Historically, the public health concept of the community is related to a geographic entity, but this limited concept no longer obtains. The term, now used flexibly, refers at times to a population within geographical boundaries but more often to high-risk populations regardless of local, state, or other political subdivisions. Other terms used are "vulnerable" and "high incidence," and for those exposed to infectious disease "contacts" and "suspects" are frequently used. For example, today a case of smallpox entering a country, having traveled through other countries, sets in motion an international chain of events to vaccinate all persons "at risk" (unvaccinated) along his path. Populations are not equally or similarly "at risk" for specific health problems; epidemiological studies have generally been able to identify those susceptible to the different categories of disease, or the "categorical community," as to age, race, sex, occupation, and the many other variables about which data have been collected and analyzed. It is now known that older white males, for example, are proportionately at greater risk of developing tuberculosis than children under age five and that a positive tuberculin reaction, formerly thought to be a protection against development of the disease, is more appropriately a danger signal.

A frequent comment is made to the effect that "the community is the patient" in public health. Some resource people resisted this theory, on the premise that the emphasis should be on health rather than illness. The significance of the idea is that a public health physician follows the same process with a community that clinical medicine follows with a patient—a process involving diagnosis (screening), treatment, rehabilitation, and supervision.

Mortality and morbidity rates and other parameters—In one group, a question was raised as to why public health emphasizes mortality rates more than morbidity. It was explained that mortality, the most valid health index available, establishes a frame of reference within which to study any relevant parameters or characteristic of a population. For example, study of the mortality rates for coronary heart disease showed that this disease was the leading cause of man-hours lost during working years. Through the statistical device of correcting the rates for the various age groups in the populations under study, the health officials could then direct attention to measures to lower the rates. Social work could utilize mortality rates in statistical score-keeping.

One participant suggested that morbidity rates-of-occurrence of a particular problem could serve social work. Measurements of growth and reduction of a particular social problem could be made. He urged social workers to be as adept as public health workers in collecting data on the kinds of problems that social work is most competent to handle. Furthermore, he said this could direct the overall efforts of the social work profession to social problems requiring priority attention. Others held that social work does not need some of the scientific tools found useful in public health; they recognized, however, that social work needs measuring instruments.

Sanction, mandate, and use of authority. Four of the five discussion groups analyzed the ways public health and social work differ with respect to sanction, mandate, and use of authority in solving problems. At first various participants, drawing sharp contrasts between the methods used by the two professions, made these points:

1. A high degree of authority and many sanctions are vested in the public health structure. The field of social work, on the other hand, is traditionally non-authoritarian.

2. The community sanctions public health programs more readily than social welfare programs because people want protection from contagion, and they realize protection is beyond the individual's control.

3. The community perceives threats to health more readily than it perceives threats to social welfare, which is a nebulous concept to many.

4. The public accepts the authority and methods of public health. Many people also accept the ends of social welfare but not the methods.

5. The centralized authority of local health departments enables them to make decisions and administer programs in a unified way. Social agencies as a group have no such unity.

6. Social work, although accountable to the community, defends the right of the individual to make his own decisions on matters affecting him.

Thus were lines drawn at the beginning. As this discussion wore on, however, some of these contrasts faded, and for a time it seemed to some that the two professions, facing similar problems at almost every turn, frequently reach similar solutions— that public health and social work are both alike and different in many vital ways.

As to mandate, public health departments are charged with the responsibility of protecting the health of the public; public health rules and regulations are official, legal devices, but public health officers invoke the law only when there is no alternative. The social worker's position is not wholly dissimilar. Although no one centralized authority has a general mandate to protect the social well-being of the public, there are laws, rules, and regulations that govern specific social situations: the adoption of children, for example, the licensing of some types of institutions, the protection of children, the support of relatives.

One participant pointed out that social workers see themselves as members of a nonauthoritarian profession, yet sometimes recognize they have a "moral responsibility" tantamount to a mandate. Occasionally they act without first seeking the community's approval; effecting the removal of a child from a destructive home, the discussant observed, is as authoritarian an act as many by public health officers.

Several groups noted that the present structure and functions of social agencies produce conflict in the use of authority. The agencies recognize social hazards and have a good deal of information (that is not, however, "scientifically documented") about the groups most endangered; but except for a few protective services they are not set up to take an authoritarian role or even to speak out against the hazards with a single authoritative voice.

A major concern of public health is to find improved ways of increasing compliance in the use of available services—poliomyelitis vaccines, for example—by the very populations for whose protection they are designed. A participant pointed out that in New York City only ten beds are reserved for tuberculosis patients hospitalized by legal action. Even this small number is of great concern to public health workers for it indicates some failure of the agency, and it means that the profession still has much to learn about motivating people to accept health services. Someone observed that the records of these patients might give clues as to why they rejected treatment and help determine the criteria for earlier intervention. Considerable research has been done on these questions and studies are continuing with a vast amount of data available but so for largely unused.

A public health official summed up his profession's approach this way: "Public health encounters many situations in which it moves cautiously and seeks community cooperation. First we find out who is responsible for making decisions and what changes are needed. Although a great many approaches are possible, the status, authority, even the personality of the person (or agency) who decides the timing, nature, and method of change inevitably affect its result. If possible, the community is motivated to spearhead the activities which will bring about change."

How the public health officer sees himself and his role is a crucial point in his use of authority. His willingness to use his legal mandate is often proportionate to his estimate of the community's readiness to accept change, and to accept his function in bringing about change. Although the public wants protection from infection, and sanctions many measures designed to provide that protection, it may not accept *every* measure proposed by the public health officer. Like the social worker, then, he sometimes finds himself trying to protect a public which accepts the ends but will not support the means.

Many beneficial changes in the pattern of living can be made only if the patient himself wants to make them and recognizes the expertness of the person who is trying to help him. In these respects, the experiences of social workers and public health personnel are similar; both see that motivation is necessary. A public health participant stated that the principle of self-determination is no less important in public health than in social work; but in situations hazardous to the community, public health must weigh the community's need for protection against the preferences of the individual.

A ready method of resolving social work's conflict over the use of authority was not found by any group. Indeed, concluding statements simply reiterated the view that social work, caught between its knowledge of social hazards and its commitment to self-determination, needs to be more flexible in its attitude toward the use of legal authority as a means of protecting the community. Before moving on to the next topic, however, all groups agreed that public health and social work differ less with respect to sanction, mandate, and use of authority than most participants had thought when the discussion started.

Prevention—One group addressed itself to a set of questions which included the following:

1. How are primary and secondary prevention carried on by social work as contrasted with the field of public health?

2. Can social work identify the agency (mosquito), the host (victim), and the environment (swamp) in social problems? If they can, do they then contribute to primary prevention? If they cannot, are they restricted, at this time, to secondary prevention?

3. Are social workers on the same level of operation in their work as public health workers are regarding chronic diseases, i.e., having to base action on tentative assumptions regarding etiology?

4. Can social workers engage in "early detection" of individual malfunctioning as public health workers do, for example, of diabetes and glaucoma?

5. Can social workers develop some screening methods for early detection of groups in the population who are subjected to special stress in their social functioning, and devise a program which will reach vulnerable populations before problems become overwhelming—for example, school dropouts, unmarried mothers, juvenile delinquents, parents with handicapped children, mothers of premature babies, young couples in the early years of marriage and expectant mothers? What early treatment can be offered to prevent the onset of acute social dysfunctioning which otherwise may become chronic?

In contrast to public health, social work seems to emphasize the individual as an entity, not as a member of a family, in finding solutions to the presenting problem. The concept of entity was introduced in one discussion group as the focus for beginning to identify a particular segment of society which is considered a "population at risk." This led to discussion of the continuum of prevention—case-finding—treatment—rehabilitation, with intervention possible at any point along the way. However, there seemed general agreement that intervention should take place at the earliest possible moment and that social work has tended to focus on rehabilitation, public health on prevention. There was general recognition that social work, in its aim to restore people to healthy functioning, has made substantial contribution to secondary prevention.

Social work's lack of data was cited repeatedly, and numerous ways social workers might collect information on essential clues to primary prevention were suggested. In public health, incomplete information about people with illness is not permitted to deter advancement in preventive efforts.

A situation was considered relative to intervention measures that might be used. John Brown, male Negro, plans to leave school and work in a bowling alley. The family income is borderline; the boy's I.Q. is 100. Most of the group agreed that a social problem, a mental health problem and an educational problem is suggested. In a well ordered universe, timely intervention may help prevent the development of incipient problems. But who would intervene and how? These questions were discussed from the point of view of John Brown, his family, and the community. Where would social work intervene in this instance to prevent the development of problems: When the family applied for relief? Through a social worker in the school? In the neighborhood house or earlier in school with the first symptoms of poor attendance? Would the public health nurse in the school be the first person, other than the teacher, likely to learn that trouble was brewing? A good deal is known about school dropouts, one discussant pointed out, but information has not been adequately structured into preventive approaches.

Two ways to move ahead were suggested: One would be to search case records for patterns of social phenomena and for clues to new approaches which could be tested. At any stage of the continuum of care, the factors contributing to deterioration or to improvement can be studied. The earlier in the continuum these factors are identified, the greater likelihood of discovering incipient manifestations of dysfunctioning and the more numerous the possibilities of early intervention. Public health strives continually to intervene at the point of primary prevention, but when the extent of knowledge does not permit this, intervention is sometimes at the point of service. It was agreed that no contradiction exists between providing both prevention and service.

Another way of moving ahead would be to look at both ends of the continuum of life—the prenatal period and old age —from the standpoint of preventive approaches. Prenatal care reduces the rate of abnormal births—this is primary prevention with which social workers can assist; as they visit homes and consult with women who are pregnant they can encourage them to obtain prenatal care. They also know how to evaluate the total situation, (including any problems to be solved before prenatal care is secured) and to deploy community resources. After the baby's birth, what can social workers do to prevent social dysfunctioning? What knowledge can they contribute about physical illness and social functioning of children? What would be required in program-building for primary prevention at this stage of life?

The aged were cited as an example of a subpopulation which often constitutes a problem in the social structure of the community. This problem has many facets: the disengagement of older persons from productivity for retirement; their need for medical care, home care, housing, and income—studies of which could influence the development of procedures leading to change in attitudes and eventual change in social policy. A public health approach to the aged involves awareness of the multiplicity of concerns that must be attacked, noting clusterings in subgroups, priorities that must be established. Care must be exercised that age in itself not automatically be considered a problem, but rather that note is taken of signposts pointing to any difficulties associated with this process. Social work could concern itself with the occurrence of symptoms of aging rather than arbitrarily establishing an age span, as from 60 to 80 years, as the universe for preventive approaches.

Another possibility for social work, similar to a procedure used in public health, would be to consider the total needs of populations within small geographical units instead of categorizing people according to the kinds of health and social welfare problems they have. Social workers would then be able to concentrate, as settlement workers do, on the people in the neighborhood as a whole, and observe the total impact of social, emotional, and health problems. Reference was made to a project in one state where the county guidance clinic took responsibility for the people in the area covered. This plan would contribute to early case-finding, and would structure social welfare services to the needs of people vulnerable to certain stresses and impositions. The integration of services would permit intervention at any point from prevention to control, and would make information and referral services part of the community, a friendly neighborhood service.

During the discussions, questions of ethics arose with regard to self-determination and prediction (or the "labeling" of people as risks). The aggressive implications in the term "intervention" were also bothersome to some participants. If prevention is achieved by identifying people who will probably develop problems, is it then implied that problems will arise under certain conditions? Does the labeling of certain people "predestine" them to develop problems? Social workers believe that people can and do change; if "reaching out" does or should follow prediction, then the "labeling" has destined which persons shall be offered treatment for problems which are now only potential.

A contrast was drawn between the ability of physicians and social workers to prevent on the basis of prediction. If certain types of physical or emotional disability are diagnosed by a physician, a man in the armed forces may not be sent overseas. This is a preventive measure based on the physician's ability to predict. A social worker may be able to predict that sending a man overseas, out of touch with his family, may so upset his wife and children that the children become delinquents. Social workers are often not in a position to *prevent* social dysfunctioning with a diagnosis of *social disability*—even though they may foresee the risks they are often unable to prevent many destructive or threatening things that happen to people. Unable to effect primary prevention, they have to resort to secondary prevention, and in this case, work with the family. Most participants seemed to agree that:

1. Social workers can identify the populations at risk but have not developed the tools to categorize or classify them.

2. Social workers may attempt to intervene at times that prove to be neither effective nor appropriate. With more experience they will discover an optimum opportunity for intervention as they observe and record the processes, the successes, and the failures.

3. Social functioning and social dysfunctioning could be indices for social work which might compare with health and morbidity as indices for public health.

4. Social work needs to be aware of and characterize subgroups in the population for whom programs should be developed to help in the solution of social problems.

5. Social work should pool what is known and use it.

6. Continuity of care for any population at risk is an essential part of community services.

EPIDEMIOLOGICAL METHODS

The groups discussed the potentials for use of epidemiological concepts and methods in social work practice. A major question was whether the continuum of public health, with health and disease as the endpoints, has a parallel in social work, which is concerned about social functioning and dysfunctioning. The groups handled the topic in diverse ways.

One group re-examined the epidemiological methods used in public health against an outline prepared by Arnold Gurin listing four types of research in social work:

1. *Studies and services.* These studies, essential to sound administration, involve the collection of data on the volume

and the cost of services, and sometimes include information on the characteristics of those served. Because they
show trends, they are helpful in projecting future needs
in money and manpower.

2. *Estimates of need.* This type of research is carried on by
Councils of Social Agencies and other planning bodies
more often than by single agencies. A device known as
the Social Breakdown Index has fallen into disuse, indicating that social work has not found a useful way of
relating social problems to the planning of services. Estimates of need are based primarily upon requests for
specific services.

3. *Studies of the characteristics of clients.* This research is
analogous to retrospective epidemiological studies in
which the investigator searches backward from the effects of a problem—for example, delinquency, long-term
dependency, or chronic illness—for clues to its causes.

4. *Evaluative research.* In evaluative research, the investigator attempts to measure the effectiveness of a social
service; some such studies, however, have evaluated
aspects of professional competence, such as the reliability of social workers' judgments.

Several major evaluative projects are under way, among them
the development of the movement scale and the studies of motivation—capacity—opportunity being done by a university. Others
have dealt with the question of whether clients continue in treatment; some have been concerned with those characteristics of
clients which seem to be related to their motivation to continue in
treatment, others with the way agencies handle clients. A major
example of a new kind of evaluative research is the prospective
study of Meyer and Borgatta, who are comparing the effects of
treatment on high school girls judged as predelinquent with a
control group. By manipulating the caseloads and training programs in social agencies, other investigators have attempted to
measure the effect of certain administrative techniques on professional performance.

Mr. Gurin pointed out that all four types of research in

social work are based on the actual services rendered by social agencies—a major difference between epidemiological research in public health and research in social work as it has developed to date. Epidemiological research analyzes problems, then looks for various methods of attack. Social work studies methods, tending primarily to ask why people need social services and how effective these services are in helping them solve their problems. In practice, however, social workers make epidemiological decisions when they say, for example, that social casework is not an appropriate method of treating children with character disorders. Such decisions should be examined scientifically, starting with the problem rather than with the service. Newer approaches in practice, such as aggressive casework and the multiproblem studies of Community Research Associates, are introducing more flexibility in social work research. One of the fruits of this seminar may be to accelerate this trend in both social work practice and research.

A research consultant for one group pointed out that the several kinds of research studies serve various purposes, but all derive from well-constructed hypotheses and that, before arriving at hypotheses, social work will have to define the variables in the problems to be studied. Although it may be unfair to expect most social workers to design and carry out sophisticated research projects, they should be expected to raise questions that aid in formulating hypotheses to be tested. Their perceptivity, professional curiosity, and skilled observations of "problems in action" should assure their cooperation to this extent, regardless of limited technical competence.

Although the ultimate goal of public health is the prevention of socio-economic loss caused by disease, the intermediate goal may be the reduction of mortality. In programing, therefore, the health officer sometimes has to rely on his judgment in handling a problem, although he might prefer to depend on the objective findings of a well-designed research study.

Dr. Cassel's paper, a participant recalled, emphasized that research by public health workers has shown the significance of environmental factors in human problems; when social workers study the influence of human factors in a group of cases and compare them to a control group they are using the epidemiological method. Social work wants the answers to various problems, but does not take the necessary preliminary steps before drawing conclusions on which the solutions will ultimately depend. Public health, on the other hand, takes the time to *describe* a phenomenon before trying to analyze its effects.

Another participant stressed that a profession gains stature as it adds to the store of knowledge and raises the level of professional practice by applying the findings of research. Experimentation, a vital part of professional responsibility, cannot be delayed until all the answers are known, for experimentation is itself a process of finding answers. Social work succeeds in helping some people, fails to help others; research is the process of finding out why.

Once again some in the group mentioned social work's stress on "the principle of uniquity" and the profession's evident inability to see past the uniqueness of the individual to the characteristics and problems common to many. One participant proposed that an agency handling adoptions place half the children in homes selected at random, the other half in homes selected by the criteria now used. A study of the results might enable social workers to make some generalizations about adoptions which they cannot perceive so long as they view each baby and each adoptive home as wholly different from every other.

A major question was whether social workers should study the factors which contribute to a social problem or concentrate instead on those which influence recovery, control, and secondary prevention. In the course of the discussion, the group directed its attention to mental illness, and agreed that the responsibility for determining its *causes* lies with psychiatry; social work must concern itself with the *effects* of mental illness on the patient and his family. Tuberculosis was another example of a health problem which affects the family, but whether the etiology constitutes a social problem was a moot question. A really complicated social problem—the prevention of narcotics addiction, for example—challenges professional skill in identifying the research question; that is, what kinds of investigations should be made and which of them can social work or public health appropriately and competently undertake? Whatever the answer to these questions, whatever the scope and nature of the investigations, they will need to rely heavily on social work's penetrating insights into the individual and his social groups.

The groups brought out the crucial differences between the utilization of knowledge and resources in the community for research on recovery, which is closely tied to clinical practice, and research on etiology. An epidemiological study of families receiving aid to dependent children could show, for example, why some no longer need public assistance and why others remain dependent. In general, participants expressed the hope that social work would broaden the scope of its investigations beyond the limits of clinical practice. Public health looks to social work for information on well people; should social work undertake studies which compare populations composed of both the socially adequate and the socially inadequate?

Several groups turned their attention to the theory of multicausation. A consultant on research cautioned against misuse of this theory on the grounds that improperly manipulated variables and misinterpreted findings could paralyze social work and inhibit the profession in its attempts to take preventive action.

This raised three other questions: What mechanisms enable social work to classify, generalize, and evaluate social problems and methods? Can other disciplines help social work refine its research methodology? Just how well equipped and skilled are social workers for solid, substantial research? Pursuing the idea that social work ought to move out into the community for extensive epidemiological data, a participant pointed to the specialized knowledge of people and their problems that is acquired by teachers, ministers, businessmen, bankers, grocers, druggists, bartenders, law enforcement officers. This information, rarely sought by social workers, would broaden social work's perspective and enrich its generalizations.

Mention was made that social work failed to put to work all the knowledge gained from research, either in fortifying theory or in improving practice. The fault, someone pointed out, may lie with the agencies, for they have more to say about who is served, and when, and under what conditions than do other members of the social work profession. One viewpoint expressed was that if the boards and staffs of the agencies refuse to investigate why their services are not used, or not used more effectively, a "third force" should intervene and help them.

A single agency cannot find the answer to a complex problem—the causes of dependency, for example—but there are ways of breaking it down, attacking it piecemeal, and in time obtaining some useful answers to this broad question. One agency might start by comparing groups of low-income families—samples, within the limits of statistical probability, of all low-income families in the United States. Another might start by analyzing census data. Other ways of escaping the limitations of a single agency would be to study a sample of the caseloads of several agencies or to accumulate information from repeated studies. All are acceptable practices in epidemiology.

When a social agency studies only one group—its clients—it introduces a bias. For instance, in the United States toxemia of pregnancy has been characterized as a disease of poverty and associated with inadequate prenatal care, but other countries have not found this to be the case. As an example of the influence of bias, assume a community with 1,000 white and 1,000 Negro pregnant women. Assume also that 10% of each group are toxemic and that 90% of all toxemia patients are hospitalized, 90% of the white women and 60% of the Negro women go to the hospital for delivery of their babies.

	PREGNANT HOSPITALIZED PATIENTS					
	900 White Women			*600 Negro Women*		
	Not			Not		
	Toxemic	Toxemic	Rate	Toxemic	Toxemic	Rate
Assumption	810	90	10	540	60	10
Findings	801	99	12	444	96	18

Instead of a 10% rate for each group, the findings show that 12% of the white women and 18% of the Negro women are toxemic. Further studies by this hospital and/or other hospitals of the rate of toxemia in pregnant hospitalized patients of both races would be necessary for comparison.

A number of relatively good sampling techniques—one is area sampling—could be used by social workers in designing studies that would permit generalizations. Polansky's *Social Work Research*[1] deals with many of these matters, a discussant pointed out. As an example of the kind of information that can be obtained by comparing sample groups, a participant described a study of group cohesiveness in relation to health and disease. Investigators comparing matched groups of industrial employees who worked on the same shift with the same people every day with matched groups on rotating shifts found that serum cholesterol was four times higher in the groups on rotating shifts than in the groups working the same shift every day. Other participants pointed to the need for replication of small studies, and said this can be done only if information about them is available. Social workers have tended to resist "repeating" studies, either in the same locale or in another.

The importance of disseminating the results of research in social work was expressed in many ways. Some thought there was a paucity of research, others that research is going on but not being reported, and still others that much has been done and reported but not reviewed or applied. Most held that unless some means are found for sharing and pooling information for retesting and supplementing findings, progress in social work research will be slow indeed. Among the recommendations were these:

1. A national center should be established where epidemiological studies could be reported. The National Social Welfare Assembly is considering this proposal.

2. "Scientific sessions" at conferences and meetings would provide opportunities for the exchange of information on research in progress and on the findings of completed studies.

3. Information should cross disciplinary as well as program lines, enabling several fields to use one another's findings.

---

[1] Norman A. Polansky, ed. *Social Work Research*. Chicago: University of Chicago Press, 1960. 306 pp.

Research should not have to be duplicated for lack of information about what has already been done.

RECIPROCAL CONCERNS AND METHODS OF APPROACH

All groups reported consensus that health and adequate functioning of people are shared goals, that both fields are concerned about the prevention of disease and social dysfunctioning, and that recognition of their shared values makes more fruitful the examination of respective methods to attain mutual goals. Although each field has its area of responsibility, both are viewed as social institutions dedicated to the promotion of physical, mental, and social well-being.

The groups identified these mutual components:

1. Both public health and social work have developed from similar concern about the problems of human deprivation and disease.
2. Both are responsible to the public.
3. Both have an impact on the community by providing a network of services and are seen by the community as intervening agents.
4. Both have a value system based on the principle of self-determination and self-improvement by the recipients of services.
5. Both stress the concept of prevention, attempt to "start where the client is," and are reluctant to be authoritarian.
6. Both believe in multi-causation of problems and emphasize scientific methods in solving these problems, but both may intercede before all causes are known.
7. Both use an interdisciplinary approach to problems.
8. Both fields are giving attention to the following:
   a. more adequate means by which problems and persons with problems can be identified and the persons reached before they are in trouble;
   b. prevention of socio-economic loss to the community,

with concern for such loss to *each person* in society
as well as to society in toto;

c. discovery of problems "under the umbrella" and the
factors which contribute to their occurrence and
which in themselves constitute potential problems;

d. helping people use the services available—holding the
conviction that this is a professional responsibility;

e. appropriate timing of services;

f. relating intervention to prevention, both primary and
secondary (i.e., in relation to the occurrence, recurrence, or reduction of resulting disability);

g. identifying factors in the community which produce
or ameliorate problems;

h. moving into new services and ways or working while
holding on to ways found to be effective;

i. finding ways in which public health and social work
can work together effectively.

Distinctive Approaches Used in Each Field

The groups recognized that differences too are vital and that
an understanding of these is as important as recognition of what
is held in common. Distinctions were made of four types, with
varying amounts of elaboration.

Community versus individual approach. The public health
approach is to the total community; public health deals with all
strata in the community. The traditional social work approach is
to individuals who come to agencies seeking help with their
problems or those referred; social work deals primarily with the
disadvantaged and the socially less acceptable.

Bases for programing. In public health, epidemiological
studies are the basis for programing as well as for ascertaining
etiology of health problems. The classical approach was described
as follows: when a health department becomes aware of a potential problem, it considers the extent of the problem; what can
be learned about the incidence and prevalence of the disease, its
natural history, where it occurs, what populations are the high
risk groups, what social, environmental, and medical factors are
associated with contracting the disease; what are the treatment

approaches when the disease occurs. The control program is based on this knowledge. Through a continual analytic process, it learns when and how intervention can be most effective, obtains leads to prediction, and establishes priorities for services.

Social work has relied heavily on case studies as the source of data. Study of total individual cases makes a contribution that cannot be made by studying selected common elements in the situations of groups of individuals. However, social work has been able to make only limited generalizations from such case studies. Social work research has been impoverished by such concentration. In their concern with diagnosis and treatment, social workers have lagged in quantifying data. Although social work is aware that all unmarried mothers, for example, are not alike and cannot be treated alike, it must recognize that some subgroups can be identified which have some similar characteristics. The knowledge and values, attitudes, and skills which are used in the study and treatment of individuals is transferable to study of communities. The taking of steps "to get the big picture" results from conviction that prevention rests heavily upon methods other than that of treating the individual.

Flexibility in programs. Public health work radiates from a central established auspice; public health has freedom to shift its priority of attention from one method to another and from one program to another. Social work is fragmented and is limited by the functions of the various agencies in which it exists; having a variety of auspices and sources of support, it has less flexibility.

Public health involves the efforts of many voluntary and private associations and agencies, of physician and others in private practice, of hospitals and professional schools. A basic philosophy and long-established methods of operating are the determinants of the program rather than the auspices. Examples were given of stages of development of two public health programs. Toward the goal of reducing the recurrence of congestive heart failure in individuals, efforts were made to increase the availability and utilization of new knowledge by the professional persons providing medical treatment. Many forms of interpretation were given in professional literature, at meetings and conferences, and particularly in medical and nursing schools. Education was the primary method used. The steps in the development of an obesity control program were: a fact book was developed; attitudinal studies were next carried out; then an epidemiological survey, followed currently by consideration of a plan for a broad attack upon the problem. The control program which evolves may well involve the use of a wide variety of resources, including those for mental health.

Public health tries new programs and sometimes uses a variety of approaches to the same problem until an effective method is found. Public health sometimes tries out experimental methods with specific questions that are believed to have significance in trying to find the answers to the bigger questions. The questions being investigated may be done in "small bits," with relatively small groups, provided the projects are soundly conceived and the hypotheses to be tested are clear.

In the discussion of social work, relative to flexibility of program, searching questions were asked. An underlying rigidity seems to prevent social workers from being ready to expand their functions and alter ways of working. Does this rigidity produce the inflexibility of agency structure or does the agency structure cause the rigidity? Is a realignment of agencies and services indicated, such as would place clinical services under one auspice and "reaching out" services under another? Although social work finds it difficult to withhold services from a control group, it may be necessary to embark on research that requires withholding services from control groups or offering different services to control groups. Partializing the caseload and treating the two parts differently would throw some light on two treatment methods.

Trends in reverse. A current trend in public health is increasing attention to individual behavior. Social work is showing movement toward focus on problems existing in the community. Public health remains largely problem-focused and social work remains dominantly individual-focused. Public health has always recognized that any constellation of factors is unique for any individual. For purposes of identifying the significance of one factor, consideration of the constellation of factors is often submerged. As public health moves further into the study of chronic diseases and of their control, it is encountering difficulties in identifying contributing causes, similar to those of social work in analyzing social problems. Social work is recognizing to a greater extent that it needs to submerge consideration of the constellation of factors in one individual in order to increase its understanding of the significance of selected factors in a number of individuals. These movements are significant with reference to efforts of these two fields to work together.

Interdisciplinary Cooperation

The presence in each group of physicians, nurses, social scientists, and social work practitioners and educators brought a variety of points of view into the discussions. The participants recognized that each discipline could learn much from the other through informal discussion and working together as well as in formal educational programs. Threaded through the group discussions, references were made to what public health and social work could learn from each other. In various contexts, bodies of knowledge and skills were identified that one field has developed highly and that could supplement the knowledge and skills of the other field.

Public health has developed highly and could share with social work the following:

1. collection, quantification, and classification of data;
2. handling of multiple factors in epidemiological studies;
3. methods of studying the natural history of disease;
4. determination of high risk groups;
5. assessing the possibilities for preventive measures at the primary as well as secondary levels;
6. flexible use of authority and legal powers.

Social work has developed highly and could share with public health the following:

1. understanding of and ability to work with persons who are the recipients of services, singly or in groups;
2. the relationship of the individual to his environment;
3. the process of making a full case study;
4. permission of self-determination and self-involvement in a non-authoritative climate;

5. mobilization and use of community resources, based on evaluation of the situation;
6. structuring of interagency relationships and modes of collaboration.

Some hindrances to good working relationships were also noted. Comment was made that social workers often feel that they have exclusive rights to the use of relationships as a tool in treatment although other professionals also use this tool. Some social workers are said to be too status and agency conscious. The teamwork approach, which public health has so well demonstrated, will be promoted by increasing an ability to accept and rely on other professionals in carrying out services. In devising the best community services, one must ask, "To which professional person does the family ordinarily look in time of crises?" In mental health, as well as other public health programs —because of the great shortage of professional personnel—the question is often raised, "What are the needs and who (of whatever profession) is there best able to serve them?"

The public health nurse is seen as the public health agent by every community in the country. In many instances, registered nurses, without public health nursing education, are exposed to a rather poor level of social welfare. Because the delineation of the role between public health and social work is often unclear, the plea was made that social work and public health nursing students should work together more, thus reinforcing mutual interdisciplinary training.

Some discrepancies were noted in the overtures made by each field. Social workers are being increasingly employed in health departments and are often used as consultants to public health nurses, but seldom are public health nurses used as consultants to family, children's, and public welfare agencies. It was suggested that the network of public welfare programs should consider bringing health personnel into their employ. A trend was noted toward public health and public welfare moving closer together. One of the public health members of the group questioned how much effort public health has made toward helping the solution of social problems. It was agreed that neither field is making the contribution to the other that it might.

Implications for the Social Work Curriculum

Two group sessions were devoted to consideration of the applicability and potential contribution of public health concepts to social work education. The goals for these discussions in six groups were to determine what of the content, method, and philosophy from public health is useful for social work and should be included in the master's curriculum; to anticipate what curriculum revisions, if any, or difficulties would be involved in adding content that was deemed valuable; and to decide what content was of an advanced nature and more appropriate for the doctoral program.

The seminar participants were permitted election of groups giving concentrated attention to one of four broad subjects which, among others, are emphasized in social work education: programing and planning for the provision of services; services to individuals in families and groups; human potentials and limitations; research with particular reference to epidemiology. Although these subjects are highly suggestive of the major sequences in the social work curriculum, the groups were asked not to limit their attention to any one sequence.

Summaries of the discussions showed that, although each group gave attention to a particular subject, it also reviewed some basic problems in social work education. Further clarification of concepts was often necessary, particularly those which have distinctive meanings to public health and to social work. All groups gave primary attention to ways of enriching the curriculum and enlarging the students' point of view by broader use of exciting new material.

The following summary of reports from all groups shows

six strands of thought that interwove the discussion of specific subject matter in the curriculum:

1. The relevancy of public health content to social work education.
2. The need to develop the inquiring mind—interest in and capacity to learn what lies underneath.
3. The need for a two-dimensional point of view—a composite of knowledge, skill, and concern for the individual and the community.
4. The need for compatibility in field and class learning experiences.
5. The need for compatibility of curriculum offerings with the needs in practice.
6. The need for preparing for tomorrow's practice.

The relevancy of public health content to social work education

There was consensus that certain public health principles might well be included in the basic social work curriculum but it was pointed out that these concepts, like those from other fields, would have to be integrated into social work theory rather than imposed *in toto*. Experience has shown that the curriculum can be enriched by working new ideas and material into existing courses. This has been demonstrated in many schools in the incorporation of content on aging, mental retardation and rehabilitation. Some public health related concepts are already included in almost all of the curricula; the discussion groups considered their focus to be appropriately upon the possibilities for integrating additional relevant material as will provide enrichment. An acceptance of the mutuality of health and social welfare concerns and a recognition of common goals (if not always common methods) would be a step in that direction.

One group summarized the major contributions to an enriched curriculum that may be expected from the use of public health concepts and materials as follows:

The *attitude and approach* implicit in epidemiology, prevention, and community planning for health will be major influences in broadening the base for social work practice.

Public health materials will usefully illustrate concepts now being taught. Students will find stimulation in selected public health studies, such as those described by Dr. Cassel.

More opportunities for *field placements* in public health will arise as public programs of medical care develop. A shift toward community-centered, less hospital-based care and the increasing community support of rehabilitation and after-care programs, and of ways to prevent the incidence of illness, will augment the social work role in the public health program.

Broader knowledge and appreciation of related disciplines will be gained by students through such content as:

1. interdisciplinary relationships and collaboration;
2. information about operation of the public health system similar to the knowledge of the public welfare system;
3. the roles of different public health workers and the common goals they share with social work;
4. awareness of the vital public issues in health as well as those in social welfare.

Two valid approaches to incorporating the new material were seen: (a) by stimulating the student to look at people and their problems in new ways—to add a new dimension, the epidemiological point of view, to present thinking; (b) by enriching the present curriculum content with more material from public health, particularly the following: prevention, need (differentiated from problem), and criteria for intervention to prevent individual need from becoming a problem for the community, "effective demand" as presented in Dr. Kandle's paper, commitment to the continuous evaluation of programs, "developmental provision" as discussed in Professor Kahn's paper, and collaboration with other professions.

Several groups discussed the educational levels at which public health content might be introduced. A broad underpinning in the undergraduate years is essential if social workers are to have a breadth of view. The tightening up of the undergraduate curriculum generally was cited; master's programs could expect a better trained student body with successive collegiate generations. One school which has had a heavy concentration of research content in its undergraduate curriculum has witnessed a different receptivity to research in the graduate curriculum and an acceleration of learning for students who have this background. An oft repeated question arose: Can the curriculum differentiate students who come with specific knowledge from the undergraduate courses? It would be possible to deal more sharply and directly with social work material in the first year if the student had more of the background knowledge upon entering the course. One participant suggested that perhaps the essential message of the Curriculum Study, not yet grasped by the field, was that the graduate curriculum should be dealing with professional knowledge for professional performance. Devices may be found for establishing prerequisites or for moving ahead faster those students who come with preliminary knowledge. Another point of view was that the first year of the graduate curriculum as currently planned need not be repetitive of undergraduate work but should deal with the same material in a way that makes different demands upon the student's use of the knowledge.

Concern was expressed that an attempt might be made to inject too much new content from sources such as public health into the social work curriculum at the master's level. It was questioned whether students could integrate these multiple approaches; and there was disagreement on this point. Some participants expressed the opinion that the student must begin from his entrance into professional education to develop an attitude of broad concern, an awareness of the community as well as the individual, even if he had only limited immediate opportunity to translate some of this knowledge into practice. Also expressed was the idea that if social work is to be comparable with other professions alongside which it works, and to meet them on an equal level of competence, more than the master's program is necessary and an internship program will eventually be required.

Although there was consensus that the social work curriculum on the master's level could be enriched by public health content, the groups did not consider this an easy task, involving as it did convincing other members of the faculty. This would require a philosophical reorientation on the part of schools of social work to the realization that public health and social work have many more common denominators than were recognized prior to the seminar.

Spirit of inquiry

Some participants expressed the view that something seems to occur in social work training which stifles creativity and curiosity in too many students. What that "something" is no one seemed sure. There was consensus that an inquiring mind and interest in the scientific method are essential for professional growth and that schools of social work should nurture these qualities in students.

Some suggestions were made of ways that schools and agencies might stimulate a spirit of inquiry in students. Schools must be aware of the barriers to epidemiological thinking that now exist in many social agencies, and bear them in mind in preparing new social workers. It was recognized that it is desirable to create in both the school and field work agency a climate in which the student feels free to question. He will then be more likely to follow through on his impressions about unmet needs; often the initial formulation of an hypothesis used in research is purely intuitive. Schools should help students develop more curiosity about research and a clear view of the scope and purpose of any research project. Beginning with a course on research in the first semester, the "research attitude" should permeate the curriculum. At every turn the faculty should encourage students to observe facts, follow hunches and clues, and trust their intuitive thinking as they grow more aware of the wider implications of individual problems. Educators can sensitize students to the vast number of community surveys lying dormant and encourage them to inquire: "If the citizens committee made 25 concrete proposals for action ten years ago, why has none been acted on?" Data in the literature can be culled, analyzed, and appropriately applied in new or improved services.

In courses on health and disease, the faculty, whose own attitudes toward epidemiology are likely to color those of their students, can show how to use the findings of research to see the picture as a whole. A participant mentioned that they must make sure, however, that they have developed an underpinning of fact for social work's key theories, for in exposing students to "the big picture" they may also expose them to facts that challenge social work's cherished beliefs. Commenting on this, a participant pointed out that "first-year students enter our schools ready to question current social policies and help people solve problems—and then we hit them over the head with 'self-determination.' " A study of one first-year class disclosed that as undergraduates, these students had avoided science courses; they had seen themselves as wanting to help people, not to be scientists. During their first semester in the school of social work, therefore, the faculty's task was to give them a view of themselves as learners in a profession that is both an art and a science.

If educators agree that the schools are trying to develop practitioners with inquiring minds who can look beyond specific cases to their broader implications, all the faculty will need to help students learn to be observant, skeptical, and curious. As one participant put it, a student should be taught to notice "when the same thing happens in sixteen cases," to ask why it happens, and to try to find an answer in the literature of the field. To cultivate this kind of careful observation, one school instituted a new system for recording social data observed in a given geographic area, thus providing students with an overview of human phenomena in a specific population.

Neither all physicians nor all social work practictioners engage in research, but to become skilled practitioners all must become skilled observers, with keen curiosity, who use scientific methods purposefully: to find answers to their questions.

Two-dimensional view

In the conviction that one responsibility of schools of social work is to guide students in their search for knowledge and skills useful in helping both the individual and the community, participants raised two general questions: in teaching, to what extent do we go beyond the easy generalization that the nature of the community affects the social health and functioning of the individuals who live there? Is enough knowledge available about the specific points at which the social system affects the functioning of the individual to enable us to systematize our teaching of this material? The discussants did not directly answer these questions, but they brought out pertinent points.

The students' success in learning to look beyond the individual case to others with similar characteristics and to relate needs and resources depends to a considerable degree on their instructors' success in revealing the social forces at work and the techniques by which their effects may be predicted, analyzed, and ameliorated or controlled. From the time students enter a school of social work they should learn to see the individual and his problem and simultaneously the implications of that problem for the community.

Beginning students generally fall into two groups: those with experience in social work who are interested in *methods,* and those straight from college who are interested in *problems* which they see in broad terms. Although in developing their concern for the individual, schools of social work sometimes "train them out of the broad view," the goal should be to help them develop a concern for the individual who can be helped through casework or group work, and simultaneously an awareness of community needs which can be resolved through the application of epidemiological techniques. In communicating this dual approach, instructors may need to select better teaching cases than those they are now using; it is probable, however, that they can use more productively the epidemiological implications of many cases now available.

A public health nurse, in the group, pointing out that physicians who enter schools of public health sometimes have difficulty in shifting their focus from the individual patient to the entire population, asked what problems confront social workers when they begin working in public health agencies. The public health social workers responded that they too have to enlarge their perspective so as to see the presenting problem in relation to the community. In addition, in public health agencies social workers must consider priorities of service, and in discharging their responsibilities to the community may have to avoid giving direct help to individuals.

Although other public health workers share this difficulty in extending their sights with social workers, *as a field* public health has more successfully developed a philosophy and practice of intervening on behalf of the community. When, for instance, the federal Old Age and Survivors' Disability Insurance program was developing rehabilitation services for the disabled, it turned to the Public Health Service and to other health agencies for help, not to agencies in which social work predominates —despite the fact that most services needed by the disabled are social, not medical. It recognized that public health habitually looks at problems in relation to the community and to the resources that are or might be made available.

At this point in the discussion, warning signals went up. "Don't be too readily seduced," the public health people said, "by the prospect of teaching the epidemiologic point of view overnight. Schools of public health encounter tremendous resistance from their students when the concepts of epidemiology are introduced." Would they face this resistance, a participant asked, if their physician-students had learned in medical school to look at problems epidemiologically as well as clinically? Can a professional school teach both methods at the same time or must students learn one before they can absorb the other?

What, asked another, are the prospects for preparing expert clinicians who are able to see the relation between clinical practice and social forces? Is it possible to teach, simultaneously, how to help people with problems and how to see the relation between this process of helping and the social context in which human problems arise? The group considered this a difficult task, but most thought the social work curriculum contains the elements necessary for accomplishing it. The challenge lies in helping to integrate these elements so that each student will not have to do it alone.

In the process of developing the two-dimensional view, students will begin to see the function of the laity in the collaborative effort to solve the problems of society. One of the responsibilities of the school is to help them grow in political sophistication, in the ability to search out and work within the power structure of a community without sacrificing their democratic values. In give-and-take of professional service they will need not only the courage of their convictions but the flexibility, judgment, and political wisdom that enable them to work effectively and democratically with powerful laymen who do not share their values, as well as those who do.

Need for Compatibility in Field and Class

Field instruction was recognized as a most significant area of the curriculum in which students during both years may be exposed to public health concepts and content. It was seen as having great, though largely unused, potential for aiding in the development of "multidimensional" practitioners. It is important in all field work placements to find direct and indirect ways of equipping students with both knowledge and beginning skills in a broad approach to social dysfunctioning. School and field must collaborate closely to provide students with sound beginning experience.

The fact that students frequently take as their role model their field instructors and not their classroom teachers was thought to be no hindrance, except when a conflict in perception of the roles of social work exists between the school and the field. However, involved is the necessity of getting across to field instructors any innovation which might occur—such as the introduction of or increased emphasis on, an epidemiological approach. Conceptual teaching alone will not do the job. Concepts need to be reinforced by examples and research in school and field and by opportunities for students to observe this practice. Experimentation with new and different approaches to field instruction, and assessment of the impact of different teaching methods on groups of students should be promoted. It was noted that difficulties may arise when the student acquires knowledge in class which he is not permitted to apply in practice because of the agency's limited view of its functions.

This idea was expressed in different terms. The students in the field might be more purposefully drawn into careful consideration of certain agency administrative problems that reflect community need. For example, students might profitably digress from casework practice to study what happens to applicants who are denied service, or to compare the composition of a waiting list to the composition of the community as a whole, or to investigate new ways of calling attention to an agency's services. Some schools, through their field instruction programs, consciously encourage students to pursue particular human welfare problems in their various community ramifications, including the social structural roots of these problems, and the nature of social, political, and other intervention needed to prevent their recurring. Perhaps field instruction is the logical place for putting together the various pieces related to epidemiology that the curricula already contain. For students to incorporate this approach requires that all teachers demonstrate it in their content, philosophy and performance; it needs to permeate the curriculum.

Other examples were given of field experiences that have been developed to meet the educational needs presented:

1. Selected special placements within the state governmental structure, e.g. for a public administration student at the highest level in the state department of welfare.
2. A combination field placement in a public health setting where a student both provides service to individuals and helps a small nearby community to develop a health program.
3. Moves in one or two schools toward developing a "training center agency," where a district office of the family and children's agency is already on the campus, with other agency branches to follow; or of one welfare center of the department of welfare, and the possible development of a clinical center in mental health. These units would be used for experimental research and educational purposes with participation of students at both the master's and the doctoral level.

Need for Compatibility Between the Curriculum and the Demands of Current Practice

Are schools of social work keeping pace with the demands of social work practice? Are they sending out new social workers who can deal competently with the problems they will confront in actual practice? One participant observed that if practice is changing, changes in the curriculum are bound to follow; but *is* practice really changing? Most social agencies still demand practitioners with good clinical training, social workers who are ready to hold their own on a clinical team providing direct casework, group work, or community organization services. If clinical knowledge and skill are not brought to bear on community problems, the community and its social agencies can be catapulted into unwise decisions and activities. One group agreed that effective community organization and social policies will not come from poor clinicians and that all social work students must have sound basic preparation for clinical proficiency.

Another group focused its attention on the demand for competent administrators, supervisors, consultants, and community planners; competent performance in these roles, singly or in combination, requires training. What is the solution? Some graduates go from school into administrative positions. Many students come to school from administrative and supervisory positions and will return to them. Those returning to case supervision, for example, look to the schools for academic experiences that will increase their skill in service caseloads and at the same time teach them the functions of consultation and administration. Should schools provide a single curriculum for experienced workers and inexperienced students preparing for clinical positions? Should students interested in policy-making, administration, and community planning be selected according to specific criteria and tutored in these special subjects?

The issues were clear: Can a school prepare a student in two years for the full range of professional practice? Should social work education establish two patterns of training for two different kinds of social work—clinical practice and policy-making? The questions were not resolved, but everyone recognized the varied, often conflicting demands of practice and the realities of trying to prepare both generalists and specialists in two years.

Returning to the question of whether practice is really changing, one participant commented that a more vital question is not whether schools are preparing students for the demands of today's practice but whether they are preparing students who can *change* practice as new knowledge dictates.

Need for Preparing for Tomorrow's Practice

The chairman reminded one group that many of those present were inadequately educated for present-day professional activities, and that in modernizing the social work curriculum there is need for broad imaginative thinking to envisage future developments. Students must learn not only to function skillfully in the services of today but must be able to develop the broad outlook and skill which can be successfully transferred to meeting the needs in the professional activities of tomorrow.

One reporter recorded that perhaps the most important single goal defined by the group, for both practice and education, was that of moving in the direction of offering social welfare services not just to avert some danger, but because they are necessary for the preservation of society. Too often, professional persons, as well as citizens, view social services as being available to "welfare" clients, but not to everyone as prerequisites for an abundant life. If social workers can begin to think of making provision for community need—rather than solving problems individually after they come to light—two results may occur: first, social workers may move away from more or less exclusive preoccupation with their clinical role; and second, the public may support services for their vital social utility rather than because they might keep something bad from getting worse.

One group reported general agreement that the responsibility for making agencies more truly responsive to the real needs of the community must be shared jointly between social work education and social work practice. The student's learning should result in his developing both recognition of present lacks and a feeling of responsibility for broadening agency services. Faculty members should become involved in community activities relating to unmet needs and schools communicate new approaches and new content in the curriculum to field instructors and to the administrators. Seminars or institutes in "community process" for agency administrators and supervisors might help avoid role conflict that would be likely to occur if schools were to teach from an epidemiological base, while agencies continue to practice primarily on a clinical base. There was not general agreement that the barriers to an epidemiological approach in social work are peculiarly the property of either voluntary or public agencies. Changes must be made in most agencies' concepts of their roles before substantial progress can be made.

An example of the split in agency practice—as between the clinical and the community (or epidemiological) orientation—was cited: of agency administrative practices which do actual violence to social work principles of human needs and human responses to stress. Some agencies seem to operate under the assumption that community demand for service is created by the visibility of the waiting list, or they utilize waiting lists to justify their existence and to protect the agency, or employ them as a means of competing with other similar agencies. Development of an effective demand for service by the public, through education and information about the agency, is thus thwarted and distorted by these practices.

Students in social work will need more of the *training for uncertainty*, that is described by Merton et al, as required by the rapid development of knowledge in all fields and that is now an objective of medical education.[2] The curriculum must cover the changes that are taking place rapidly in the practice of social work and related professions and also identify for the students the *stage of development of social work knowledge*. If social work is to move increasingly in the direction of influencing social determinants, social workers will be needed who have a sense of dissatisfaction but also a sense of direction in which changes must be made. The social work curriculum must therefore be imaginative and flexible if it is to prepare practitioners who are able to cope with uncertainty and rapid social change.

CURRICULUM CONSIDERATIONS WITH REFERENCE TO PARTICULAR SUBJECT MATTER

The discussion of the curriculum provoked lively interchange of thought on particular content as well as on basic problems in

---

[2] Renee C. Fox, "Training for Uncertainty," in *The Student-Physician: Introductory Studies in the Sociology of Medical Education*, edited by Robert K. Merton, George G. Reader, and Patricia L. Kendall (Cambridge: Harvard University Press, 1957), pp. 207-41.

education. Much of the content of these discussions served to clarify concepts and implications for social work practice, presented quite fully in the preceding chapters. To avoid repetition, only those points which relate specifically to particular subject matter in the curriculum appear in the following summaries.

Programing and Planning for the Provision of Services

In both groups, social work educators identified difficulties they encounter in getting the desired responses from students:

1. Although the configuration of person-problem-situation is taught, and an important part is the community, the educators have difficulty in presenting students with a useful, workable idea of the community as a whole.

2. Difficulty is encountered in teaching first year students a range of major social problems and variations in social services so that they move beyond a superficial view of facts. Some who have had undergraduate courses in social welfare look upon the introductory course as a review and do not delve into the underlying factors.

3. Although the idea of *provision as a policy* is not hard to get across to students, their field practice gives them little, if any, opportunity to engage in provision as a function.

4. The process of specialization itself within social work is one barrier to training all practitioners to think in community terms. One group explored at length the public trust concept of the community-as-patient (or as client). To what extent would the social workers' capacity to plan and develop programs be enhanced through the translation of this concept into the curriculum and thence into practice? Although the exploration served to further clarify the concept, it was clearly not one which could be translated *in toto* into social work; nor did all of the discussants consider it useful for the curriculum.

A public health physician observed that the concept of the

community can become an oversimplified interpretation of the practical working philosophy of public health. A public health social worker suggested that a whole array of methodologies is implied by the phrase, "community-as-patient;" it must be thought of as a whole system, not as a single entity. The concept might be relevant if social work, like public health, could apply specific measures against specific ills. In the final analysis, public health must think of the impact of broad epidemiological forces on individuals. The "health of the community" is a useful abstraction but, in programing for public health, coordinating and planning contribute nothing until they touch the lives of people.

Although social work educators have always taught in general terms that the community affects the client, they have only begun to look for systematic ways of showing students how social forces affect the individual. Not only is the individual affected by these forces but he has the capacity to affect and change them. This group agreed that the concept of the individual as an "agent of change"—an important idea in community organization—sharply conflicts with the idea of the community as a sick interacting system, passively waiting for public health or social work to intervene and cure. As the group tried to decide whether its "backing away" from the concept of the community-as-patient arose from the term itself or from the underlying ideas, the focus shifted to the uncertainty and the ambivalence about the answer to the over-all question as to whose job it is to try to modify community forces? Other related questions raised were:

1. Is the concept of the community as a social system influencing and in turn influenced by individuals a legitimate concept for social work education?

2. Should social workers assume the responsibility of prescribing for the community specific remedial action against social ills whenever their expertise—although not necessarily great nor complete—exceeds that of others?

3. If social workers reject the idea of the community-as-patient, in what other terms can they justify not only the need for social change but their role in bringing about change?

An example was given of the serious and growing problem of out-of-wedlock births and suggestions were made for specific remedial action. During the discussion that followed, someone pointed out that the social workers have been loathe, at least in recent years, to "impose" solutions to problems on the public; they have tended to leave to others the job of prescribing remedies. A social worker said that "we really aren't experts on illegitimacy" but did not suggest who else might know more about it than social workers. Another countered with a reminder that doctors know little about the causes or cures of many diseases, but the medical profession is still looked to as the best available source of help, even in illnesses that tax the limits of medical knowledge.

The discussion of responsibility for modifying forces in the community led this group to attempt to schematize the relationships between public health and social work in a chart depicting the gamut of services in a community. Social welfare and social work services were on one side of the chart, public health services on the other. Down the middle was a dividing column labeled "community organization." But the division lacked validity, they realized, for public health agencies provide certain social services and social agencies—for example, welfare departments provide a range of public health services. Another way of depicting this relationship was tried with two overlapping circles, one representing public health, the other social welfare services. If to some extent the services overlap, is it valid to assume that the concepts which gave rise to these services also overlap?

Other points brought out were that the responsibility of developing social services that are relevant and responsive to the needs of a community has usually been delegated to social workers who are specialists in community organization, or to the community welfare council. The public must participate in the planning and must support the goals, if programs are to succeed. This philosophy reflects social work's democratic values, and acknowledges the citizen's inherent right to veto the changes that professionals define as needed. Here the group left open the question of whether the changes recommended by the public health expert are less subject to veto than are those of the social worker; but they agreed that the vested interests which oppose or support public health programs may differ from those which take one position or the other on social welfare programs. Social work, and public health too, can learn a great deal from political science and economics about the dynamics of power and influence, social change, changing patterns of need, and community organization and *reorganization* as well. A participant humorously suggested that schools of social work would do well to arrange field work placements in state legislatures!

With the exception of certain specified functions of public agencies, social agencies carry functions which are broadly and variously defined as "community concerns." The accountability expected by the community, particularly of the public agencies, seems to be largely for social *control* rather than social *provision*. Perhaps this is because the major functions of public agencies bring to them the socially disadvantaged groups, which the community expects to provide for, but in circumscribed ways.

Can social agencies, lacking the relatively unified statutory base of the public health agencies, transmute community goals and ideas of need into an effective demand that will support social services on a broad, institutionalized base? Public health workers in the new nations of the world are asking themselves this same question. Americans who are helping these countries have found they must postpone their plans for preventing illness and improving the level of health, to meet the immediate needs of sick people. Preventive measures must wait until the hungry are fed and the sick made well. This is somewhat analogous to the challenge facing American social work today.

Human Potentials and Limitations

This group agreed that all social workers should understand man in society. To achieve this objective, they must comprehend biological, psychological, social, and cultural forces. In addition, they must be able to respond to other people with feeling and develop a skill in helping them. Thus, social work rests on the triad of knowledge, feelings and skill. It follows that social work education is committed to the task of nurturing these qualities in every student.

Toward these educational aims, what does the field of public health offer? Both social work and public health work toward the goal of achieving social health in people, and both recognize the forces operating in the social system. Social work is concerned with society and individuals and sees them along a continuum ranging from adequate social functioning to social dysfunction-ing—analogous to the continuum from health to disease. By eliminating hazards to health, public health agencies enhance the social and economic climate of a community and improve the health and social status of the people who live there. Thus, the efforts of social work and public health are often pointed in the same direction, as for example toward the problems of the aging, child welfare, mental health, juvenile delinquency, illegitimacy, and many other aspects of human behavior.

Although their efforts are similarly directed, social agencies and public health programs differ in their emphasis. Social agencies, concentrating upon improved social functioning, incorporate the aims of health; public health agencies, directed toward improved health, incorporate the values of social work. Increasingly, both emphasize interdisciplinary collaboration, but the leadership differs—in a public health agency a physician is usually in charge, in a social agency a social worker.

The group identified a number of health concepts and methods that they believed schools of social work could usefully apply in dealing with the subject of human potentials:

1. Hazards to health affect social functioning and must be understood and considered in social planning. The over-all goal of public health—the maintenance and improvement of health—incorporates the over-all goal of social work—the enhancement of social functioning. Students should be helped to recognize that these are different expressions of similar goals.

2. Public health considers the entire population "at risk" not merely those with health problems; specific public

health programs, however, may be directed toward particular groups of people.

3. Health departments are charged by law with a broad responsibility: "the health of the people." Public welfare departments, by law, have more specific responsibilities; they are usually charged with providing aid to the needy and with rendering certain child welfare services. But nowhere in the social welfare structure is there an agency charged with the social welfare of the entire population.

4. Health problems are useful illustrations for presenting to students the biological, psychological, and social factors affecting the development of human potentials. The effect of diseases on the individual is an element in the etiology of social problems.

5. Concepts of prevention should be covered in presenting any social problem to students whether the problem affects an individual, a group, or a community.

6. The biological concept of predisposing factors may be applied to social problems and the one of homeostasis is helpful in the teaching of social adaptation.

7. The concept of intervention can be related to social phenomena and social planning, and has applicability to social casework, group work, and community organization.

8. The practice of setting priorities in planning programs for community health is applicable to social planning for community welfare. The pioneer spirit in social work can be evoked by examples of early and current pioneer efforts and programs in public health.

9. The interdisciplinary approach to program planning and problem solving demonstrated in public health can be presented as one model of collaboration. The student's perception of the role of social work would be broadened, as would his understanding of the ways various personnel are deployed. They should understand the responsibilities of other professions in dealing with the social problems of the people they serve and the role

of the expert, of any profession, in providing consultation. More exposure to the functions of various public health personnel, including those of public health social workers, would broaden their perspective.

What would be involved in the incorporation of these concepts and methods into the social work curriculum? A basic public health concept, such as the continuum from promotion of health through restoration, would involve more than additions. It would require specific consideration of prevention, case-finding, treatment, and restoration in the sequence on social work methods, in field instruction as well as in the classroom. In most schools the current curriculum content on health is probably not adequate to give students the biological information they need to understand the development of human potentials, problems of maturation, predisposing factors, the etiology of social problems, and social adaptation.

More attention might be given to the concept of the population at risk than is now given. In this relation, several suggestions seemed to merit exploration by social work educators:

1. The reciprocal etiologies in the problems coming to the attention of public health and of social work should be examined. Disease may be viewed etiologically if the social consequences are considered; social conditions may also be evaluated for their contribution to the onset of a disease process. The label of "cause" or "resulting problem" depends upon the locus of attention, but their relationship can be established.

2. The concept of predisposing conditions, particularly as linked with the natural history of disease, could be further developed through study of the natural history of social problems.

3. Social intervention could be studied with more intensive examination of the following questions: what kinds of social intervention are currently available? What kinds are possible and appropriate under the circumstances faced by the community, the client, and the social worker?

4. What leads for epidemiological studies might be derived from the biopsychosocial data on the face sheet? Perhaps this information has not yet been sufficiently utilized by practitioners, research workers, or educators.

5. With regard to the nosology of medicine in public health, terminology needs to be devised that would describe social competence; for example, such terms as chronic-hospitalized; chronic-home, convalescing; chronic-home, unemployed; chronic-home, working. Perhaps this could be done through the combined efforts of social work and public health.

Services to Individuals in Families and Groups

Two groups gave major attention to the contributions of specific public health concepts to social work knowledge and methods of solving problems. They recognized that learning experiences pertinent to services to individuals appear in all the sequences of the curriculum, not just the sequences on methods.

Several generalizations were made in each group:
The principles of epidemiology, prevention, and community planning apply to the practice of casework, group work, and community organization and should pervade the curriculum rather than relate to one sequence. Some schools are taking a greater responsibility for stimulating social action by disseminating throughout the curriculum a variety of ideas on ways of serving the general community. It is necessary to show the student the whole spectrum to avoid becoming fixed at any one level. The curriculum would be strengthened by enriched teaching in methods of community intervention and community planning.

The "scientific approach" was discussed by one group in relation to values. Dr. Kahn's paper implied that social work has values which do not require validation. The tendency of social workers to avoid statements of values was examined. One participant questioned whether this was because social work was preoccupied with a scientific approach to problems. The group recognized that professional convictions do not have to be set aside; they are not incompatible with the use of scientific techniques. Is avoidance of stating social work values because the public does not really accept them? Although there was acceptance of the responsibility for social work to convey these values to the public in a way which can be understood and accepted, it was noted that confusions often arise in public understanding of social work values as they are translated into service. For example, the public, in its present criticism of the A.D.C. program, appears to have lost sight of the value on which the A.D.C. program was based, the right of the child to emotional and physical security. The morality of the mother has been at the center of recent public criticism. On services to the delinquent, the goal of social work to help the child towards healthier living has become confused in the public view with condoning offenses. Has social work been preoccupied with a scientific approach but not able to convey to the public that its practices stem from a scientific view of the problem?

Concern was expressed that when social workers intervene on behalf of individuals or groups they do so in ways that are harmonious with social work values. This must be true of means as well as ends. Social work's concept of eligibility was contrasted with public health's provision of services for all. Some public health personnel tend to view social workers as rigid and restrictive because of the requirements for public welfare services. If the public health philosophy were applied to social welfare, it is probable that social workers would seek out dependent children and help their families establish their eligibility for A.D.C.

The making of a "diagnosis" was considered from various points of view, particularly as the basis for action which may be subsequently revised. It was suggested that although in social work education instructors discuss "the dynamic, ongoing diagnosis," they may at times use the term "accurate diagnosis" in such a way as to make it sound static to the student. It was suggested that William Gordon's terminology—"a confronting situation which needs assessment and intervention"—has value in relation to understanding the formulation and use of diagnosis. There was consideration of social work's use of the term "psychosocial diagnosis." The latter can be useful to the social worker in evaluating the constellation of pertinent factors.

Through the ongoing case study process the social worker often acquires more data than he gives himself credit for possessing; his problem may lie in organizing the facts meaningfully. Use of a tentative diagnosis as a basis for planning action, followed by simultaneous action and continued fact-gathering leading to a refined diagnosis, was recognized as a useful process. Public health can contribute to social work skill in systematization and in ordering of facts. The faculties of many schools include internists and pediatricians for the sequence on human growth and behavior, but not all physicians have interest in prevention and a public health approach to health problems. In some instances an epidemiological approach has been introduced by the social work teacher in the methods sequence but in many cases, prevention is not included in any sequence. Not only knowledge but attitudes toward health must become part of social work's educational objectives. Students should want to help every client attain his highest level of social, emotional and physical health. Public health looks to social work education to foster in students an attitude of responsibility for the promotion of well-being, prevention, and protection.

Research with Reference to Epidemiology

One work group concerned itself with the similarities and differences between epidemiology and research in the master's curricula of schools of public health and of social work. Although these two types of professional schools solve their common educational problems in different ways, both aim at developing in students an attitude toward research which will serve as a foundation for their use of educational experiences and will influence them later in practice. The nature of the learners, therefore, determines the methods used by the schools to inculcate the desired attitude.

A medical educator suggested that generalizations from medical education may be applicable to social work education if one equates medical students to social work students in the master's program and medical residents to social workers in the second year of practice or in a post-master's training program. Medical students are expected *to learn* accepted medical knowledge, but the psychiatric residents are expected *to challenge* accepted medical knowledge. The first years in each educational program lay the groundwork for broad knowledge and meaningful identification with a profession. The desired attitude toward research grows out of the student's respect for knowledge and his identification with a profession which searches for knowledge.

The principal value of learning with respect to research lies in developing analytic reasoning powers, not in collecting data. A suggestion was made that schools should provide students with opportunities to analyze data already collected rather than ask them to secure new information. Recent experiences in public health education point to the value of a "bank of problems"; schools could draw kits of raw data from the "bank" for use in teaching students how to formulate and/or test hypotheses, solve problems, and develop skill in analyzing raw or partially proved material. The kits could illustrate a wide range of content and a variety of problems.

Implicit in this proposal is the idea of continuity in research. Multiphasic research projects over several years, with follow-up studies built in, would accumulate data for the stockpile. These coordinated projects would be carefully planned and designed and participation in them would provide good training in research for students. The projects themselves could also produce substantial research information for the profession.

Much of the research done by social work students at present has exercise value for them but does not produce significant data. A study designed to train them in research methodology differs in dimension from one designed to produce new knowledge; the one produces informed *consumers* of research; the other competent *producers* of research. In the master's curriculum—a learning experience primarily for consumers—it is possible to identify those students whose interests and abilities point toward careers in research. Experience indicates that they are best served by intensive systematic training in methods of research and by related field work in their second year. Some schools have modified their usual requirements for these students, so they may obtain learning experiences in other areas of the curriculum, by exempting them from the customary "information" course in research.

Underlying these considerations is the relationship between basic and applied science. Public health, using the epidemiologic method, can initiate investigations of a practical problem and seek a solution in research whereas social work, because of pressure tends to limit its investment in research to immediate issues; as a result, it has "farmed out" basic investigations. The integration of research related to social programs and basic research could infuse the curriculum with a fresh spirit of inquiry.

Current trends in the social work curriculum forecast this integration. The concept of social functioning permits a wider field for inquiry than does social dysfunction. In investigating the natural history of disease, epidemiology has covered a great deal of ground; in applying the concept of social functioning throughout the curriculum, research in social work will also evolve a *qestalt*.

What the group referred to as "a research stance" becomes part of the student's image of himself as a learner in a profession to the extent that a spirit of inquiry and a respect for research are projected by the curriculum. The group saw field work instructors as most important members of the teaching team because of their influence on the attitudes of their students. The problem is not resistance to research, but the demands of teaching and of developing appropriate resources for field work. If those in this sensitive teaching group were more involved in research, their experiences would enrich the curriculum. Various ways were discussed of affording these teachers additional experience in research, for as they become more identified with research, its importance to practice will be communicated to students.

One solution would be to train groups of field instructors in a common facility, thus reducing the demands on individual schools and agencies. Another opportunity is provided through funds available to social work educators who wish to pursue advanced study leading to careers in social work research. The addition of a social scientist to the faculty of a school of social work could in time involve all the teaching staff, class and field instructors alike, in common research enterprises.

The primary need is a redistribution of the workload so that those who wish to undertake research may do so. Their investigations would stimulate others and "seed" the atmosphere with the spirit of inquiry. An increase in research by social work educators would directly influence teaching throughout the curriculum as well as produce new knowledge.

ANALYSIS OF IMPLICATIONS OF THE SEMINAR

Analysis of the Implications of the Seminar for Social Work Education

by MILTON WITTMAN, D.S.W.*

It would be difficult to prepare an analysis of the implications of the Princeton Seminar on Public Health for social work education without first briefly considering the general context of this meeting.

The seminar occurs at a time which finds professional social work education in deep ferment following publication of the Curriculum Study of the Council on Social Work Education and the move toward revision of the curriculum policy statement of 1952, an event which, when accomplished, will set the general framework for graduate education in social work for the next decade. The restructuring of curriculum policy occurs in a milieu influenced by interacting socio-economic forces which have exerted perplexing pressures on the field of social welfare in general and on the social work profession in particular. The rising tide of welfare expenditures and the desperate, apparently insoluble, shortage of trained manpower to man the burgeoning welfare programs have created a personnel situation of crisis proportions. Accompanying this development is the rapid expansion of the health field, which, along numerous lines of diverse dimensions, has created additional demands for social work participation

* Chief, Social Work Section, Training Branch, National Institute of Mental Health, National Institutes of Health, Public Health Service, U. S. Department of Health, Education and Welfare, Bethesda, Maryland. The writer is grateful for the valuable comments on this manuscript provided by Dr. Elmer Hill, Eleanor Morris, Elizabeth P. Rice, Ruth Taylor, and Grace White.

and involvement. Therefore, the Public Health Seminar has performed the function of highlighting for social work education and, perhaps more pervasively, yet emphatically, for the whole field of social welfare, the strategic potential role for social work in relation to public health programs in the United States.

In its basic organization, the seminar was planned to present to educators and practitioners in public health and social work a summary of the status of public health as a field and elaboration in depth of three selected major areas of the field, epidemiology, prevention, and community planning. The principal papers deal with the history and development of the field of public health and of each of three areas of public health practice, and in each case assessed the potential role for social work. The work groups were composed to provide a variety of personnel with experience in the fields of public health and social work, thus affording a rich opportunity for interchange, questioning, and discussion.

This analysis will direct itself to an assessment of the potential implications for social work education in the seminar proceedings. Implications will be drawn for social work education in its broadest sense, including graduate professional education, covering master's, third year and doctoral levels of preparation, and inservice or staff development forms of education. Moreover, the discussion of Seminar content will touch on several aspects of curriculum, including the three major social work methods (casework, group work, and community organization), and administration, research, and field instruction. The conclusions will have a bearing on content related to social services and human growth and behavior, as this content might be considered in the structure of formal and informal educational programs.

A central objective of the seminar was "to promote within social work education better understanding of the field of public health and to encourage working together in developing ways in which this content may be incorporated in the social work curriculum." That the better understanding of public health should extend not only to the participants, but, through these proceedings, to social work educators and to the field of social work in general was a secondary, but no less important, goal.

Public Health Content in the Curriculum Study

The curriculum policy statement of 1952 listed public health content under the rubric "human growth and behavior." The Curriculum Study volume directed toward assessment of the components of human growth and behavoir, after careful study of existing content, suggested a reorientation of total emphasis to a sequence described as "understanding the potential for social functioning."[1] The investigator compiled materials which provided a basis for a ten-point outline dealing with the life cycle aspects of human growth and development and the nature of pathology. The completed study endeavored to view the "biopsychosocial" aspects of human growth as these might be learned by the graduate student intending to enter professional practice in social work. The final goal in the projected plan deals with "theories of total man." This volume explicates the nature of homeostasis and the process of adaptation to stress by the individual and family. The continuum of health and disease is elaborated as is the emphasis on normal human behavior. However, this volume does not to any length emphasize public health methods and public health concepts. There is no development of content on prevention and this seems in general to be a neglected area of the social work curriculum.

The Field of Public Health

Public health practice is a significant institution in American communities today. Public health legislation at the Federal and State levels outlines a wide range of protective and service activities carried on today in the 53 states and territories and the 3,100 counties of the United States. The field of public health is as much beset by problems of public understanding, underfinancing, and manpower difficulties as is social welfare. A number of the work groups touched on the problems of public acceptance when public health is compared with social welfare. The similarities became more visible with careful study.

Unfortunately, few social workers in daily practice have

---

[1] Ruth M. Butler, *An Orientation to Knowledge of Human Growth and Behavior in Social Work Education* (New York: Council on Social Work Education, 1959).

frequent occasion to collaborate directly with public health personnel, although most, in their ordinary functions, become intimately aware of disturbing health problems in the caseload and in the community. A considerable percentage of social disability is directly related to, or derives from, major or minor health problems. This being the case, there is an apparent need for increased knowledge of public health concepts as these can be applied in social work education and practice. There is also an acute need to amplify the awareness of the student and the practitioner concerning public health structure and function. The integration of health concepts in social work practice and education must inevitably follow increased understanding and acceptance of these concepts.

As Dr. Porterfield's paper has so clearly enunciated, the field of public health has its own history, its own patterns of function, its own structure, and its own very pressing problems. He correctly saw public health as a "universe" which functions with varying degrees of effectiveness, depending on public acceptance and support. There is an educational process involved in training for public health practice, which, by its nature, is perhaps more interdisciplinary than might be true of any other of the service professions. The public health personnel include not only public health physicians, but also public health nurses, sanitarians, social workers, sanitary engineers, nutritionists, dentists, biostatisticians, laboratory specialists, public health educators, and, in some instances, social scientists. A well-staffed and well-financed public health department offers a myriad of services which presuppose a high degree of proficiency in technical and professional ability. Increasingly social workers serve as members of public health teams in local and state public health departments in a number of important ways. The pattern of services may include the provision of casework, but is more likely to involve social work consultation, community planning, administration, teaching and research. This field of social work practice is exceedingly complex and increasingly involves modes of professional behavior based on sound theoretical preparation in one of the major social work methods and a high degree of awareness of the others. In few social work positions will be found such complex demands for research and administrative knowledge including awareness of how bureaucratic structures function within the community framework.

Without substantial basic understanding of the structure and function of public health services, the social work student will be limited in his future ability to provide a full range of social services in the community. This means that instruction in public health content must extend beyond the descriptive input so frequently found in social work educational programs. On the other hand, it should be acknowledged that some social work educators have recognized the importance of public health content and have done a great deal to develop meaningful curriculum content derived from didactic and field resources for students at all levels of training. Thus some educational content can be found at the undergraduate, graduate, and post-master's levels in schools of social work and undergraduate departments and, in addition, in the inservice education programs of health and welfare agencies.

One work group raised three questions outlining the issues involved in the integration by social work education of public health content.

1. What does any social worker need to know?
2. What does every social worker need to learn of environmental factors?
3. What does any field of practice teach?

This group explicitly agreed that the general objectives of social work and public health are concordant and have in common the goal of improving the social, mental, and physical well-being of the general population. The group quickly recognized that certain segments of the population, more vulnerable than others, may be considered "at risk"; thus, for example, infant mortality is a matter of vital concern, as is reactive depression in the aging.

In general the public health worker studies the environment of the individual and family in the context of human behavior and physical interaction. There are many variations in public health practice, however, according to the particular constellation of qualifications of the personnel charged with developing a program and by the latitude granted by legislation and local sanction.

The spectrum of public health practice reviewed in the papers by Bauer, Porterfield, Knott, Kandle, and James, suggests a vital and complex organizational structure, in the main legally constituted, which embraces the protective network of community services intended to enhance and preserve community health. There was noted the historical movement of public health practice from primary concern for environmental sanitation to the present position which views health as including the biopsychosocial aspects of health problems as matters of importance to the public health practitioner. The transition in dominating emphases in public health programs (from communicable to chronic diseases) also was noted. Some question of the extent to which history of public health, structure and function of public health services, and health concepts in general, are included in social work curricula was raised by a number of the work groups. In some instances this seemed superficially accomplished and in others, a substantial segment of time was allocated to the description of public health structure and services, in the United States and in the international field as well.

Epidemiology and Social Work Education

Following an effective presentation by an epidemiologist and a penetrating analysis of this paper by a psychiatrist in public health and a social worker with a public health orientation, the seminar found itself engaged in a detailed assessment of the implications of epidemiology for social work practice and education. As a science, epidemiology provides a basis for systematic and effective study of populations to determine the incidence and prevalence of illness and the decisive factors in threats to human well-being as a basis for intervention. The study of a disease process involves examination of the natural history of the disease and its manifest and latent impact on the individual, family, and community. The evolution of control methods flows from the knowledge obtained through such study. Where the cause cannot be detected or removed, the individual or community may be protected from invasion so that the disability does not occur or may be otherwise controlled so as to limit morbidity. The many protective devices around infancy and child care are ready examples of the application of findings from public health research and epidemiologic studies. For the field of public health, the science of epidemiology endeavors to answer several questions: What causes the illness? Why do some people become ill and some not? What can be done to prevent or control illness? What can be done to help well people stay well?

The objectives of epidemiology with reference to illness closely parallel those of social research with reference to social pathology and dependency. Social work needs to develop further working relationships with scientific health research and to explore channels for the cooperative study of health and social disability. The tools of the epidemiologist have been tested through generations of study of sick and well populations. A section of the research component of the social work curriculum could profitably include an orientation to epidemiologic methods.

The introduction of epidemiologic content in classroom and field instruction of social work students will require either the direct participation of a consultant or teacher with training and experience in epidemiologic methods or the introduction of selected teaching materials from epidemiology at appropriate points in the curriculum. Perhaps as epidemiology becomes better understood, social work practitioners and educators will more easily see its relevance and importance in preparation for social work practice.

Community Planning

Education for work in community planning is still in the early stages of development as a definitive part of the social work curriculum. Of the three major methods in social work, community organization is the last to achieve common agreement on structure and content in master's level education. Development of suitable academic content in community planning is hampered by the lack of systematic organization of theory and practice in this method. It is generally recognized that the effort in this field made by the Curriculum Study of 1956-59 left much work to be done in the structuring of curriculum content in community organization.

The implications for social work education from the seminar discussion suggested the need for close scrutiny of the broader aspects of community planning and of the need to consider conjointly the health and welfare aspects of agency functions in the community. The impinging aspects of health and welfare suggest it would be an error to consider community planning content without including an active consideration of the health aspects of community life. One speaker noted that in addition to the network of public agencies there are 2,000 community councils and chests, and 50 national health agencies, all concerned with the organization and function of health and welfare programs. The fact that the field of social work has extensive experience in agency operations and in the development aspects of community services should be brought to bear on health problems in the community. The consensus of a number of work groups in this seminar suggested the need to break the walls of isolation which seem to hamper good collaborative efforts in health and welfare. The foundation of such collaboration and improved communication probably rests in the educational process in both fields. Since this seminar was directed toward educational content in social work education, there was no effort at this point to look at the implications for social work content in professional education in public health. The joint concerns for improved collaboration suggest that the latter might in time be a profitable endeavor.

Prevention as a Component of the Social Work Curriculum

It was generally recognized by the seminar members that the papers on prevention provided such stimulating and evocative interaction among the participants that full justice could not be done to the implications raised by this segment of the seminar. The introductory paper reviewing the several levels of prevention in public health and the ensuing papers on prevention in mental health and on "developmental provision" sparked some spirited discussion of the feasibility of the integrating concepts of prevention in social work education and practice.

A major obstacle appeared to be the problem of feasibility

of application of these concepts in social work if a literal interpretation of primary prevention is assumed. The field of social work has not yet evolved adaptations of practice which can equate satisfactorily with the health promotion aspects of primary prevention (as exemplified in health education programs) or with the specific protection aspects (as found in fluoridation of water or vaccination). Where beginnings have been made, as in parent education, there is still some reluctance to see this as a part of professional education.

A second consideration is the general notion that much of what is done in welfare practice today is preventive in intent, if not in actuality. The welfare structure is devoted to relieving the effects of poverty and the categorical aid programs are intended to meet the specific financial and (in time) the service needs of the aged, blind, disabled, and dependent children, among others. It was recognized, however, that economic provision, by itself, is insufficient to meet the full range of social problems which occur regardless of economic circumstances. Thus the need for social work to determine more precisely the effects of welfare programs in terms of prevention became vividly apparent.

The role of social work in secondary and tertiary prevention seems more easily applied in the health and welfare structure; but, here too, the questions of manpower and research entered as intervening obstacles. Early detection and treatment of social problems seem valid enough, but there are still too few trained practitioners to man existing services. Thus, the full activation of resources providing services at the secondary and tertiary levels is difficult even where community support can be actively enlisted. Moreover, existing research has not yet produced effective guidelines for optimum use of professional personnel.

The seminar participants reacted strongly to the description of a mental health program in a rural setting (Kiesler) which patently resisted becoming overwhelmed with a treatment case-load, but devoted its major professional time to consultation, research, and education functions. It was generally agreed that, in this instance, the quite distinctive roles for all professional staff, including the social workers, involved a level of function not ordinarily taught within the framework of master's level cur-

riculum content. It appeared to most that social work practitioners who would be involved primarily in consultation, community
education and research, would need first to have accomplished
basic professional education to provide a foundation for what
seemed to be a superordinate cluster of professional responsibilities. It was readily apparent that the clinic staff in the situation
described was moving actively and aggressively into social policy
considerations in the three counties served and was playing an
aggressive role in intervention and interdiction in meeting crises
in individuals and families. This involved not a limited but a comprehensive and aggressive form of collaboration with the medical profession, the school system, welfare agencies, and the clergy
in this predominantly rural area.

Another aspect of prevention which challenges social work
educators and practitioners is the problem of theoretical definition. Kahn, in his paper, postulated that the public health model
can apply to social work services, but need not be completely
tied to the "pathology continuum." The notion of "developmental
provision" suggested for social work action the assessment of
social institutions to determine which of these could, through
their normal functioning, meet and resolve critical situations in
individuals and in families, and which would need special efforts
to permit the resolution of social problems.

For example, the incorporation in the public school system
of supporting social and mental health services might eventually
permit this institution, by itself, to resolve most of the continuing
psychosocial problems coming to the surface in the pupil population. The function of social work in such a development would
be to explore the means by which direct services and educational
efforts could be developed to permit the basic staff in the educational system (the school teacher and school administrator) to
become increasingly capable of handling mental health and social
problems as they arise. The supporting role for social work would
occur through consultation, rather than through direct involvement with cases.

It was generally recognized that prevention content as such
is not ordinarily found in the structure of the social work curriculum. There was positive recognition of the need for more

content in this area, but latent confusion and uncertainty about the methods by which this might be accomplished.

Public Health Practice and Field Instruction

There were several noteworthy aspects relating to the field instruction area of the social work curriculum which appear in the reports of the group discussions and in the presentations illustrating the several roles for social work in public health. It was recognized that, in one sense, public health concepts should apply throughout the full scope of service provided by all medical care and health facilities. Thus, any aspect of service to patients, regardless of diagnosis and treatment implications, needs to be considered if the social environment is recognized as having a bearing on disease processes. Social work education has a long history of liaison and close cooperation with health and medical care facilities. In collaboration with medical and psychiatric social service departments of hospitals and clinics, student field instruction has been firmly and soundly integrated with social work education. A number of clinic services provided by health departments have served as a base for sound casework preparation in the public health setting. It is apparent, however, that learning the social work methods *per se* may not necessarily involve the absorption of a public health approach to professional practice.

The public health social workers reflected general dissatisfaction with the input of knowledge, attitudes, and skill in the master's level curriculum which would, in fact, prepare for practice of public health social work. While the latter has not yet had the benefit of systematic definition,[2] the generalized impression and acceptance of common characteristics suggests that, as in social psychiatry, public health social work deals with the community in total, that it is concerned with groups of people, that it frequently involves employment of group methods or group process in its functions, and that it is directed toward the

---

[2] An Ad Hoc Committee on Public Health established by the National Association of Social Workers is currently working on a definition and description of this field. The content of public health social work is outlined in *Social Work Activities in Public Health* (Boston: Massachusetts Dept. of Public Health, 1961).

use of clinical knowledge in broader applications to psychosocial and heath problems in the community. The active provision of field work instruction in this phase of effort in the public health department or in voluntary health agencies, involves a number of ingredients which could be added to existing basic professional educational content. Perhaps the most important of these ingredients is the teaching of social policy as it operates in the health setting. This involves a measure of skill in organization and interpretation of social data in health and medical care. Here is where the social worker, with his knowledge of individual and group behavior, and with his orientation to community structure, can make his contribution to the understanding of incipiency, vulnerability, and predisposition in preventing social breakdown. The diffusion of improved understanding of illness and the social complications of disease is the task of public health social workers. This requires ease of communication with other members of the health professions and with agency personnel in a host of community resources. The acquisition of skill in such functions requires suitable models in practice.

There was described for seminar members a few instances in which an internship plan for a training experience immediately following master's level education is being used as a means of incorporating into the professional knowledge of the emerging practitioner some specific content in public health practice which can then be used in ensuing professional practice. The internship itself is not yet fully developed, but the content tends to involve supervised field experience in a health department with broad educational and research functions and a pattern of seminars on public health practice, epidemiology and similar public health subjects not found in social work curriculum.

An alternative to the internship is the third year or doctoral program involving combined social work and public health content. This occurs in training centers, where schools of social work and schools of public health are found in juxtaposition and can provide combined experiences. Master's and doctoral training in schools of public health is more frequently sought by social workers. The field of public health employs a number of social work practitioners with combined training in social work and in public health. There is a small group of social work educators with public health training in schools of social work.

The field instruction experience should be manned by personnel with adequate preparation in public health so that the cluster of experiences involved in field instruction will have relevance to the academic content in the program. The block plan of field instruction might serve to open field instruction centers for public health social work training not readily accessible under the concurrent field instruction system.

There was an obvious need for better knowledge of existing programs of public health social work and some move toward more formal agreement as to what the total educational component should be. In this respect, public health social work seems at a clear disadvantage when compared with what now exists in descriptive terms in other fields of social work practice, including the significant and growing number of fields involving interdisciplinary collaboration.

Teaching Manpower

The field of social work is currently hampered by the lack of a sufficient supply of well-qualified teachers in social work education. This deficit is particularly acute where teaching of health concepts is involved. The incorporation of public health content in social work education might best be advanced by faculty or by consultants with dual training in both social work and public health. Presumably, such individuals would be able, on the basis of sound theoretical grounding in public health, to select suitable content from public health which will enrich and extend the knowledge content at the master's level. Such content would be of benefit not only to the graduate intending to enter the public health field, but for all students, regardless of the field of practice they might enter. Public health content should be found in the social service sequence, in the human growth and behavior sequence, and in the several social work methods courses. Students would be informed, not only of the structure of public health programs, but would know the history, philosophy, and concepts of public health as these relate to and impinge upon the history, philosophy, and practice of social work. Epidemiology would not be a strange word to the social work graduate and the cluster of public health personnel would be seen as collaborators in the achievement of social goals in the community health and welfare network.

Of particular importance would be the better understanding and acceptance of research implications in public health practice. In being exposed to public health research, students would, through class and field experiences, become readily aware of the possibilities for preventive efforts and the quest for knowledge on which to base intervention and prevention. Students would grasp some of the difficulties involved in experimental designs getting at the improved understanding of individuals and families and their responses to health procedures and health measures. They would be exposed to study of the evaluation and testing of new and experimental public health methods. The ultimate gain for social work practice would be increased breadth of practice regardless of method.

The development of educational manpower needed to accomplish such tasks will be an urgent problem for the near future. More social workers will need to be motivated to seek public health training and there will be an acute need to examine social work participation within the framework of schools of public health. A social work contribution is currently found in some but not in all schools of public health. The involvement of public health personnel in social work education is as yet uneven and incomplete in most educational programs. Social work education is faced, as it has been in relation to psychiatry and medicine, with a deficiency of strong educators from this importantly-related field. What is needed is inspired teaching, in depth, of well-organized content which does in fact represent a cohesive part of the total curriculum and not a superficial addendum.

Public Health Content in Undergraduate and Inservice Education

The exploration of public health content at this seminar has some direct implications for undergraduate and inservice education. In many instances, a quantity of content covering the health field is found in undergraduate curricula. As is true in the case of content in social welfare, the explication of health and medical care has an appropriate place in undergraduate education. Therefore, efforts directed at extending teaching content in this field should include the undergraduate area of education, and any move toward carrying forward the Curriculum Study recommendations with reference to undergraduate education should give careful attention to the components from health and medical care which are included in the total curriculum.

Inservice education and staff development remain the universal forms of continuing educational preparation for personnel in practice regardless of level of training. For agency staffs at the practice level, the opportunities should be made available for periodic exposure to public health content and methodology, whether this be on the basis of incorporation in annual institutes, or ongoing seminar types of education. Training consultants at state and local levels should have knowledge of the resources for education in public health and should make active use of these. At the inservice and staff development level, every effort should be made to teach public health in context so that it will not be seen as an isolated effort, but as a collaborative enterprise with social work to achieve appropriate health and welfare goals.

A question might be asked as to the existence of adequately trained teaching personnel who might be drawn on for this purpose. There will be a need to survey the existing potential faculty for such teaching responsibilities and to explore the needs for further development of additional teaching personnel who might be of service to every region of the country. There is need for a pattern of training institutes which will teach leadership personnel as well. Supervisory, consultative, and administrative personnel are also in need of periodic refreshment and review of theoretical content. This can be provided only by active instigation, through state, federal, and national resources which can provide funds and consultant services for regional planning and activation of projects directed towards these purposes.

Financing of Education for Public Health Social Work

The seminar, in pointing up the urgent needs for new and extended content from public health in the social work curriculum and for increased undergraduate and inservice educational efforts, did not touch on the inevitable question of financing for such efforts. Implied are additions to faculty and field instruction resources, or increased resources for training for existing faculty in public health and in education for public health. The models which best serve for recruitment to a given field are successful and productive educators and practitioners. Funds which will foster increased training for leadership in social work practice and education should be used more extensively and additional resources for faculty and students should be developed. The importance of scholarship aid in increasing entrance into a given field has been amply demonstrated.

Conclusions

The seminar on public health content in social work education has brought to the surface a number of important and crucial considerations. Social work education cannot be content with an existing social work curriculum which includes only a superficial approach to public health content. What is apparently needed is a careful assessment of existing content and educational resources of the faculty, in related departments, or in the community, which can be drawn upon to increase and improve public health content. This is seen as something which affects the education of the total student population and is by no means regarded as a specialized emphasis in the curriculum. However, it is obvious that as the public health field increases in size and in scope of responsibility, the rounding out of state and local public health staff will include increasing numbers of social work practitioners. Private health agencies will seek increased numbers of qualified social workers. Thus, the existence of a career pattern for public health social work suggests that this field of practice will eventually become one of the several emerging fields in which master's level social work education will be seen as appropriate training. The amalgam of social work methods required for this work suggests that means for combining casework, group work and community work experience will need to be uncovered and used. This cannot be accomplished without the development and incorporation of appropriate field experiences which involve engagement in public health practice. Conversely, a program involving such field experiences can be seen as suitable preparation for other fields of social work practice, including family and child welfare, psychiatric social work, and medical social work.

The deliberations of this seminar produced a large quantity of teaching material which is available for immediate use. These materials can be employed at all levels of education in social work and in public health. The papers in themselves represent a substantial contribution to both fields and the group discussions provide a sensitive and thoroughgoing assessment of the various aspects of application which might be possible in both fields.

The relationship which began at Princeton is not one which should be permitted to decay and diminish. It should be seen as a foundation on which to build increasing collaboration and cooperation on the part of two fields dedicated wholly to the advancement of physical, mental and social well-being in the United States and in other countries as well. Therefore, it is certainly necessary that periodic efforts be made to re-assess and re-evaluate the nature of the collaboration of social welfare and public health in the direct practice of these two fields and in the professional preparation members of both must have to be of effective and lasting service to mankind.

REFERENCES

Selected References on Public Health

ANNOTATED BIBLIOGRAPHY

I. General Public Health Practice

Standard references on general public health practice include the following books:

Confrey, Eugene A., ed. *Administration of Community Health Services.* Prepared in consultation with the Committee on Public Health Administration, American Public Health Association. Chicago: International City Managers Association, 1961. 560 pp.

Emerson, H., ed. *Administrative Medicine.* New York: Thomas Nelson, 1951. 1007 pp.

Hanlon, John J. *Principles of Public Health Administration.* 3rd ed., St. Louis: Mosby, 1960. 714 pp.

Leavell, H. R. and Clark, E. G. *Preventive Medicine for the Doctor in His Community.* New York: McGraw-Hill, 1958. 689 pp.

Mustard, Harry S. *Government in Public Health.* New York: Commonwealth Fund, 1954. 219 pp.

Mustard, Harry S. and Stebbins, Ernest L. *An Introduction to Public Health.* 4th ed.; New York: Macmillan, 1959. 338 pp.

Smillie, W. G. *Preventive Medicine and Public Health.* New York: Macmillan, 1952. 603 pp.

Many other equally pertinent materials could have been selected; these given below are a mere sample. We suggest reviewing issues of *Public Health Reports,* published by the Public Health Service, and the *American Journal of Public Health,* official organ of the American Public Health Association, for other valuable articles. A useful source of references is

"Excerpta Medica," Sect. XXVII, *Public Health, Social Medicine and Hygiene,* Vol. 6, 1960, Index Number. This latter publication lists, by subject and reference numbers, abstracts of articles published in this and other countries on topics related to public health. These are classified under (1) General aspects, administration, and legislation; (2) population; (3) infectious diseases; (4) medical preventive measures and aspects; (5) industrial medicine and hygiene; (6) dental hygiene; (7) sanitation; (8) military medicine and hygiene; (9) tropical medicine and hygiene; (10) nutrition; (11) veterinary hygiene; (12) miscellaneous; and (13) medical zoology.

Baumgartner, Leona. "Public Health in an Affluent Society." *American Journal of Public Health*, 50,10:1521-28, October 1960.
The editor's introduction to this article states: "A recent president of the Association (APHA) makes a number of observations on today's public health problems, and probes some of the influences which led up to them. She offers some projections into the future in a searching analysis which should stimulate public health workers in their visualizations of the whole field as well as in their everyday tasks."

————. "What about Soviet Medicine and Public Health?" *American Journal of Public Health*, 49,5:590-600, May 1959.
Dr. Baumgartner's fascinating account enables us to compare Soviet medical practices with those in the United States.

Chronic Disease and Rehabilitation; A Program Guide for State and Local Health Agencies. American Public Health Association, Inc., 1790 Broadway, New York 19, N. Y. 1960. 116 pp.
This material was the work of the Program Area Committee on Chronic Disease and Rehabilitation of the Association's Technical Development Board. In relatively few pages the publication surveys a broad spectrum of subjects: historical efforts of public health to cope with chronic disease, current responsibilities and activities of official health agencies, the "epidemiology of health" and an epidemiological approach to chronic illness, the levels of prevention, therapeutic and restorative services to patients. Indirect services—coordination, consultation, education, and research—are also briefly discussed.

Determinants of Health Beliefs and Behavior: I. "Psychological Determinants," by Eugene L. Hartley; II. "Sociological Determinants," by Robert Straus; III. "Cultural Determinants," by Margaret Mead. *American Journal of Public Health*, 51,10:1541-54, October 1961.
In these papers (part of a series by social scientists which began

in the September issue and continues in the November issue) a psychologist, a sociologist, and an anthropologist indicate the significance of recent studies for health education and health services. They remind us that we all have a "culture," regardless of social class, and that beliefs and behavior are influenced by that culture.

Dunn, Halbert L. "High-Level Wellness for Men and Society." *American Journal of Public Health*, 49,6:786-92, June 1959.

On the premise that public health is concerned with promotion of positive health, the author explores the "factors responsible for good health" and proposes a scale of degrees of health. The changing demographic, social, economic, and political aspects of civilization require a fresh look at health. The author bemoans the "fragmentation of man into areas over which various groups struggle to maintain their jurisdiction"—the physician, psychiatrist, psychologist, educator, and religious preceptor, to mention only a few—and advocates the "study of man as a unity living within a total environment" as a means of achieving the objective of "peak wellness." Procedures similar to those used to measure illness and disability should be applied to positive health. Steps to quantify positive health are suggested, as a prelude to the goal of wellness, and ways of achieving this goal are described.

Four Decades of Action for Children: A Short History of the Children's Bureau. Government Printing Office, Washington, D.C. U.S. Children's Bureau Publication No. 358, 1956. 90 pp.

This report covers almost five decades—from the preliminary steps leading to the Bureau's creation in 1912 to the comprehensive programs conducted in 1956.

Freeman, Ruth B. "Impact of Public Health on Society." *Public Health Reports*, 76,4:277-80, April 1961.

An associate professor of public health administration at Johns Hopkins University, Dr. Freeman defines public health in its broad aspects.

Ginsberg, Ethel L. *Public Health is People; An Institute on Mental Health in Public Health at Berkeley, California, 1948.* New York: Commonwealth Fund, 1950. 241 pp.

The book-jacket describes the content: "Here, new concepts illuminate one after another all phases of public health work: administration, intra-staff relationships, community relationships, clinical services. The purpose of this book is threefold: to help public health workers realize that through their everyday activities they can promote mental health within the community; to offer leads and suggestions to those who wish to incorporate mental health concepts in staff development programs; and to reaffirm the conviction that this sort of training should be available to students in professional schools for the training of practitioners in health and welfare."

Hanlon, Julian G. "The Role of the Mental Health Service in the Local Health Department." *Public Health Reports,* 72,12:1013-97, December 1957.

Mr. Hanlon holds that the responsibilities of the local health department for promoting mental health programs are the same as for physical health. He adds that the department itself does not necessarily provide the services, but it should stimulate the development of appropriate resources in the community. Some examples, with commentary, are given of local health department activities, both clinical and preventive.

"The Local Health Department—Services and Responsibilities; An Official Statement of the American Public Health Association, Adopted November 1, 1950." *American Journal of Public Health,* 41,3:302-307, March 1951.

This statement, which supplants earlier ones, summarizes those services and responsibilities which can be incorporated into efficiently organized and adequately staffed full-time local health departments. A guide to an effective program, it contains recommendations on: recording and analyzing data; health education and information; supervision and regulation; provision of direct environmental health services; administration of personal health services; operation of health facilities; and coordination of activities. Health department organization and staff and the relation to state and federal health agencies are also discussed.

"Man and His Changing Environment": "The Changing Physical and Biological Environment of Man," by Abel Wolman; "Historical Perspective," by Fred B. Rogers; "Public Health and Some Major Changes of Our Time," by N. J. Demerath; "Public Administration," by Robert G. Webster. *American Journal of Public Health,* 51,11:1631-46, November 1961.

This symposium is a companion to one on the social environment in the July issue (abstracted under "Epidemiology" in this bibliography). The influence of water and air pollution, food technology, and occupations and their hazards on current and future public health programs and practices are discussed, and the need for additional research on their short- or long-term effects is emphasized. The historical resume describes the changes in the last century in the environment and in public health approaches to the problems created by man-made "physical forces which may destroy himself and his kind." The third paper refers to the Medical Care and Research Center of the Jewish Hospital and Washington University's Social Science Institute, established to perform multidisciplinary long-term cooperative studies on health care and preventive programs.

Medical Care in the United States; The Role of the Public Health Service. A Report from the National Advisory Health Council. Government Printing Office, Washington, D. C., 1961. Public Health Service Publication No. 862, 37 pp.
Distinguished public health and other medical personnel and educators survey trends in medical care and current public health activities. Recommendations for future programing emphasize innovation and experimentation for improved medical care. Some tasks assigned to the Public Health Service are already being undertaken.

Mountin, Joseph W. "The Health Department's Dilemma—Definitions and Functions." *Public Health Reports,* 67,3:223-30, March 1952.
An elder statesman of public health describes the transition from environmental sanitation to broadened attention to many other health needs, including medical care. He mentions the importance of involving many related disciplines and of augmenting the training of the medically oriented to include more understanding of social factors. His comments of ten years ago are in line with the best thinking today.

Muller, Jonas and Bierman, Pearl. "Cooperation Between Departments of Health and Welfare," *Public Health Reports,* 71,9:833-48, September 1956.
The results of a study by former staff members of the American Public Health Association and the American Public Welfare Association in eight states are commented upon in relation to public health nursing, services for children, tuberculosis control, services for the chronically ill and disabled, institutional standards and licensure, nutrition consultation, payment for institutional services, consultation to outside institutions, and general administrative services. The conclusions indicate that there is still considerable room for improvement in cooperation, in spite of progress on some fronts.

"Public Health is One World." Supplement to the June 1960 issue, *American Journal of Public Health*, 50,6:Part II. 94 pp.

Here are speeches presented at the association's 87th annual meeting on international health problems and programs by Dr. M. G. Candau, director general, World Health Organization; Dr. Abraham Horwitz, health director, Pan-American Sanitary Bureau; Dr. John Grant, professor of public health and medical care, University of Puerto Rico School of Medicine; and Dr. Brock Chisholm, former director general, World Health Organization. Dr. Chisholm's paper on the "Expanding Concept of Public Health" gives immediacy to problems faced by a troubled world.

Review of Intramural Research, 1960. U.S. Public Health Service, National Institutes of Health. Government Printing Office, Washington, D. C., 1961. 368 pp.

This is the second annual review of intramural projects conducted by the institutes studying cancer, heart, allergy and infectious diseases, arthritis and metabolic diseases, mental health, neurological diseases and blindness, and dental research. Although many of these projects are highly technical chemical or physiological studies, several have social or psychological aspects of particular interest to social workers.

"The State Health Department—Services and Responsibilities; An Official Statement of the American Public Health Association, Adopted November 11, 1953." *American Journal of Public Health,* 44,2:235-52, February 1954.

This companion to the association's statement on the local health department describes the structure, organization, responsibilities, and services of a state health department, and discusses the health officer's role, board of health, personnel policies, major departmental units, planning and staff organization, and state-local health department relationships, and presents illustrations of reverse patterns for bureau structure.

Terris, Milton. "The Changing Face of Public Health," *American Journal of Public Health*, 49,9:1113-19, September 1959.

This paper spells out some implications and consequences of the changing character of public health. As the major communicable diseases disappear, emphasis shifts to the control of noninfectious diseases. There is a need to mobilize the actual and potential resources of public health to solve these problems. A sharp increase in local, state, and federal support for public health services is essential.

Tobey, James A. *Public Health Law*, 3rd ed. New York: Commonwealth Fund, 1947. 419 pp.
This informative book traces the progression of legislative bases for public health activities. It discusses the sources of public health law, police power accruing to the official health agencies, in general and with specific reference to communicable or occupational diseases, sanitation, food and drugs, etc. School hygiene is also presented in some detail. The last sections are concerned with liability and a discussion of law enforcement and court procedure. A famous decision is presented in the appendix.

Winslow, C. E. A. *The Cost of Sickness and the Price of Health.* Geneva: World Health Organization Monograph Series, No. 7, 1951. 106 pp.
The author, consultant in public health administration of the World Health Organization and professor emeritus of public health at Yale University, draws on his authoritative knowledge to develop the thesis that "prevention is not only better than cure; it is also cheaper." The report describes methods of reducing the burden of world-wide disease, in collaboration with other disciplines.

II. HISTORY OF PUBLIC HEALTH

Anderson, Odin W. and Lerner, Monroe. *Measuring Health Levels in the United States, 1900-1958.* New York: Health Information Foundation, 1960. 38 pp.
This report describes the development of measurements of mortality and illness and disability, and presents statistics to show changes in health levels. Because of the decrease in death rates in this century, illness and disability rates have become more important in measuring health levels. Changes in illness patterns have also occurred. The consequences for society of the decline in mortality and of increased survivorship are discussed.

Bierring, W. L. "Preventive Medicine—Its Changing Concepts, 1859-1959." *Journal of the American Medical Association*, 171,16:2190-94, December 1959.
Among the changes in the last century are the reemergence of the environment as an important factor in the causation of disease, currently in relation to water and air pollution, fluoridation, and

radiation; the lengthening of the life span; the continuing increase
of the aged in the population; and the greater incidence of long-
term or chronic illness. All influence the character of medical practice and require new aspects of preventive medicine. Current efforts
aim at the attainment and maintenance of positive health, and may
lead to the conversion of community hospitals into positive health
centers.

Fifty Metropolitan Years in Public Health, 1909-1959. New York:
Metropolitan Life Insurance Company, 1959. 16 pp.
This booklet presents speeches on the 50th anniversary of the
Metropolitan Life Insurance Company: "Metropolitan's Interest in
People;" "Insurance as a Social Problem;" "Health Needs—Today
and Tomorrow;" "Medical Research—1909-2009;" and "Science, An
International Highway."

Hanlon, John J.; Rogers, Fred B. and Rosen, George. "A Bookshelf
on the History and Philosophy of Public Health." *American Journal
of Public Health,* 50,4:445-58, April 1960.
These references, with commentary, cover a wide range of subjects
under general history, disease and epidemic disaster, public health
development in some countries other than in the U.S.; and public
health development in the U.S. for the historical section, and a
larger number of categories for philosophy, past and future.

Rosen, George. *A History of Public Health.* New York: M.D. Publications, 1958. 551 pp.
A professor of public health education tells a readable story of
the origins and progress of public health. Developments are traced
from Greek and Roman times to recent years. There is also valuable
information on bibliography, memorable personalities, international
lists of periodicals, societies, and schools of public health.

Williams, Ralph Chester. *The United States Public Health Service,
1798-1950.* Washington: Commissioned Officers Association of the
United States Public Health Service, 1951. 890 pp.
This illustrated tome by a former assistant surgeon general traces
the development of the Public Health Service from its beginnings
—providing medical care for merchant seamen—and gives a broad
background of the different phases of the Service.

Winslow, C. E. A.; Smillie, Wilson G.; Doull, James A.; and Gordon,
John E. *The History of American Epidemiology.* St. Louis: Mosby,
1952. 190 pp.

The four chapters in this volume, first presented at the twentieth anniversary session of the epidemiology section of the APHA in 1949, were augmented for publication. The authors respectively discuss: "The Colonial Era and the First Years of the Republic (1607-1799);" "The Pestilence that Walketh in Darkness: the Period of Great Epidemics in the United States (1800-1875);" "The Bacteriological Era (1876-1920);" and "The Twentieth Century— Yesterday, Today, and Tomorrow 1920-   )."

Zimand, Savel, ed. *Public Health and Welfare; The Citizens' Responsibility*. Selected Papers of Homer Folks. New York: Macmillan, 1958. 475 pp.

The concurrent progress of public health and social welfare, and the part played in both fields by an outstanding social worker, is presented in this book. It reproduces many speeches and writings in which Mr. Folks documents the social problems of the late 19th century and the remedial steps in which he participated, in various roles, for many full and active years. A citation he received in 1940 stated, ". . . He has labored for the cure and for the prevention of disease, has fought the most dreaded of man's physical enemies and, in his home state, all but overcome it. . . ."

III. EPIDEMIOLOGY

Apple, Dorrian, ed. *Sociological Studies of Health and Sickness; A Source Book for the Health Professions*. New York: Blakiston, 1960. 350 pp.

The editor's preface states that "there are many problems in patient care which involve human behavior and relationships. The solution of these problems by the practitioner requires an understanding of the social and psychologic forces at work." These articles by psychiatrists, social scientists, and health educators report on studies in these areas.

Cameron, Charles M. "Better Measures of the Impact of Accidents on the Community." *American Journal of Public Health*, 49,6:771-77, June 1959.

An epidemiological analysis of various types of readily available records is described as a method of providing data for intelligent program planning. The sources are health departments, their various sub-units, and outside agencies including hospitals, fire departments, schools, industry, health insurances, and safety councils.

Clark, E. Gurney. "Modern Concepts of Epidemiology" (Editorial). *Journal of Chronic Diseases,* 2,5:593-96, November 1955. (Reprinted by the Public Health Service, U. S. Department of Health, Education and Welfare.)

In three succinct pages this public health expert describes the concepts and methods of epidemiology, historically and as currently applied. He defines epidemiology as "a field of science which is concerned with the various factors and conditions which determine the occurrence and distribution of health, disease, defect, disability, and death among aggregations of individuals; it has application also to problems other than those of health and disease." Thus, epidemiology, the basis for prevention, has become far more than "the science of epidemics," as it was originally defined.

Corwin, E. H. L., ed. *Ecology of Health: The New York Academy of Medicine, Institute on Public Health, New York, 1947.* New York: Commonwealth Fund, 1949. 196 pp.

These papers and discussions by outstanding public health figures are titled: "Genetics and the Public Health;" "Maternal Health and Nutrition;" "A Problem in Preventive Medicine;" "Animal and Insect Reservoirs of Disease;" "Climate, Geography, and Disease;" "Realities in Preventive Psychiatry;" "Trends in State and Local Health Service;" "The Hospital Survey and Construction Act and a Nationwide Health Program;" "The Preparation of Professional Workers in the Field of Public Health;" and "Education of the Layman in Health Responsibilities".

Dubos, René. *Mirage of Health: Utopias, Progress and Biological Change.* New York: Harper, 1959. 236 pp.

One of America's most distinguished scientists (a biologist) dispels "the illusion that perfect health and happiness are within man's possibilities [which] has flourished in many different forms throughout history." He holds that although modern medical science helped to clean up the mess of urban civilization, historically much was achieved by humanitarians and social reformers. This is fairly characteristic of the book, which stresses social factors. This historical resume of epidemiological theory, ranging through many cultures and livened with frequent literary allusions, makes interesting reading.

"Epidemiology of Cardiovascular Diseases, Methodology, Hypertension and Arteriosclerosis." Report of Conference, Princeton, N. J.,

April 24-26, 1959. *American Journal of Public Health*, 50,10, Supplement, October 1960. 124 pp.

This report devotes over one-fourth of its 124 pages to cultural, societal, familial, psychological, and genetic influences. It was presented by Dr. Harry Kruse of the New York Academy of Medicine for other committee members, who included social scientists as well as physicians. The content, too extensive to abstract, deserves careful reading. It has implications for more than cardiovascular disease. The description of current research projects which follows this section should also be of considerable interest.

"Health Studies of Human Populations" (conference summary); Pond, M. Allen, "Interrelationship of Poverty and Disease"; and Shock, Nathan W., "Public Health and the Aging Population." *Public Health Reports*, 76,11:955-63, 967-74, and 1023-28, November 1961. Three separate articles, in the same issue of the publication, are presented jointly because of their epidemiological emphasis. The conference report, on some of the more technical aspects of epidemiological study of populations, commends itself to social workers interested or engaged in research. The conference, at the University of Pittsburgh School of Public Health in November 1960, was attended by many "veteran investigators," who were asked to draw on their experience "to mark the trail for future inquiries."

Although the information presented by Mr. Pond on the relationship between poverty and disease is not new, he applies these data to some less recognized disease categories and provides interesting documentation. He comments that the exact nature of this relationship is not understood; however, it is not necessary to wait for a thorough investigation of these aspects to apply the knowledge that raising the standard of living will be an important contribution toward the improvement of public health.

Dr. Shock describes the efforts of the gerontology branch of the National Heart Institute to apply epidemiological methods to the problems of aging. Some of these studies are longitudinal and follow large populations throughout adulthood. These projects refute some preconceived beliefs about the biological effects of aging and emphasize individual variations among adults of advanced years.

Hueper, N. C. *A Quest into the Environmental Causes of Cancer of the Lung*. Government Printing Office, Washington, D. C., 1955. Public Health Monograph No. 36. 54 pp.

This publication is of interest to social workers primarily as an example of epidemiological research with a purely medical approach; the content is somewhat technical. The extensive bibliography exemplifies the breadth and scope of research on a single diagnostic entity.

James, George and Greenberg, Morris. "The Medical Officer's Bookshelf on Epidemiology and Evaluation: Part I—Epidemiology." *American Journal of Public Health*, 47,4:401-408, April 1957.
This is more than a bibliography, since the authors engage in a fairly full discussion of the subject. They also evaluate some of the writings, grouped under headings of: classic and historic, general texts, chronic disease (with several subtitles), experimental epidemiology, serological epidemiology, and cautions.

Leonard, Alvin R. and Arnold, Mary. "An Epidemiologic Approach to Health Education." *American Journal of Public Health*, 51,10:1555-60, October 1961.
A local health officer and an instructor in a school of public health apply the concepts of epidemiology to the learning process. This experience, they say, "involves sets of conditions that affect the host (the person learning), the agent (the material to be learned), and the environment (the situation bringing these two together)." The thesis is expanded in this article, and applied to health education but with broader ramifications.

Lipscomb, Wendell R. "Epidemiological Methods in the Study of Alcoholism." *American Journal of Public Health*, 49,3:327-33, March 1959.
This article describes and exemplifies epidemiological methods and applies them to a major public health problem, alcoholism. To discover the populations most affected and the etiological factors, the author resorted to numerous sources of data for clues, and comments on the fruitful possibilities of social agency records. He also discusses longitudinal studies in progress to determine the validity of initial impressions. He was chief of the Study Investigation Section, Division of Alcoholic Rehabilitation, California State Department of Public Health.

Plunkett, Richard J. and Gordon, John E. *Epidemiology and Mental Illness*. New York: Basic Books, 1960. 126 pp.
This reference was reviewed in *Social Work* (6:122, April 1961) by Eleanor Clark, Massachusetts General Hospital, who describes it as a "well-written, cautious, brief statement of the principles of

epidemiology and its application to the study of mental illness, and is a reminder that the search for causation of mental illness demands an intensive scientific study of the individual and of his social environment. It is unlikely that either one will yield answers unless studied in interaction with the other."

Pope, Lawrence A. and Chen, William Y. "A Project for Studying the Geographic Distribution of Cancer in a Single County as Related to Environmental Factors." *American Journal of Public Health,* 49,5:668-73, May 1959.

This scientific article has some elements of a mystery story. It tells how this project got underway, describes the elements which spontaneously arose during the research, and pays proper tribute to the local health officer who stimulated the investigation.

Stainbrook, Edward. "Man and His Changing Environment; Health and Disease and the Changing Social and Cultural Environment of Man." *American Journal of Public Health,* 51,7:1005-13, July 1961.

This article is one of a series on the general subject which includes a description of the changing physical environment (as abstracted above under the heading "General Public Health" and appearing in the November 1961 issue of the American Journal of Public Health). In this July periodical there are other related articles: "Historical Perspective," by George Rosen, M.D.; "Health Administration Viewpoint," by Ralph E. Dwork, M.D.; "Engineering Viewpoint," by Frank M. Stead; and "Public Administration Viewpoint," by A. P. Hamann—professor of health education at a school of public health, a state health officer, a sanitary engineer, and a city manager, respectively. The lead article is by a psychiatrist, who holds that "every disease, in some balance of etiologic patterning, is a psychosomatic, a psychosocial and a biosocial ill-at-easiness." The other writers support this thesis.

Symposium on World Medicine. *Public Health Reports,* 76,9:793-816, September 1961.

Although this report covers more than the concepts of epidemiology, they are a primary consideration. The lead article by Dr. Candau, director general, World Health Organization, is titled "Epidemiology and World Medicine;" other contributors include Dr. Parran, former surgeon general, Public Health Service; Dr. Horwitz, director, Pan-American Sanitary Bureau; Dr. Shannon, director, National Institutes of Health; and other public health authorities. Dr. Candau defines "epidemiology as the study of the distribution of disease in large or small populations [which] . . . now takes in account man's whole environment and his own reactions to that environment." He describes WHO's international epidemiological investigations. Dr. Parran discusses the need for additional epidemiologists, and for training other professions in epidemiological methods, in this country and others.

Dr. Horwitz elaborates on opportunities for epidemiological studies in Latin America, and on some current methods. Dr. Shannon considers the study of "disease in the aggregate, particularly those factors that are contributed by man himself and his environment" a "neglected avenue to knowledge." The next paper is a fairly technical exposition of the epidemiological method applied to viral encephalitis. The last, "Future of Immunization" (a subject related more to prevention than epidemiology), refers only briefly to social factors, recognized by the others as important.

IV. PREVENTION

Anderson, Odin and Rosen, George. *An Examination of the Concept of Preventive Medicine.* New York: Health Information Foundation, 1960. 22 pp.

Following a fairly full discussion of the history of disease patterns in Sweden, selected because of the completeness of the data available, the authors briefly discuss some current preventive processes: good health habits, environmental sanitation, communicable disease control, health education and health promotion, and health services for individuals. Data on surveys in this country among the general population show that "A substantial proportion of the public believes that a person can consciously take care of his own health and not depend on fate or luck," but that many fail to take such care. The authors conclude: "The key (to improved health conditions) would seem to be the intelligent use of health services by the general public and assurance by public and private agencies of health resources and methods of providing and paying for care."

Blomquist, Edward T. "Tuberculosis Casefinding, 1961." *Public Health Reports,* 76,10:871-76, October 1961.

The chief of the tuberculosis program, Public Health Service, describes a principal preventive technique in public health—the screening of apparently healthy populations to uncover hidden disease. He discusses changes in this procedure for tuberculosis, because of fewer new cases discovered, and the need to concentrate efforts on groups at high risk. The importance of a comprehensive approach to tuberculosis control is emphasized, particularly in the follow-up of suspects, contact examinations, and care of known patients in areas of both high and low incidence. The tuberculin test has become an increasingly important tool as a preliminary screening method for some groups.

Buell, Bradley. *Implications for Social Work Education of a Concept of Prevention.* Discussion by Mary R. Baker. New York: Council on Social Work Education, 1960.

Buell, Bradley. *Is Prevention Possible?* Edward C. Lindeman Memorial Lecture, 86th Annual Forum, National Conference on Social Welfare, San Francisco, California, May 25, 1959. New York: Community Research Associates, n.d. 20 pp.

The speaker directs his comments to prevention of social disorders and explains the importance of prevention in the light of increased knowledge about causes. Drawing largely on Community Research Associates' studies of multiproblem families, he concludes that, with the exception of some public health agencies, community services are not now planned to prevent or control community problems. The concept of primary prevention, or of onset, although useful in public health in relation to contagious diseases, was discarded in these projects since this writer believes it is not applicable to social problems. A "therapeutic concept" of preventive programing was used, on the assumption that the applicant of resources after the detection of pathological symptoms can delay, halt, or cure the course of a disorder. A distinction is made between the goals of "providing service" and "solving problems."

"Cancer: Progress Toward Prevention and Control." *American Journal of Public Health,* 51,8, Part II:1-28, August 1961.

This symposium reports on studies of causal factors in cancer morbidity and mortality and calls for preventive action even though research is incomplete. This primarily clinical approach stresses secondary prevention through adequate diagnosis and treatment. The search for a method of primary prevention, however, continues with some optimism that one will ultimately be found. In the interim, already available knowledge must be applied to counteract the rapidly increasing rates resulting, at least in part, from changes in human behavior patterns.

Caplan, Gerald and Insley, Virginia. *Concepts of Mental Health and Consultation; Their Application in Public Health Social Work.* Government Printing Office, Washington, D. C., U.S. Children's Bureau Publication No. 373, 1959. 269 pp.

This report covers the presentations and discussions of two institutes for social workers in public health, and includes content much broader than the subject of prevention. Dr. Caplan's papers on the "Role of the Social Worker in Preventive Psychiatry for Mothers and Children" and "The Mental Hygiene Role of the Nurse in Maternal and Child Care" are appended. The family health clinic conducted by the Harvard University School of Public Health is also briefly described. Supplementary chapters prepared by Miss Insley, chief of the medical social work section of the Children's Bureau, discuss "Social Work Consultation" and "Program Consultation."

Chen, E. and Cobb, S. "Further Study of the Nonparticipation Problems in a Morbidity Survey Involving Clinical Examination." *Journal of Chronic Diseases,* 7,4:321-31, April 1958.

This report of a field study of arthritis presents some of the factors influencing participation and suggests ways of increasing public acceptance of screening programs.

Steps Toward Prevention of Chronic Disease; Summary of the National Conference on Chronic Disease: Preventive Aspects, held in Chicago, March 12-14, 1951. Sponsored by the Commission on Chronic Illness and the U. S. Public Health Service and National Health Council. Raleigh, N. C.: Health Publications Institute, 1952. 32 pp.

The committees for this conference included many leaders in public health, welfare, social work, and medical care. Their report covers evaluation of scientific data, prevention in medical practice, professional information and training, community organization and services, and public education. Social work and other professions are dealt with briefly.

Concepts of Prevention and Control: Their Use in the Social Work Curriculum. Report of the Workshop on Use in Curriculum of the Concepts of Prevention and Control, New York City, March 29-31, 1961. New York: Council on Social Work Education, 1961.

Cruikshank, R. and Glynn, A. A., eds. *Rheumatic Fever; Epidemiology and Prevention.* Proceedings of a seminar held at the International

Children's Centre, Paris, September 1956. Springfield: Thomas, 1959. 193 pp.

This book's heavy emphasis on the clinical aspects of rheumatic fever may deter some readers. A medical approach to a public health problem on an international scale, it refers in passing to the social factors involved.

Dunn, Halbert L. and Gilbert, Mort. "Public Health Begins in the Family;" and "The Family—a Focal Point in Health Education." *Public Health Reports*, 71,10:1002-31, October 1956.

These articles cover epidemiological and preventive aspects of family health. In the first, the authors urge better use of data on families as an epidemiological tool to discover groups at risk, and discuss some factors in the family that are statistically significant in relation to health problems. The second compilation of "briefs" on the family covers a wide range of related subjects dealt with at a health education conference at the New York Academy of Medicine. They discuss family education, the changing family profile, psychological dynamics of family life, family health maintenance, the physician and the family, education for parenthood, culture and health practice, the study of family mental health, and social work for the family.

Hilleboe, Herman E. and Larimore, Granville W., eds. *Preventive Medicine; Principles of Prevention in the Occurrence and Progression of Disease.* Philadelphia: W. B. Saunders, 1959. 731 pp.

This book stresses the importance of preventing the occurrence and progression of disease and disability. The material comes from lectures, seminars, and articles by experts in preventive medicine and public health, and is divided into three parts: (1) prevention of occurrence: control of environmental factors, prophylactic measures against diseases, provision of proper and adequate nutrition, and elimination of predisease conditions; (2) prevention of progression: periodic health inventories, early detection of disease, follow-up of screening and diagnostic examinations, rehabilitation, and alcoholism; and (3) supporting services for preventive medicine: role of education in preventive medicine and services aiding the practice of preventive medicine.

Mattis, Grace. "Accident Prevention and Nursing." *Public Health Reports*, 76,10:853-56, October 1961.

A nurse describes the knowledge needed by nurses and their responsibilities in regard to accidents.

"Prevention and Control of Heart Disease; a Symposium." *American Journal of Public Health,* 50,3, Part II:1-34, March 1960.
This symposium considers the relationship of heart disease to heredity, nutrition, hypertension, elevated blood cholesterol, and smoking. Although primarily clinical, the section on nutrition makes two points of importance to social workers: (1) conditions occurring simultaneously do not necessarily have a cause-and-effect relationship, and (2) a disadvantageous physical condition may be prevented or remedied without its exact damaging effects being known.

Scheele, Leonard A. "Progress in Prevention of Chronic Illness, 1949-1956." *Public Health News* (New Jersey), 38,2:40-46, February 1957.
The issue also contains papers presented at the Governors' Conference on "Advancing Together for the Prevention and Control of Chronic Illness." The former surgeon general of the U.S. Public Health Service discusses four concepts: unity of services (instead of segmentation into preventive, curative, and restorative); the new "map of disease;" personal health; new medical and psychological methods of prevention in community programs. He considers an understanding of multiple causation of disease basic to preventive planning.

Selye, Hans. *The Stress of Life.* New York: McGraw-Hill, 1956. 324 pp.
One of the great pioneers of medicine presents for the general public, his concepts of stress in its medical and health aspects, and what should be done to alleviate its deleterious effects.

U.S. National Health Survey; Attitudes toward Cooperation in a Health Examination Survey. A study of factors associated with stated intentions of cooperation. Washington: U.S. Department of Health, Education, and Welfare, Public Health Service, 1961. PHS Publication No. 584-D6. 45 pp.
This report was prepared by the National Opinion Research Center, University of Chicago, in cooperation with the Bureau of the Census, from a study stimulated by people's non-response to several community programs for health examinations. The purpose was to discover, through interviews, major factors influencing attitudes and behavior. The findings are summarized on pages 12-14, in the conclusions; one was that "Cooperators more often indicated that approval of the health examination by their spouse, friends, doctors, or other prestige groups influenced their decisions. . . ."

Wittman, Milton. "Preventive Social Work: A Goal for Practice and Education." *Social Work*, 6,1:19-28, January 1961.

Dr. Wittman points out that most social work has been geared to treatment and that very little effort has been devoted to prevention and "extension of coverage to the total population." He pleads for research and experimentation in social work which will enhance the profession's contribution to primary, as well as secondary and tertiary, prevention.

V. COMMUNITY PLANNING

Ballard, John H. *Community Planning for Rehabilitation; Proceedings of the Workshop: Practice of Social Work in Rehabilitation,* June 20-26, 1960, Chicago, Illinois. Edited by Mary W. Green. Chicago: University of Chicago, n.d. # pp. 68-80.

A case illustration is presented of the community organization process designed to improve services for the handicapped, instituted by the Welfare Council of Metropolitan Chicago. The problem was not wholly lack of resources, but of splintered and uncoordinated services which left a large segment of the disabled without rehabilitation. The objective was to develop a Central Rehabilitation Service, the planning of which is described.

Chicago Institute of Medicine: A Comprehensive Community Plan for Meeting the Problems of Chronic Illness in the Chicago area. Chicago: Proceedings of the Institute of Medicine, 22,9:227,95, May 15, 1959.

The conclusions and recommendations in this report are the result of 15 years of study and experience, largely by the Central Service for the Chronically Ill under the direction of a social worker, Edna Nicholson. In providing information and referral services, this agency collected facts on needs of the chronically ill and on facilities for their care. The several presentations by different disciplines were summarized by Miss Nicholson into recommendations which form a truly "comprehensive plan" involving more than 1,000 agencies and institutions which were currently providing some direct services to the chronically ill in Chicago.

Community Organization in Social Work—Its Practice in Old and New Settings. New York: Council on Social Work Education, 1956. 68 pp.

These papers, presented at the National Conference of Social Work in May 1956, were written by Violet N. Sieder ("What is Community Organization Practice in Social Work?"), Mildred C. Barry ("Assessment of Progress Made by Community Organization in Identifying Basic Concepts and Methods for Utilization in Social Work Education") and Ernest F. Witte ("Community Development in India, Iran, Egypt, and the Gold Coast"). All are particularly applicable to public health.

Community Health Program Materials; Selected References. Government Printing Office, Washington, D. C., 1960. U.S. Public Health Service, Bureau of State Services; PHS Publication No. 783. 59 pp. The annotated bibliography should be helpful to workers in health departments, professional organizations, schools of public health, voluntary health and other community agencies. It includes guides to organizing and administering public health programs.

de Garcia, Jacinta Muriel. "Yambele: An Experience in Community Organization in a Public Health Setting." *Social Work,* 6,2:87-93, April 1961.
Mrs. de Garcia, assistant professor and field work supervisor, University of Puerto Rico School of Social Work, illustrates the broadening of traditional social work activities from individualized casework services to efforts to meet the needs of a total population. The community is Yambele, Puerto Rico. The report describes the experience of a field work student whose activities were stimulated by a patient whom he had helped through casework.

Dixon, James P. "The Community Responsibility for Medical Care." *American Journal of Public Health,* 49,1:76-81, January 1959.
When he wrote this article Dr. Dixon was Philadelphia's commissioner of health; he is now president of Antioch College. A more accurate title might be the "role of government in the provision of medical care" since he focuses on public agencies' inherent responsibilities for health services. The author comments: "It is the role of government taking the responsibility to assure that proper planning, counseling and leadership are incorporated into our community efforts for better medical care." He recommends active collaboration with voluntary agencies in community planning.

Donahue, Hayden H. and Jones, Granville L., M.D. *A Mental Illness Control Program: Planning a Continuum of Care as It Relates to Health and Welfare Services.* New York: Council on Social Work Education, 1960.

Eller, C. Howe; Hatcher, Gordon H.; and Buell, Bradley. "Health and Welfare Issues in Community Planning for the Problem of Indigent Disability." *American Journal of Public Health,* 48,11, Part II:1-49, November 1958.

This report compares the findings of the Community Research Associates' study in Washington County (Hagerstown), Maryland, to those in San Mateo, California, and Winona County, Minnesota. Numerous factors relating to the three population groups are analyzed in considerable detail, with particular attention to Washington County. The aim was to determine the extent of chronic illness and disability in a "typical" American community. The implications of these data for programs are summarized.

"Financing Medical Care for the Aged." *American Journal of Public Health,* 49,2:161-85, February 1959.

This symposium report includes the following papers: "The Problem—the Role of the Federal Government," by Dr. Franz Goldmann, Harvard University School of Public Health; "Public Welfare Viewpoint," by Mary S. Weaver, formerly principal medical assistance specialist, Bureau of Public Assistance; "Viewpoint of Organized Medicine," by Dr. Henry A. Holle, commissioner, Texas State Department of Health; "The Hospital's Viewpoint," by Dr. James P. Dixon, commissioner of health, Philadelphia, and "A Voluntary Health Insurance Viewpoint," by J. F. Follmann, Jr., director, Information and Research Division, Health Insurance Association of America.

Guide to a Community Health Study. New York: American Public Health Association, 1961. 156 pp.

This committee report, for use by various official and voluntary agencies and public health workers, fully recognizing differences in communities, furnishes an instrument for inventorying community health needs and resources, and for formulating plans for health programs and services.

Haldeman, Jack C. and Flook, Evelyn. "The Development of Community Health Services." *American Journal of Public Health,* 49,1:10-21, January 1959.

The authors, who are on the staff of the Bureau of State Services, Public Health Service, discuss: trends in organization, deficiencies in service, the need for new patterns of community health services, current health needs, old health problems requiring new methods, meeting newer health problems, limitations of health department resources, services from other sources, the need for research in

public health practice, and experimental methods in various localities under various auspices. They urge agencies to adapt services
realistically to meet health problems, and caution them against
slavish adherence to traditional patterns of service.

Harper, Ernest B. and Dunham, Arthur, eds. *Community Organization
in Action; Basic Literature and Critical Comments.* New York: Association Press, 1959. 543 pp.
This volume presents the ideas of many experts on the principles
and skills involved in community organization. The content is more
related to social work problems and programs than to those of
public health, but the methods apply to either field.

Jaco, E. Gartly, ed. *Patients, Physicians and Illness; Sourcebook in
Behavioral Science and Medicine.* Glencoe, Illinois: Free Press,
1958. 600 pp.
This sourcebook brings together the writings, research and ideas
of behavioral scientists on aspects of medicine, and explores recent
developments leading to the introduction of behavioral science into
medicine. It considers social and personal components of health;
health and community; sociocultural aspects of medical care and
treatment; the patient as a person with an illness; healing practices and practitioners; and the medical setting: hospital, clinic, and
office. The second section, on health and the community, deals with
studies of the conditions which affect health and of successes and
failures of health programs in a community.

King, Clarence. *Working with People in Small Communities.* New
York: Harper, 1958. 130 pp.
This small book by a professor of community organization uses
case records of community development projects in several countries to illustrate principles and methods. That the countries are
largely underdeveloped does not detract from the applicability of
these principles and methods in parts of the United States.

Koos, Earl Lomon. *The Health of Regionville; What the People
Thought and Did About It.* New York: Columbia University Press,
1954. 177 pp.
The author presents the results of periodic interviews with more
than 500 families over a four-year period. They show the "widely
different approaches to illness among members of that community
. . . [which may be] real obstacles to providing adequate health
attention." Understanding of these attitudes is basic to community
planning.

Memorandum on Implications for Social Work Curriculum of Community Research Associates' Materials. Report of Study conducted by Mary R. Baker, Council on Social Work Education, for the Louis W. and Maud Hill Family Foundation. New York: Council on Social Work Education, 1960.

Planning for Health Services; A Guide for States and Communities. Government Printing Office, Washington, D. C., 1949. Public Health Service Bulletin No. 304. 69 pp.

Despite its age and brevity, this committee report on the processes for health planning contains much valuable information in sufficient detail to be helpful in most types of geographical or problem areas.

"The Politics of Public Health: APHA Symposium, 1958." *American Journal of Public Health,* 49,3:301-21, March 1959.

This symposium points out the need for the public health worker to understand the political process and the way things are accomplished through organized political action, and illustrates how public acceptance was gained for several public health programs. To solve some public health problems it is often necessary to disregard political boundaries, especially in urban areas, and attack on a regional basis, try coordinating the planning and effort of many institutions, agencies, and groups. Another political facet discussed is the preparation of health regulations. (An editorial on this subject appears in this same issue; it stresses the importance of recognizing and developing a facility for dealing with the power structure of a community.)

Roney, James G., Jr. *Public Health for Reluctant Communities; An Anthropological Interpretation of Community Health for the Laity.* River Edge, N. J.: River Edge Printing Co., 1961. 71 pp.

This slim volume provides laymen with information about the nature of community health and the implicit responsibilities and actions appropriate for individual citizens. The author, who has spent much of his "professional life working at the establishment of effective public health services in communities which did not want them particularly," has developed an approach easily understood by nonprofessionals. The chapters discuss "What Is Public Health?", "Who Are Public Health People—and How Did They Get That Way?", and "What Health Departments Do—And Do Not Do," "Helping the Unable—Welfare Services" clarifies the difference between the functions of health and welfare workers with respect to medical care.

Schlesinger, Edward R. "The Role of Community Health Services in Meeting the Needs of Mothers and Children." *American Journal of Public Health,* 49,5:585-89, May 1959.
The associate director of the Division of Medical Services, New York State Department of Health, attempts to answer "What guidelines should govern the development of these services?" on the premise that they should provide "comprehensive care."
He calls for further research on new techniques, the spread of basic health services to populations not now reached, and increased depth of services to those receiving some type of care, illustrating with experiences of the New York State Department of Health.

VI. MANPOWER AND THE HEALTH PROFESSIONS

Albee, George W. *The Manpower Crisis in Mental Health. Proceedings of the 1960 Annual Conference of Surgeon General, Public Health Service, with State and Territorial Mental Health Authorities, Washington, D. C., January 6-7, 1960.* Government Printing Office, Washington, D. C., 1960. PHS Publication No. 771, pp. 6-14.
A professor of psychology at Western Reserve University covers the range of professional needs in public health, emphasizing mental health. He discusses some social factors contributing to growing problems and to continuing manpower shortages in all professions. Without much optimism regarding the possibility of remedying this imbalance, Dr. Albee makes the cogent comment that "what we need are techniques and methods that will enable each professional worker to reach far more people."

Alt, Edith S. "Social Work Consultation in a Prepayment Medical Care Plan." *American Journal of Public Health,* 49,3:350-54, March 1959.
The director of the Community Resources Division, Health Insurance Plan of Greater New York, describes activities of the plan's social workers in four boroughs of this metropolitan area. Services include some direct casework, but consultation with other professions and intra- and interagency planning for this large-sized subscriber population are emphasized.

Bartlett, Harriett. *Social Work Practice in the Health Field,* Monograph II. New York: National Association of Social Workers, 1961. 286 pp.
The past chairman of the National Association of Social Workers' Commission on Practice illustrates a method for analyzing social work practice, a subject discussed in a previous publication. In this volume she covers essential elements of social work practice, charac-

teristics of the health field, the multidisciplinary approach, knowledge and methods, implications and trends.

Bowes, Anna de Planter. "Nutrition Services in State Departments of Health; Retrospect and Prospect." *American Journal of Clinical Nutriton*, 9,5:638-42, September-October 1961.
The author presents an historical resume of public health nutrition services which have continued to expand. She lists some guidelines for making consultant services more effective, and prognosticates that research now underway will contribute to future gains.

Bryant, Zella. "The Public Health Nurse's Expanding Responsibilities." *Public Health Reports*, 76,10:857-60, October 1961.
The chief of the public health nursing branch, Public Health Service Division of Nursing, describes some influences contributing to changes in public health nursing practice, such as scientific discoveries, new resources, and increased public demands for services.

Buell, Bradley and Kandle, Roscoe P. "Bookshelf from Social Welfare and the Social Sciences for the Public Health Worker." *American Journal of Public Health*, 44,4:421-31, April 1954.
These references were selected to provide the public health worker with some understanding of social welfare and social science. The social science material primarily concerns community and group relationships. The social work references cover public assistance, child welfare, and corrections, but provide little on social work in public health.

Cockerill, Eleanor. "A New Philosophy of Social Work in Chronic Illness." *Public Health News* (New Jersey), 38,2:54-61, February 1957.
Miss Cockerill discusses social work's role in considerable depth, and recommends ways of making casework services more meaningful to the individual or family, particularly in preventing adverse effects of stressful situations. She comments on the necessity for social agencies to gear their services to individuals "toward the achievement of limited as well as advanced social goals" (from self-care through the other levels of restoration to full social competence). Evaluation of services and participation in community-wide efforts to develop other needed services are part of the caseworker's responsibility.

Commonhealth, Massachusetts Department of Public Health, Vol. 4, No. 6, June 1956.
This entire issue on social work in public health, contains brief articles by several specialists on functions, recruitment, and educational opportunities and methods.

"Engineering for Health." *American Journal of Public Health,* 49,3:366-67, March 1959.

This editorial comments on the progressive extension of engineering services as a supplement to "the promotion of health and the prevention and cure of disease." Sanitary engineering is recognized as "a basic arm of public health."

Freeman, Ruth B. "The Public Health Nurse as a Family Counselor." *American Journal of Public Health,* 42,11:1379-87, November 1952. The author, associate professor of public health administration at Johns Hopkins School of Hygiene and Public Health, describes methods for improving nursing skills in family health counseling. Social workers will note the similarities between the concepts of nursing and those of their own field, a factor which often contributes to improved collaboration.

Galagan, Donald J. "What the Dental Profession Has to Offer in the Development of More Adequate Chronic Disease Programs." *American Journal of Public Health,* 46,4:450-56, April 1956.

The assistant chief of the division of dental public health, Public Health Service, comments on the little attention paid to dental needs of a growing population with chronic illnesses. He discusses the role dental consultants should be playing in prevention, treatment, and rehabilitation, and describes the obstacles they face.

Health Careers Guidebook. Supported by the Equitable Life Assurance Society of the United States. New York: National Health Council, 1955. 153 pp.

This illustrated recruitment manual, written in popular style, includes material on medical and psychiatric social work, briefly discusses professional education and career opportunities.

Health Manpower Source Book—Section 12. Medical and Psychiatric Social Workers, by William H. Stewart, Maryland Y. Pennell and Lucille M. Smith. Government Printing Office, Washington, D. C., 1961. PHS Publication No. 263, Section 12. 65 pp.

One of several manpower studies produced by the Division of Public Health Methods, Public Health Service—others concerned physicians, nurses, medical record librarians, dentists and dental hygienists—this survey was made in 1960 by the Bureau of Public Assistance, Children's Bureau and Public Health Service in cooperation with the U.S. Department of Labor's Bureau of Labor Statistics and the National Social Welfare Assembly. Data are presented on an estimated 12,000 medical and psychiatric social workers in health and related programs, in regard to type of employment, educational level, salary, and employment practices, with special attention to 1,140 workers in official public health agencies.

Maddux, James F. "Psychiatric Consultation in a Rural Setting." *American Journal of Orthopsychiatry*, 23,4:775-84, October 1953; and "Consultation in Public Health," *American Journal of Public Health*, 45,12:1424-30, November 1955.
In describing the role of the psychiatric consultant the author interprets consultation methods for any health profession.

McGuiness, Aims C. "The Importance of Public Education for Health on the World Scene." *American Journal of Public Health*, 49,3:339-42, March 1959.
Following a discussion of the age-old problem of the public's lack of motivation to take advantage of health programs, the special assistant to the Secretary for Health and Medical Affairs, U.S. Department of Health, Education and Welfare, mentions the increasing importance assigned to health education activities in various national and international agencies.

Medical Social Services for Children in the Maternal and Child Health and Crippled Children's Programs. Government Printing Office, Washington, D. C., 1953. U.S. Children's Bureau Publication No. 343. 49 pp.
Stemming from the deliberations of a group of social workers in public health and other related settings, this pamphlet describes and illustrates the various functions of medical social workers with case examples; and discusses the processes used, developments in social work in maternal and child health and crippled children's programs, and trends for the future, many of which have now materialized.

Nurses for a Growing Nation. Prepared by the Committee on the Future. New York: National League for Nursing (2 Park Ave.), 1957. 31 pp.
This brief pamphlet presents graphic data on nursing personnel, and estimates future needs.

Perrott, George St. J. and Pennell, Maryland Y. *Health Manpower Chart Book*. Government Printing Office, Washington, D. C., 1957. Public Health Service Publication No. 511. 57 pp.
This statistical survey of health professions—physicians, nurses and dentists—gives data on characteristics, distribution, and trends. Limited information is provided on other categories. In 1950, the 4.9 million employed professional, technical, and kindred workers in-

cluded 850,000 in health service industries. Of over 75,000 social and welfare workers (exclusive of those in group activities who are listed with recreation workers), roughly 5,600 were in health programs.

Reports of the Committee on Professional Education. New York: American Public Health Association (1790 Broadway).
"Educational Qualifications" have been published in various issues of the American Journal of Public Health or are available from the Book Service of the association for administrative personnel, physical therapists, industrial hygiene personnel, public health laboratory workers, public health educators, directors of public health departments, medical administrators, dental hygienists, dentists, sanitary engineers, statisticians, veterinarians, sanitarians, and school physicians. Others are being prepared. A revision of the statement on social workers was published in the Journal for February 1962. Considerable information is provided on functions.

Rice, Elizabeth P. "Social Work in Public Health." *Social Work,* 4,1:82-88, January 1959. (Reprinted by the Public Health Service, Department of Health, Education, and Welfare, #OM 1226.)
Changes in public health and in the several functions normally carried by the social worker in a public health agency are described. Skills required of this profession in these programs are also discussed, especially in moving from the patient-by-patient basis to responsibility for total populations which are the concern of public health services.

Rosen, George and Wellin, Edward. "A Bookshelf on the Social Sciences and Public Health." *American Journal of Public Health,* 49,4:441-54, April 1959.
A discussion of the human factor and the role of the social scientist in public health programs precedes a lengthy bibliography grouped under history; theory and general orientation; organization, institution, and community; socialization and the health professions; social class, cultural differences, and health; cultural beliefs and practices related to health; methods of social research; problems of interdisciplinary work; applications and results; publication series of joint public health—social science interests; social science texts; and social science journals.

Roueche, Berton. *Eleven Blue Men and Other Narratives of Medical Detection.* New York: Berkley, 1953. 189 pp.
This 35-cent paperback contains stories of medical detection which first appeared in *The New Yorker.* They are described as factual accounts of epidemiology and epidemiologists at work.

Smillie, Wilson G. and Luginbuhl, Martha. "Training of Public Health Personnel in the United States and Canada; A Summary of 10 Years' Advance in Schools of Public Health, 1947-1948 to 1957-1958." *American Journal of Public Health*, 49,4:455-62, April 1959.
An article describing the educational programs of the current schools of public health contrasts the two periods in regard to faculty, departments of study, facilities, degrees, required courses, field training, research, and consultation services.

The Scientist in the U.S. Public Health Service. Government Printing Office, Washington, D. C., Rev. 1961. Public Heath Service Publication No. 41. 29 pp.
This small pamphlet covers a wide range of medical scientists, describes kinds of work they do and types of settings in the Public Health Service where opportunities are presented. It refers briefly to psychologists, the only behavioral scientists whose work is described.

Youland, Dorothy M. "New Dimensions for Public Health Nutrition; The Challenge of Chronic Disease and Aging." *American Journal of Clinical Nutrition*, 9,2:211-16, March-April 1961.
A nutritionist in the Public Health Service describes several ways in which this profession can contribute to programs for chronic disease and the aging.

Other "Bookshelves" on health professions published in the *American Journal of Public Health* are:
Axelrod, S. J. "The Medical Care Bookshelf." 43,4:381-98, April 1953.
Barron, J. Lloyd and Henderson, John M. "The Public Health Engineer's Bookshelf." 42,4:353-63, April 1952.
Deming, Dorothy. "The Public Health Nurse's Bookshelf." 41,4:375-82, April 1951.
Felix, Robert H. "A Bookshelf on Mental Health." 46,4:397-407, April 1956.
Harris, Albert H. "The Laboratory Bookshelf." 40,4:375-84, April 1950.
Rosen, George. "The Health Educator's Bookshelf." 39,4:433-42, April 1949.
Shank, R. E. and Mrak, Emil M. "A Bookshelf on Foods and Nutrition." 45,4:419-28, April 1955.
Williams, Huntington. "The Health Officer's Bookshelf." 38,4:467-75, April 1948.